PATIENTS AND AGENTS

Transference-Countertransference
———————————in Therapy———————————

Maria Carmen Gear, M.D.
Ernesto Cesar Liendo, M.D.
Lila Lee Scott, M.D.

New York JASON ARONSON London

Library of Congress Cataloging in Publication Data

Gear, Maria Carmen.
  Patients and agents.

  Bibliography: p. 317
  Includes index.
  1. Psychotherapist and patient.   2. Trans-
ference (Psychology)   3. Countertransference
(Psychology)   I. Liendo, Ernesto Cesar.
II. Scott, Lila Lee.   III. Title.
RC480.8.G4   616.89'14   82-24468
ISBN 0-87668-497-5

Manufactured in the United States of America.

The tendency which falsifies judgement in this respect is that of *idealization*. . . . The ego becomes more and more unassuming and modest, and the object more and more sublime and precious. . . . The object has so to speak consumed the ego. . . . There is the same humble subjection, the same compliance, the same absence of criticism . . . the same sapping of the subject's own initiative.

Freud, Group Psychology

There is an extraneous influence at work, and it is this that decides what is to be called good or bad. . . . [The cause of the subject's submission to it is] his helplessness and his dependence on other people, and it can be best designated as *loss of love*. If he loses the love of another person upon whom he is dependent, he also ceases to be protected from a variety of dangers. . . . At the beginning, therefore, what is bad is whatever causes one to be threatened with loss of love.

Freud, Civilization and Its Discontents

Contents

Preface   ix
Acknowledgments   xi

The Pathological Dyads

1. The Framework of Psychotherapy   3
   Two Realities   3
   Basic Client Types   8
   Differential Diagnosis   10
   Defense Mechanisms   13
   Neurosis, Psychosis, and Borderline Syndrome   15
   The Role of the Therapist   19
   High Performers as Agents of Mental Health   20
2. The Authoritarian Dyad   22
   The Masochistic Patient   23
   The Sadistic Agent   31
   Complementarity in the Authoritarian Dyad   39
   An Authoritarian Dyad Asks for Consultation   41
3. The Demagogic Dyad   45
   The Masochistic Agent   46
   The Sadistic Patient   57
   Complementarity in the Demagogic Dyad   65
   Sand and Chopin: A Demagogic Dyad   68

v

4. The Undercommitted Dyad   74
   The Masochistic Insufficient   75
   The Sadistic Insufficient   84
   Complementarity in the Undercommitted Dyad   93
   An Undercommitted Dyad Asks for Consultation   95
5. Refining the Dyadic Typology   101
   The Eight Diagnostic Axes   101
   Diagnosing the Phenomenologic Subtypes   113
   Relationship between Dyadic Typology and DSM-III   134
6. Making the Diagnosis   140
   Diagnosing Speech and Action   141
   The Multiaxial Diagnostic Decisions Sheet (MADDS)   149
   The Clinical Application of the Decision Sheet   154

Treatment

7. Transference and Countertransference   195
   Defensive Action Plan and Transference   195
   The Masochistic Patient   202
   The Sadistic Agent   207
   The Masochistic Agent   212
   The Sadistic Patient   217
   The Masochistic Insufficient   224
   The Sadistic Insufficient   230
8. Treatment Strategies   238
   Strategic Goals   238
   Tactical Stages   240
   Technical Procedures   241
   Therapeutic Reactions   245
   The Masochistic Patient   245
   The Sadistic Agent   251
   The Masochistic Agent   256
   The Sadistic Patient   261
   The Masochistic Insufficient   265
   The Sadistic Insufficient   270
9. The Typology in Three of Freud's Cases   274
   Strategic Formulation   275
   Strategic Formulation of Dora   278

Strategic Formulation of the "Rat Man"   *286*
Strategic Formulation of the "Wolf Man"   *295*
10. Some Fundamental Issues   305
  Emphasizing the Socioeconomic   *305*
  The Dyadic Model and Polyadic Relationships   *308*
  Treating Psychotics   *308*
  Inverted and Direct Speech   *310*
  Detecting Contaminated Speech   *311*
  Levels of Intervention   *313*
  Strategic Stages   *315*

References   317
Index   331

Preface

The pragmatic method of dynamic psychotherapy presented in this introductory text is based on the fundamental structure of the unconscious and the issue of power in human interaction. Power in the sense of social control and interpersonal authority is an enormously important factor in human relationships, although it is often ignored in psychodynamic formulations and the therapeutic process.

In psychotherapy, clients deal with the exercise of interpersonal authority in the microenvironment of their family, where issues of domination and submission occupy the foreground. However, issues involving socioeconomic control and the macroenvironment are frequently overlooked, making therapy inefficient or even ineffective. The classification of psychopathology in this volume is based on the distribution of power and pleasure within two interlocking frames of reference: the interpersonal and the socioeconomic. The classification serves both as a diagnostic tool and as a key to effective treatment.

The theoretical framework—including a new conception of the psychotic and the borderline phenomena—is outlined in the first half of the book. In Chapter 1 the reader is introduced to the six basic types of clients, which we classify in relation to socioeconomic control (controlling *agents*, dependent *patients*, or restricted *insufficients*) and interpersonal authority (dominant *sadists* or submissive *masochists*). The three typical pathological dyads are discussed in Chapters 2 (authoritarian dyad), 3 (demagogic dyad), and 4 (undercommitted dyad). In Chapter 5 the diagnostic categories of DSM-III are coordinated and compared with the typology described in the previous chapters, and the dyadic subtypes are defined.

Clinical case material is used extensively in the second half of the book to show how clients attempt to recreate their typical dyadic formation with the therapist. This defensive action plan, with its complementary position, represents the transference-countertransference transaction described in Chapter 7. In Chapter 8, the various therapeutic stages and treatment strategies are seen as stages in the correction of the transference phenomenon. In the first stage, the therapist mirrors the client's pathology by playing the complementary role in the dyad—by containing the client's projections. During the second and third stages the therapist helps the client to work through power and pleasure imbalances in the interpersonal and socioeconomic spheres. In the fourth stage the client finally arrives at a more sophisticated and comprehensive resolution of problems of power and pleasure in these two spheres. The quality and production of happiness is increased and its distribution is made more equitable. However, clients are unstable in this new position and should be supervised to avoid regression, especially when significant others behave in the complementary way. In the fifth stage the improvement stabilizes and the client becomes autonomous. In Chapter 9, the model is further demonstrated in an objective confirmable way when it is applied to three of Freud's cases to give a diagnosis and strategic treatment plan. In Chapter 10, the authors answer the frequent questions that have come out of previous discussions with diverse audiences.

Readers can undertake a fuller exploration of our approach in *Working through Narcissism* (Gear, Hill & Liendo, 1981).

Acknowledgments

Dr. Melvyn Hill, of the Department of Political Science at the New School for Social Research, New York, was directly involved in the design of this book.

We are also indebted to our multidisciplinary team of consultants: Leon Grinberg, M.D., Training Analyst of the Buenos Aires Psychoanalytic Association; Harry Prosen, M.D., Head of the Department of Psychiatry, University of Manitoba; Professor Luis J. Prieto, Head of the Department of Linguistics, University of Geneva; Professor Morris Eagle, Department of Social Sciences, York University; Gene Supinski, Senior Commodity Specialist, New York; Professor Rizal Grimau, Head of the Department of Informatics, Central University of Venezuela; and Professor Daniel Glauser, Department of Sociology, University of Geneva.

We are also grateful for the fruitful interchanges with Drs. Jose Bleger, Alejo Dellarosa, Horacio Etchegoyen, Juan Miguel Hoffman, David Liberman, Enrique Pichon-Riviere, Heinrich Racker, and Reggy Serebriany, of the Buenos Aires Psychoanalytic Association; as well as Drs. Carlos Featherstone, Frederick Lowy, Patrick Mahony, Elliot Markson, and Peter Thomson, from the Canadian Psychoanalytic Society; Dr. Silvia Amati, from the Swiss Psychoanalytic Society; Drs. Francisco Corrao, Claudio Neri, Adolfo Pazzagli, and Stefania Turillazzi Manfredi of the

Italian Psychoanalytic Society; Antonello Correale, Giorgio Corrente, Enrico Meneghini, Domenico Perri, and Lorena Prato of the Centro de Ricerca de Gruppo. Also helpful were Drs. William Bebchuk, Sandford Fleming, Philip Katz, Robert Martin, Rodney Slonim, and Rivian Wienerman, of the Department of Psychiatry, University of Manitoba, and Drs. Yolanda de Venanzi, Rocio Martinez, Caridad Lopez Mendez, Auxiliadora Posadas, Jorge Posadas, Elio Sanchez, Esperanza Sanchez, and Jose Zamora, of the Venezuelan Society of Psychotherapy.

Finally we especially would like to mention Dr. Carlos Sluzki, Director of the Mental Research Institute of Palo Alto California, who for many years has shared with us the ideal of building an effective multidisciplinary system for psychotherapy.

The Pathological
Dyads

1

The Framework of
——————Psychotherapy——————

Freud (1924a) described mental illness as a loss of contact with reality. In fact, most of us experience two realities: the *objective* reality, which has a shared social definition, and the *subjective* reality, which is individually experienced. Those who are poor at reality testing experience a great deal of dissonance between these two realities and are often considered "disturbed." Such people frequently fail to realize the private and idiosyncratic nature of their understanding of experience; they believe their definition to be universally shared and correct. Failures in their thought processes may be numerous: they may totally misinterpret the true context of events; they may not grasp some broad underlying principle of organization; they may over- or undergeneralize; or they may simply be unaware of other ways of encoding reality. On a practical level, they may totally ignore information that does not tally with their view of reality and doggedly persist in a faulty, previously invalidated plan of action. Despite past failures, such people often make the same predictions and carry out the same ineffective plans over and over again. Brute facts are not allowed to kill a pet theory. This failure to develop new action plans or register new experiences only perpetuates their interpersonal and socioeconomic problems.[1]

In order to help their clients achieve a greater measure of happiness and satisfaction in life, therapists must deal with the full gamut of human unhappiness, failure, and destructiveness. Above all, therapists must become intimate with their clients' idiosyncratic, narrow, and stereotyped world view. Toward this end, psychotherapists have primarily concerned themselves with their clients' thoughts, feelings, and interpersonal relations as they exist in the microenvironment of the family or as they are reflected in client-therapist interactions.

However, therapists cannot ignore their clients' socially shared reality—the reality of the social, economic, and political structure—even though it lies beyond the direct influence of psychotherapy. The macroenvironment is often a source of major suffering, constantly undermining clients' efforts toward self-actualization. Obviously, both therapist and client are a part of this social context; to ignore it is to engage in a delusion. Instead, it must be acknowledged and fully explored in the course of therapy, so that clients can recognize whatever damaging effect it has on their lives and take steps to improve their situation to whatever extent possible (Kessler, 1979).

Therapists must learn to distinguish between interpersonal process and social process and deal with both as they arise.[2] Otherwise the therapy will be ineffective; it will be dealing with one order of reality, for example, psychic reality, when in fact the issues involve another order, for example, political or economic reality. The diagnostic and treatment method we describe uses this

---

[1]Thomas Kuhn (1972) made clear how scientific communities resist new theories, even if they appear to be more effective.

[2]This distinction has been made within psychoanalytic theory by Jacques Lacan (1960) when he distinguishes the (interpersonal) "imaginary order" from the (socioeconomic) "symbolic order": they represent two aspects of the "order of the real." According to Lacan the subject usually escapes into the narcissistic imaginary order to avoid facing his helplessness at the symbolic order: he escapes from one reality into another.

very distinction as the point of departure for therapy. While we cannot claim to be able to transform the world through psychotherapy, we can help our clients change their social context. Such change is the real test of a successful treatment. When psychotherapy fails, it tends to do so because it looks to emotions or self-image—or even to styles of interaction—for solutions to problems that are rooted in socioeconomic reality. But changing the socioeconomic context is a most complex task, requiring changes in the conscious and unconscious perception of reality, as well as new values and goals and new action plans and skills. Hence, interpersonal and social reality are dynamically linked (Dohrenwend & Dohrenwend, 1969).

Objective Reality and Social Control

Social scientists (Della Fave, 1980) frequently classify people according to their relationship to the social, economic, and political power structure. Greater or lesser status is accorded certain characteristics, which may vary from culture to culture. These characteristics may be present at birth or otherwise immutable (for example, sex, skin color, caste) or they may be subject to change (for example, level of education, age, class). Through the socialization process people learn (often unconsciously) which characteristics are valued and which are not. They also learn which of their own attributes are valued or derogated by their particular culture. They learn, in other words, who has power—control, authority, influence—and who does not, who is entitled to pleasure and who is not.

People also learn to play the role that conforms to their particular status. (Actually, they learn many roles, since status varies not only with the culture but with social context as well.) They learn that they are free to engage in any activity that conforms to their status but are discouraged or actively prevented from engaging in activities that contradict it (Cook, 1975). Furthermore, they are encouraged to associate with those that confirm their status but are inhibited from intimate association with those who might bring it into question. Hence, the objective power-and-pleasure structure is internalized; people learn to stay in their "place" and to enjoy what pleasure is designated for them.

In our society socioeconomic status defines a person's relation to the social, economic, and political power structure. Power is associated with the control of information, resources, and rewards; those people who possess socioeconomic power are able to control those who do not. Of course this occurs in the macroenvironment, where certain groups (for example, men, whites) are able to exercise control over certain other groups (for example, women, blacks).

We call this power *socioeconomic control.* But, as we shall see when we discuss the six basic types of client, socioeconomic control plays a vital role in the microenvironment (Blau, 1964). Of primary importance to the therapist is the client's personal relationship to socioeconomic control—and the ways in which socioeconomic manipulation and control are played out in the client's everyday life.

Subjective Reality and Interpersonal Authority

It is striking that not all people with socioeconomic control dominate interpersonally. In developed countries, for example, it is more frequent to see those with socioeconomic control dominated by people who are spoiled, demanding, and childish (Henderson, et al., 1978). In effect, a clear distinction must be made between socioeconomic control and *interpersonal authority* (Dahrendorf, 1967).

In addition to learning their place in relation to society's power structure, people also learn to command or to obey others, to make judgments about their self-worth and to enjoy or give pleasure. In relation to others they subjectively perceive themselves to be intelligent or stupid, generous or selfish, sensible or crazy, strong or weak, and so forth. In other words, they adopt a position of superiority, inferiority, or equality in interpersonal relations (Lane, 1959).

The third option, that of sharing in life's pleasures and

unavoidable disappointments with equal others, is not available to disturbed individuals (Corrao, 1981). Instead they become addicted to a particular kind of frustrating relationship, adopting one or the other of the first two positions: either sadist, with feelings of superiority, which they have learned through early experiences of interpersonal domination and abuse; or masochist, with feelings of inferiority, learned through early experiences of interpersonal submission and sacrifice.[3]

The sadomasochistic alternative is fundamental because it is comprehensive.[4] Unless one is prepared to share with an equal other, one can either deprive the (inferior) other for the sake of one's own pleasure or deprive oneself for the sake of the (superior) other's pleasure. Deriving pleasure while frustrating the other is sadistic, and suffering frustration while satisfying the other is masochistic. These are the two pathologic alternatives to mutual satisfaction (Watts, 1961). One alternative cannot exist without its complement; both are necessary to complete and perpetuate the circle of interpersonal domination and submission. In this interaction, sadistic clients overvalue their subjective worth and devalue that of their masochistic partners. Complementarily, masochists devalue themselves and idealize their partners. In sadomasochism both are accomplices and both victims (Rogers-Millar & Millar, 1979).

---

[3]The addiction has been explained in various ways. Here we follow the psychoanalytic model, particularly the hypotheses of psychic inertia and fixation advanced by Freud (1895, 1916): the anxiety of facing change seems stronger than the unpleasure of continuing frustration and abuse.

[4]This alternative and its resolution has been exhaustively studied by Klein (1952) when she analyses the (sadomasochistic) "paranoid-schizoid position" and its transformation in the "depressive position." In the paranoid schizoid position the helpless infant protects his mother from his own aggression by splitting her representation into a "partial" idealized one—who is actually persecutory (sadistic) toward him—and a "partial" persecutory one—who is actually persecuted (masochistic) by him. The depressive position implies the recognition of the subject's split and inverted sadomasochism and, eventually, its being overcome.

——————————— Basic Client Types ———————————

In our system, clients are classified and diagnosed according to two psychosocial parameters. In relation to their exercise of social power (socioeconomic control) and their attitude toward objective reality they can be classified as controlling agents, dependent patients, or restrictive insufficients. But in relation to their exercise of interpersonal authority and their attitude toward subjective reality, these same clients can be classified as dominant, abusive sadists or submissive, sacrified masochists.

Agents, Patients, and Insufficients

Since socioeconomic control seems to be a more critical variable than interpersonal authority, our first task as therapists is to determine our clients' objective status.

Agents are those who create dependence in their significant others by exercising control over the socioeconomic aspects of the relationship. Objectively, their status is higher, a situation which they try to maintain by excluding others from socioeconomic control (Ellis, 1979). Agents try to take care of the therapist and act like concerned "parents," responsible for others with lower educational, occupational, and economic status. They make decisions, control resources, give rewards, control information, etc., in such a way as to infantilize the other.

Patients, on the other hand, are socioeconomically dependent. Their objective status is generally lower than that of their significant others. They exclude themselves from such activities as decision making and therefore from socioeconomic control, acting as helpless, irresponsible, worrisome "children" (Manderscheid, Rae, McCarrik & Silbergeld, 1982).

Finally, *insufficients* have such uncommitted contacts with others that they are incapable of either a dependent or a controlling relationship. Their objective status is approximately equal to that of their significant others, a situation which they do not attempt to change. Insufficients act like rigid, narrow-minded, restricted "adolescents" or restricting "elderly" (McNeil et al.,

1972) who are barely able to take care of themselves and are unwilling to assume responsibility for others.[5]

Sadists and Masochists

In addition to their typology in the socioeconomic sphere, clients can be classified according to whether they function as domineering and abusive sadists or submissive and sacrificed masochists in the sphere of interpersonal authority.

Sadists act like condescending, blaming, domineering "masters" who are entitled to be served and pleased by inferior others (Courtright, Millar & Rogers-Millar, 1979). They try to boss the therapist and those around them, they overvalue themselves at the expense of others, and they undermine and otherwise exclude from pleasure those who are close to them. They feel victimized even though they act as victimizers.

Masochists, by contrast, will idealize the therapist, deny themselves the right to pleasure, allow themselves to be dominated and abused, and act like self-denigrating, obedient "servants" (Webster & Sobieszek, 1974). They see themselves as victimizers even though they are victimized.

Blame and devaluation. Sadomasochistic interpersonal authority is usually exercised by overqualifying or underqualifying the personal status of the interactors (Sluzki, Beavin, Tarnopolsky & Vernon, 1967). This is usually done by devaluing or blaming oneself or the others. Sadists are predominantly blamers or devaluers, and masochists are predominantly blamed or devalued. Each client will act mainly—but not exclusively—in one interpersonal-qualification mode. For example, one client may be a paranoid blamer who also periodically devalues himself or others. Another may be a hypomanic devaluer who occasionally also

---

[5]Agents tend to "contain" others, patients tend to be "contained" by others, and insufficients neither contain nor are contained by others (Bion, 1962). But agents are infantilizing containers who isolate their dependent contained patients from socioeconomic reality, like a uterus which does not allow the foetus to be born.

blames herself or others. Classification is based on the strongest and most frequent pattern of interpersonal qualification: Is the client mainly a blamer or blamed, a devaluer or devalued?

———————— Differential Diagnosis ————————

On the basis of an initial clinical diagnosis in the two spheres—socioeconomic control and interpersonal authority—therapists can determine which of the six basic clinical types the client conforms to.

1. Domineering, controlling sadistic agent
2. Submissive, dependent masochistic patient
3. Submissive but controlling masochistic agent
4. Domineering but dependent sadistic patient
5. Intrusive, restricting sadistic insufficient
6. Avoidant, restricted masochistic insufficient

The first four diagnostic types are more or less self-explanatory. The sadistic agent controls the relationship entirely, while the masochistic patient is controlled in all spheres (Lane, 1959). The masochistic agent, on the other hand, relinquishes interpersonal power while retaining power in the socioeconomic sphere, and the sadistic patient takes the inverse position. The sadistic insufficient

	INTERPERSONAL AUTHORITY	
SOCIAL CONTROL	Abusive Domineering	Sacrificed Submissive
Infantilizing Controlling	Sadistic agent	Masochistic patient
Infantilized Dependent	Sadistic patient	Masochistic patient
Undercommitted Restrictive	Sadistic insufficient	Masochistic insufficient

Figure 1.   Types, Control, and Authority

may be interpersonally intrusive and socioeconomically restricting of others. The masochistic insufficient is interpersonally pleasant and avoidant but restricted by others in the socioeconomic sphere. When others become too intrusive, the masochistic insufficient will simply run away or otherwise avoid interpersonal control (see Figure 1).

Each of the six types has a specific, unconscious theory about socioeconomic power and interpersonal authority that results in an action plan that is utterly self-defeating. For example, masochistic patients have a need to achieve absolute security, but their mode of action results in total insecurity because it is based on dependence and submission (Watzlawick, Beavin & Jackson, 1967).

Pathological Dyads

In a form of *folie à deux* (Layman & Cohen, 1957) clients in each of these six basic types act out their distorted views of reality and power relationships with complementary others in their lives. It is important that the therapist recognize this for two reasons. First, the client will attempt to get the therapist to complement his or her pathological type. Second, the therapist will need to be cognizant of the complementary role of significant others in the client's life in order to help the client transcend the self-reinforcing pathological interaction (Jackson, 1961).

The syndrome of *folie à deux* was described in 1877 by Lasegue and Falret (1964). Gralnick (1942, p. 230) defined it as "a psychiatric entity characterized by the transference of delusional ideas and/or abnormal behavior from one person to one or more others who have been in close association with the primary affected partner." Solomon, Fernando, & Solomon (1977, pp. 230-235) outline the conditions for the existence of such a partnership.

1.   An intimate relationship between two partners in the same environment over a long period of time
2.   Shared life experiences and common needs
3.   Relative isolation from the outside world
4.   A dominant, usually more intelligent partner who imposes delusions on the more passive, dependent, and "healthy" partner

5. A shared delusion that is usually plausible
6. Adoption of the dominant partner's delusion by the passive partner. Secondary gain for the passive partner, specifically, maintaining a dependent relationship with the dominant partner
8. Separation anxiety experienced by the passive partner when separated from the dominant partner
9. Remission, usually occurring in the passive partner following separation

We are suggesting here that mental illness is usually shared. In addition to the sick partner, there is an apparently healthy partner—or partners—who plays a major role in precipitating and perpetuating the illness. For example, sadists and masochists share the delusional belief that the sadists are masochists and vice versa; agents and patients share the belief that agents should control and patients should depend; and, finally, insufficients share the belief that undercommitment is the best policy for them.

Hence, the six client types are always partners in one of three pathological dyads:

1. The authoritarian dyad, which consists of sadistic agent and masochistic patient. It coincides with the traditional conception of *folie à deux*.
2. The demagogic dyad, which consists of masochistic agent and sadistic patient.
3. The undercommitted dyad, which consists of sadistic insufficient and masochistic insufficient.

In Chapters 2, 3, and 4 the characteristics of the six basic types of client are described in detail. The client types are presented with their pathological complement. In this way the reader will have a clear picture of the interpersonal and intrapsychic dynamics of each type.

The power-and-pleasure structure of the dyad seems to depend strongly on the power-and-pleasure structure of the dyad's social matrix (Soni, 1974). It can be said, for example, that agent-patientism is related to a society of abundance while insufficientism is related to scarcity (Lasch, 1979).

───────────── **Defense Mechanisms** ─────────────

Certain basic defense mechanisms are brought into play in our clients' efforts to maintain the status quo. Change in the socioeconomic sphere is prevented through the mechanisms of *disavowal* through *displacement*. All perception, thought, feelings, or discussion of the negative consequences of socioeconomic monopoly, dependence, or restriction is vigorously avoided. Attention to this sector of reality is displaced onto interpersonal domination or submission (blame and devaluation) and onto trivial issues. In effect, when facing anxiety-provoking socioeconomic problems the client will engage in blaming or devaluing behavior (personalization) or trivialize the issues by switching to small talk.

For example, when directly confronted with the need to improve their socioeconomic status—by going back to school, job hunting, or asking for a raise, etc.—clients will put themselves down as stupid, lazy, or undeserving (if they are masochists), or blame others for not recognizing their true worth (if they are sadists). Having displaced the "problem" from the socioeconomic to the interpersonal or trivial sphere, the client will often bring a second systematic defense mechanism into play: *repression* through *inversion* of the direction and sequence of the sadomasochistic relationship.[6] For example, a self-idealizing sadist who initiates a sadomasochistic interaction by deliberately needling, downgrading, and attacking a depressed friend will be completely taken aback when her friend blows up and walks off, maintaining all the while that she is the victim of her friend's sadistic outburst.

Within this framework, *narcissism* becomes a deviation from socioeconomic reality combined with the use of others simply as mirrors of the subject's interpersonal sadism or masochism (Kohut, 1971).

─────────────

[6]Actually the mechanism of inversion results from the combined use of represession and denial, as described by Freud (1915), and projective and introjective identification, as described by Klein, et al. (1952). What has been repressed internally is projectively identified externally and what is denied externally is introjectively identified internally.

People tend to defend their pathological status quo in order to avoid the anxiety and emotional upheaval inherent in effecting change (Green & Taylor, 1969). Clients tend to recite the same sadomasochistic story or "script"—with the same characters, relationships, sequence of events, and outcome—over and over again.[7] It is important that therapists become thoroughly familiar with their clients' scripts and also be aware of occasional twists and turns in the plot. Within the microenvironment of the family or employer-employee relations, clients may sometimes be unable to act out their preferred pathological role and be forced to interact intensively with someone who is not their true complement. For example, a sadistic patient and a sadistic agent may be thrust together by circumstances. One member of this dyad—usually the one with less socioeconomic power—will be forced to adopt the masochistic position, returning to his or her preferred structural position as soon as circumstances permit.

In brief, individual clients always tend to displace, invert, and narrow their attention, speech, and actions in the same way. We call this *fundamental acting off* (Gear & Liendo, 1979). Simultaneously, clients tend to induce in their significant others the complementary type of deviation, inversion, and narrowing. We call this *fundamental counteracting off*. For example, Dora, one of Freud's most famous cases, was a dependent dominant blamer (a sadistic patient). She repeatedly told Freud that her manipulative others tried to cheat and seduce her, while she herself was cheating and seducing others (including Freud); she also tried to make them declare themselves guilty of cheating and seducing her. She used this stereotyped inverted sadomasochistic speech and action in order to avoid discussing and working through her overdependence on her family.

---

[7]This "eternal return of the same" that has been conceptualized by Freud (1924b) as repetition compulsion, is also emphasized by Claude Levi-Strauss (1963) when analyzing the structure of myths. The "true" version of a given myth is represented by the plot and characters which are repeated throughout all of the known versions of the myth.

Neurosis, Psychosis, and
———————— Borderline Syndrome ————————

In psychopathology the degree of disturbance is a measure of the degree of distortion and deletion in the perception of both inter-personal and socioeconomic reality.

> In neurosis a piece of reality is avoided by a sort of flight, whereas in psychosis it is remodeled. . . . Or again, expressed in yet another way: neurosis does not disavow reality, it only ignores it; psychosis disavows it and tries to replace it. (Freud, 1924a, p. 185)

Neurotics tend to experience mild distortion of interpersonal reality and a narrowing of their interpretation of socioeconomic reality. Borderline clients experience moderately severe distortion of interpersonal reality and mild to moderate distortion of socioeconomic reality, especially in relation to the consequences of their behavior. The psychotic experiences severe distortion in both spheres; interpersonal and socioeconomic reality may be disavowed altogether.

> Thus we see that both in neurosis and psychosis there come into consideration the question not only of a *loss of reality* but also of a *substitute for reality.* (Freud, 1924a, p. 187)

In effect, in both cases subjects disavow (displace the focus of their attention) their excessive socioeconomic dependence, con-trol, or restriction and replace it with an inverted and stereotyped view of interpersonal domination or submission. Consequently, sadomasochism (and triviality) seems to be the substitute for the loss of socioeconomic reality.

In neurosis the displacement, inversion, and narrowing are only partial, while in psychosis they seem to be practically total. That is, psychotics do not talk about socioeconomic reality at all, and their perception of interpersonal reality is a completely projective one.

> In neurosis the ego, in its dependence on reality, suppresses a piece of the id (or instinctual life), whereas in psychosis this same ego, in the service of the id, withdraws from a piece of reality. (Freud, 1924a, p. 183)

It is important to emphasize that neurotics suppress self-perception of their sadism or masochism by perceiving it in reverse. Psychotics do the same thing, but they also avoid all perception of their excessive socioeconomic dependence, control, or restriction and any problems in this sphere.

With respect to socioeconomic reality, usually it is the agent who distorts or disavows the perception of the patient. With respect to interpersonal reality, it is usually the sadist who distorts or disavows the perception of the masochist. However, patients and masochists do, at times, attack the perception of agents and sadists.

The degree of pathology is also played out either actively or passively in the dyads, depending upon the power that the members have at their command. Powerful sadistic agents will tend to act upon significant others in their environment as "psychoticizers" or "neuroticizers" (Searles, 1959), while powerless masochistic patients will tend to allow themselves to be acted upon, that is, to be "psychoticized" or "neuroticized."[8]

The following is a typical transaction between a devaluing, psychoticizing sadistic agent (Gerry) and a devalued, psychoticized masochistic patient (Julia):

JULIA: (Happily) I got a raise in my salary!
GERRY: (Looking surprised) Oh yes? Why you?
JULIA: (Inhibited) Well, I don't know. . . . Maybe because I've tried to do the best work I could, I don't know.
GERRY: (Still surprised) Did you? But even at your best . . .
JULIA: (Depressed) Do you mean I don't deserve the raise?
GERRY: Not exactly. You have to be more subtle, my dear. What I really mean is that the standards must be going down at your office. Don't you think so?

---

[8]Bateson and Ruesch (1945) describe the four elements of Bateson's double-bind theory, elements that are usually included in the psychoticizing situation: dependence, paradoxical instructions, censorship, and impossibility of escape. Once the psychoticizing double-binder is in a position of control, he starts sending blaming and/or devaluing paradoxical double messages to the dependent psychoticized double-binded.

JULIA: Well, certainly I'm not very smart. Maybe I cheated them.
As you said before, even if I'm stupid, sometimes I use some tricks
to hide it.

Masochistic agents are "borderliners" because they tend to
attack their sadistic patients' perception of socioeconomic reality
by accepting blame and devaluation from them and overprotecting
them from the real consequences of their acts (Kernberg, 1975).
The following is a typical transaction between a devalued, blamed,
borderlining masochistic agent, Barbara, and her spouse, Jim, a
sadistic patient.

JIM: (*Commanding*) Go to the store and buy some whisky for me.
BARBARA   (*Placating*) "Please, Jim, don't ask me to do that. You
know what the doctor told you about not drinking even a drop of
alcohol because of your liver.
JIM: (*Angry*) Come on! This is nonsense! You know a small glass
of whisky won't hurt me at all! You are the one who doesn't want
to go outside in the cold, even when there is something that I need
really badly.
BARBARA: (*Guilty and justifying herself*) Well, I don't think you
should start drinking again. I would really like to do what you ask.
The cold outside wouldn't keep me from doing it, you know that.
JIM: (*Yelling*) Don't look for excuses. You don't really care a bit
about me.
BARBARA: (*Frightened and guilty*) Well, I don't know . . .
JIM: (*Changing suddenly into a childish tone*) Please, don't do this to
me. You know that this will make me really happy. Only this one
time. Please . . .
BARBARA: (*Tenderly*) OK, OK. But only this time. (*Smiling*) My
goodness, how difficult it is to say no to you.

Insufficients, whether sadists or masochists, tend only to neuroticize the other, since they lack both the power and the intensity
to withdraw the other from reality (Erickson & Rogers, 1973).
In the following mutually neuroticizing transaction between
a blaming but devalued jealous sadistic insufficient and a blamed
but devalued jealousy-making masochistic insufficient, Bill, the

sadistic member, neuroticizes Carrie with respect to moral worth, and Carrie, the masochistic partner, neuroticizes Bill with respect to self-worth.

CARRIE: I'm very happy. I've just taken a test, with wonderful results. It seems that I'm OK. I want neither to include nor exclude anybody from my life. It seems that I'm a very easy-going person.

BILL: What about me? You didn't decide if you accept or reject me as your boyfriend. Where am I? Am I included or excluded? And what about Fred? You seem particularly fond of him—and very close to him.

CARRIE: What I told you is that I'm very happy as I am now. Isn't that clear enough?

BILL: (*Angry*) No, it isn't! Who do you want, me or Fred?

CARRIE: (*Smiling softly*) Don't get angry. I just don't know, you see. Furthermore, I don't know what all this fuss is about. You didn't make a clear proposal of marriage to me, did you?

BILL: Well, you know perfectly well that it makes me very anxious to think of becoming more commited to you. I don't know if I'll be actually capable of supporting you for the time being.

CARRIE: You see. You're also very happy to leave things just as they are. You keep saying "for the time being." I don't know what you have to complain about.

BILL: Yes, but I'm a clear and honest guy. I love you and nobody else. You *enjoy* switching from Fred to me.

CARRIE: At least he is kinder than you. He doesn't insult me. You try to control me but don't want to commit yourself.

BILL: Fred may be kinder than I. But he is also more of a hypocrite. On the other hand, I don't want to overcommit myself. One should be cautious and careful in these matters.

Neuroticizing clients will actually recognize the abuse they inflict on others but justify it on the basis of some presumed mistreatment received at the hands of their neuroticized partner. That is, they rationalize and invert the direction and sequence of the interchange. In the psychoticizing situation there are such severe reality distortions that the abuse inflicted may be denied altogether, while the presumed mistreatment from the partner may be a complete illusion (disavowal). For example, a neuroticizing husband may rationalize, yelling abusive criticism at his wife because she has "frustrated" him previously with her "hostile" silence. The psychoticizer, on the other hand, may deny that he did anything more than "slap" his wife—to "keep her in line"—when, in fact, he has severely beaten her because the steak was overdone. To the degree that the partners in these dyads—or any witnesses to what is happening—believe that the abuse they are suffering is justified, they are neuroticized or psychoticized, since they are acting in complicity to reinforce the effect of the other (Asch, 1951; Rogers, 1973). On the other hand, both masochistic and sadistic patients can experience a psychotic breakdown if they suddenly lose the protection of their respective agents (Mahler, 1952). Complementarily, some masochistic agents can have brief psychotic episodes if they lose their sadistic patients (Christodoulou, 1970).

The Role of the Therapist

As therapists we must function simultaneously on both an abstract and concrete level. Theory provides us with a general framework for understanding our clients, allowing us to make certain predictions and plan interventions. At the same time we must constantly test the accuracy of our predictions and the success of our interventions. Above all we must be flexible (Neri, 1979). If our predictions are not confirmed, we must reexamine our original hypotheses to see if some basic overriding principle has escaped our notice. To remain rigidly wedded to an invalidated theory is to lock ourselves into a losing position.

Clients tend to choose therapists whose personalities complement their own, and in the initial phases of therapy they try to confirm this complementarity by behaving toward the therapist in the same way as they behave toward their significant others (Turillazzi Manfredi, 1979). Our first task as therapists is to understand our clients' particular world view as completely as possible—without giving up our therapeutic objectivity. And in order to achieve this understanding, and initially contain our clients' anxieties, we must deliberately act as if we accept their world view; that is, we must allow our clients to play out their defensive maneuvers and preferred positions in the pathological dyad, without ourselves becoming hopelessly entangled in their pathology (Grinberg, 1969). We must consciously play the complementary role, but we must not give up control of our own socioeconomic reality to the agent, or assume responsibility for the patient's reality, or accept forever the distance that the insufficient tries to impose. Our second task is to overcome the tendency of submitting, sacrificing our pleasure, and feeling inferior to sadistic clients or dominating, abusing, and feeling superior to masochistic clients. Our third task is to overcome the agent's socioeconomic control, the patient's dependency, or the insufficient's restrictions. In order to be effective, we must remain in control of the therapeutic situation. Only then can our clients accept personal responsibility for their feelings and behavior and ultimately enter into truly satisfying relations with others.

It is up to us therapists, then, to help our clients work through their defensive postures and to introduce relevant reality to contrast with and, finally, replace our clients' irrelevant and distorted reality. (The role of the therapist in understanding the client's world view and helping the client overcome his or her basic pathological mode is discussed in detail in Chapters 6 and 7.)

High Performers as Agents of Mental Health

In some way, those who achieve mental health must be high interpersonal and socioeconomic performers, with the necessary psychological ability to enjoy their top performances. We are not suggesting, however, that such people must be desperate superachievers or sacrified workaholics who exhibit the so-called Type A behavior pattern identified with heart disease and other psychosomatic problems. On the contrary, high performers set goals, solve problems, and take risks, using techniques that allow them to manage stress well, enjoy life, and participate positively in society.

After interviewing 1200 top performers in business, education, sports, health care, and the arts, Charles Garfield (Larson, 1982) picked out some clinical traits that typify the high performer.

1. They are able to transcend their previous levels of accomplishment.
2. They avoid the so-called conform zone, that no-man's-land where an employee feels too much at home.
3. They do what they do for the art of it and are guided by compelling internal goals.
4. They solve problems rather than place blame.
5. They confidently take risks after laying out the worst consequences beforehand.
6. They are able to rehearse coming actions or events mentally.

But most of all, notes Garfield, they are "masters of delegation" (p. 33).

Thus high performers are agents of mental health; they are neither excessively dependent, monopolizing, restricted, dominant, or submissive. They are flexible, responsible, egalitarian people who can, according to the circumstances, either obey or command, take care of or be taken care of, or accept rational limits.

The ultimate goal for both therapist and client is the achievement of mental health as epitomized by such high performers. That is, we must help our clients develop the necessary skills to achieve psychologically, educationally, occupationally, and monetarily and to enjoy feelings of shared happiness with their significant others (Trivers, 1971). In order to do so, we must gain a thorough understanding of our clients' underlying pathology as it emerges in the context of a specific interpersonal and socioeconomic power-and-pleasure structure. We help them first to cope with subjective and objective reality and then to master reality to the degree that this is possible.

2

The Authoritarian
——————Dyad——————

The authoritarian dyad consists of a sadistic agent and a masochistic patient. In this partnership there is an openly declared bargain in which the sadistic agent takes full responsibility in the socioeconomic sphere and as a result reaps major benefits in both spheres. The masochistic patient submits to sadistic domination and socioeconomic control in exchange for survival and protection.

The dependency of the masochistic patient is recognized, talked about, and openly capitalized upon. The success of the sadistic agent is discussed and highly valued (Dornbusch & Scott, 1975). Sadistic agents do not discuss management and strategy with their partners because to give information is to share power. Instead they trivialize their partners' efforts in the socioeconomic sphere as those of an inferior, incompetent, ill-prepared person who is incapable of either understanding or dealing with the cruel, dirty situations which the sadistic agent must confront. Sadistic agents exclude from consciousness, or are unaware of, their responsibility in creating and maintaining dependency in their partners (Kant, 1942).

Both consider socioeconomic power to be important. Both state the fact. Both agree that the masochistic patient is dependent on the sadistic agent for survival, and that this gives the sadistic agent the right to exploit and to compel the masochistic patient to surrender all pleasure. The socioeconomic reality principle reigns supreme in this feudal contract (Toffler, 1981).

—————————— **The Masochistic Patient** ——————————

The two basic traits of a masochistic patient are (1) avoidance of socioeconomic control amd (2) submission to interpersonal authority. Such people appear to be modest and infantile; they seem to be asking others—in a very submissive, self-blaming, and self-denigrating manner—to take care of them. They usually have lower educational, occupational, or monetary status than their significant others and view themselves as baser people—stupider, crazier, less competent, etc. Affectively they experience strong feelings of anxiety, guilt, depression, and a helplessness (Freud, 1914). Their anxiety stems from their real lack of control over their lives; their depression results from the constant humiliations and attacks of their sadistic partners and their unconscious complicity in these attacks.

Let us now examine typical behavior patterns and defensive maneuvers of the masochistic patient in various situations.

The Clinical Interview

As a rule, masochistic patients perceive the therapist as a powerful, omnipotent authority, whom they idealize and submit to, all the while denigrating themselves. It is very typical, for instance, for such clients to start blaming or devaluing themselves if the therapist remains silent for a while: they feel that the therapist may not be speaking because what they are saying is aggressive, stupid, crazy, meaningless, etc. (Mensh, 1950).

On the other hand, we as therapists are pushed into feeling that if we do not assume the role of a cruel, blaming, devaluing, omnipotent authority, our client will think we are no good—weak, naive, or soft. The first paradox we experience with masochistic patients is that even though they seem to be asking for affective support, they distrust and immediately reject us. They view support as a sign for weakness.

In other words, from the very first interview such clients appear to be asking the therapist to take care of their lives, to "coach" them, but in a tough, devaluing, or blaming manner. They are eager to be obedient, pleasant children, unable to cope with reality because of their weakness and naiveté. We may find ourselves being assertive, opinionated, bragging, or condescending, even if this is not our usual style (Merloo, 1959).

Family of Origin

Usually, the masochistic patient comes from a fiercely competitive family headed by a highly authoritarian leader who uses denigration, blame, and even brutality in the exercise of his or her authority (Laing & Esterson, 1964). The family head is a despot who, in exchange for ensuring the family's social and economic survival, assumes the right to humiliate, attack, and control the destinies of the other dependent members.

Generally, it is the masochistic patient's same-sex parent who is the despot, with higher socioeconomic status than the parent of the opposite sex. In this case our client rejects the despotic parent as a role model and identifies instead with the opposite-sex parent, who is the obedient and submissive partner in the marriage (Tucker, et al., 1977).

For example, if the father is the denigrating, blaming family guardian, the mother and sons will be humiliated dependents. On the other hand, the daughters will tend to become sadistic agents, modeling themselves on their father; if the culture does not allow them to assume economic control, they will become sadistic insufficients or sadistic patients at the very least.

In the case of the families where all the children are of the same sex, the oldest child tends to identify with the parent of the opposite sex and the youngest with the parent of the same sex; the middle child can be a mixture. For example, if the father is a sadistic agent and the mother a masochistic patient, the oldest son may be a masochistic patient, the middle son a masochistic insufficient, and the youngest a sadistic insufficient with some traits of the sadistic agent.

On the other hand, if the family consists of several "generations" of children, that is, if there are large age spans between siblings, the parents may function as parents for the first group and grandparents for the subsequent group. In that case, if the father is a sadistic agent and the mother a masochistic patient, the oldest son would be a masochistic patient and the oldest daughter a sadistic agent, insufficient, or patient. But the reverse would be true of their siblings, particularly if they are much younger.

Masochistic patients learn how to behave as "bad," inferior dependents who are never allowed by the same-sex parent either to take economic control and leadership or to rebel against domination and humiliation. Complementarily, they are encouraged by the opposite-sex parent to concede economic control and passively accept the authority of "superior" others. They act out the role of "loyal servant" to the tyrannical family dictator and accept their systematic exclusion from interpersonal authority and social control (Searles, 1959).

Adult Social and Family Rules

As a result, when masochistic patients reach adulthood, they are unable to assume leadership roles; they have learned feelings of inferiority, obedience, and dependence but have failed to learn how to command or take care of others. However, patterns of agent-patientism and, to a lesser extent, sadomasochism are influenced not only by family dynamics but also by social role expectations and opportunities. Thus masochistic patients may act out distinctly different roles at home and in the larger society.

For instance, the son of a sadistic-agent father may be an obedient and effective worker to a dictatorial employer, but he may be expected to assume a more aggressive stance within the family. This presents great practical difficulties because, although he may have acquired sufficient formal education or technical skills to get a job, his father has never allowed him to exercise leadership. When this man marries, social circumstances thrust upon him responsibility for and control over the economic resources of his new family. The role of family authority is also deposited in him (Rosenberg & Pearling, 1978).

His understanding of the exercise of authority is inflexible and absolute, as was that of his father. When a family member presents a problem, his insecurity makes him attack the person rather than the problem. He tends to give orders and pronounce judgment—and then abandon the field so that his wife can solve the real problem. As his children grow older he becomes distant from them in order to preserve his "image." If he is fortunate at home he is a pseudoagent in complicity with a wife who is a pseudopatient. Outwardly, his wife appears to respect his authority, which means simply that she keeps information about family situations from him and assumes informal leadership. She is, in many senses, the real family caretaker.

In the economic field the wife may have more difficulty, since society does not allow women as much direct economic control. By manipulation and suggestion she may be the hidden economic decision maker for her frightened, reluctant "caretaker" husband. If the wife fails to recognize his need to retain family representation but not responsibility—that is, if she is a true masochistic patient—the family situation can be disastrous, since there will be no effective leadership (Gibb, 1969).

Object Relations and Clinical Traits

Because of their early family experience, masochistic patients act as if they were always facing a sadistic agent. Indeed, most of their significant others—spouse, partners, friends—belong to this type. Masochistic patients are pathologically dependent on others for control of their socioeconomic reality because they cannot (or think they cannot) survive without such help. They believe that dealing with the real world of work and money is either extremely difficult or somehow beneath them.

They live in an artificial world of romantic dreams and are as addicted to this artificial reality as a polio victim is to an artificial lung. Hence they are constantly terrified of being abandoned because objectively they appear helpless. They forcefully avoid social and interpersonal power, generally remaining inferior in education, occupation, and income to their close friends and family. Their spouse may make all the financial decisions and hold title to all family property, for instance (Prins, 1950).

Out of fear of total abandonment, masochistic patients accept the jealous guardianship of their overprotective, often exploitive partners. They assiduously cultivate ignorance in financial and administrative matters, confining themselves to trivial and domestic affairs or abstract issues. Anyone who tries to depend on them in these areas will invariably be let down, although they are reliable in areas involving minor domestic or intellectual issues that don't imply action or responsibility. They can be skillful, hard-working employees. Sometimes they can even earn a reasonable income but are unable to administer or invest it, choosing instead to leave such tasks in the hands of their spouse or professional partner.

At crucial moments in socioeconomic matters they are overwhelmed by transient emotions and tend to give up easily. As a result, they avoid risks, preferring conformity and security to independence, no matter what the cost in humiliation (Courtright, Millar & Rogers-Millar, 1979). Such people engage compulsively in small talk. When serious topics like politics or the current economic situation arise, they quickly move the conversation to a more domestic or irrelevantly abstract level. One way or another masochistic patients unconsciously manage to undermine their own status, either by encouraging otherwise neutral witnesses to attack them or demonstrating that they are unreliable, irresponsible, bad, crazy, or stupid. Having relinquished all socioeconomic control over their own lives, they become emotional hostages to a jealous, monopolizing guardian, who constantly warns them that all other people are dangerous, unreliable, and dishonest.

The following exchange is typical of the sadistic agent (Hal) who is attempting to isolate a masochistic patient (Janet) from a potential alternative source of social and affective support:

HAL: You should be careful with Vicky. She says she is your friend, but she is lying. She's manipulating you. Why are you so naive? She's intriguing, introducing mistrust, and poisoning your soul.

JANET: Do you really think so? But actually she really has proved her friendship and fairness to me.

HAL: You're blind! She has already convinced you that she's your friend. When will you open your eyes to your real friends?!

JANET: Maybe you're right.

HAL: You should remember that I am the only real friend you have. And I don't know for how long . . .

JANET: Thank you. I don't know how I would survive without your advice and friendship.

If masochistic patients still attempt to form new friendships, the guardian will accuse them of plotting and being unfaithful. And if, by chance, their guardian does not realize that a new and friendly alliance has been formed, masochistic patients will often alert their partners to the "dangerous" and "threatening" quality of such an alliance. As we will see later, this usually happens when the therapeutic alliance starts to become strong: the client unconsciously "asks" the sadistic-agent partner to criticize or even interrupt the treatment.

Masochistic patients believe that any attempt at rebellion against this tyrannical interpersonal domination will rapidly be quelled because the others in their lives are—or are perceived as—smarter, more energetic, and more powerful. Others are idealized as generous, clever, sensible, and so on. Such clients are infatuated with or hypnotized by their "protectors" despite repeated mistreatment, humiliation, and torture. In fact, as with the therapist, such clients will push others into the role of cruel, ruthless, insatiable persecutor or wise, sensible, but rigidly strict parent, all the while accusing themselves of being stupid, crazy, selfish children (Bateson, 1960).

In complicity with the sadistic agents in their lives, masochistic patients distort reality to one degree or another, maintaining that they, not their sadistic partners, are the ones who act in a domineering, exploitive, and denigrating manner. To the extent that the masochistic patient's perceptions, thoughts, feelings, and memory are distorted, to the degree that reality is disavowed, the patient is either neuroticized or psychoticized (Dewald, 1970).

Let us see how a very envious blaming sadistic agent traps a "candid" masochistic patient just by playing with words.

Rose: You're a very envious person. You keep contradicting me all the time just because you can't tolerate the feeling that I'm brighter than you are!

Howard: Is that so? I wasn't aware that I contradict you all the time.

Rose: You see? You're contradicting me again! You're implying that I'm a liar.

Howard: Oh God! You're right.

Rose: You must recognize that you are a very envious person in the back of your little dirty soul.

Masochistic patients are unconscious but willing accomplices in their own persecution. Because they fear abandonment, they resist any attempts at rescue or defense against the attacks of their tormenters. If their partners cease to behave in a sadistic fashion, masochistic patients may experience a real, but relatively minor, emotional crisis. However, if they lose the socioeconomic support of their partners, they are thrown into a panic and are unable to think or act in a coherent fashion (Kallman & Mickey, 1946).

Defense Mechanisms

Masochistic patients engage in some typical interpersonal and intrapsychic defense mechanisms in order to avoid suffering feelings of affective rejection and devastating abandonment.

Interpersonal defenses. Masochistic patients

1. Compulsively and unconsciously select sadistic agents—and reject nonsadistic agents—as significant others (selection of complementary partner)
2. Induce others to assume responsibility for and mistreat them (induction of complementary behavior)
3. Systematically avoid all discussion of their critical, crippling

socioeconomic dependence by compulsively talking only about irrelevant and trivial issues or devaluing their self-worth (displacement by trivialization or personalization)

4. Insist repeatedly that they—and not their partners—are the initiators and perpetrators of the sadistic interactions (inversion of direction and sequence of sadomasochism)

5. Repeatedly insist on their sadistic mistreatment of others in the same, stereotyped way (narrowing)

Intrapsychic defenses. Intrapsychically, masochistic patient-ism is played out as follows:

1. Unconsciously, masochistic patients view themselves as (dependent-submissive) child-servants and others as (controlling-domineering) parent-masters, while consciously they view themselves as (dependent-dominant) child-masters and others as (controlling-submissive) parent-servants.

2. They disavow their actual socioeconomic exclusion and dependence and deny their interpersonal submissiveness by maintaining that *they* are the ones who force others to submit.

3. They perceive others as masochists and themselves as sadists, idealizing others while blaming and/or devaluing themselves.

4. They always perceive themselves as mistreating others in the same way.

Misqualification and Reality Testing

Masochistic patients belong to two main groups, which can be further divided into subtypes. Masochistic patients in the first group tend to idealize their partners and devalue themselves. This group comprises the depressive, neurasthenic, conversive, and dissociative subtypes, which are dyadically related to self-idealizing, devaluing hypomanic sadistic agents. Those in the second group tend to morally entitle their partners and blame themselves. This group comprises the schizoid, anxious, phobic, and obsessive subtypes, which are dyadically related to self-entitling, blaming paranoid sadistic agents. (Subtypes are discussed in detail in Chapter 5.)

——————————The Sadistic Agent ——————————

The two basic traits of a sadistic agent are (1) total socioeconomic control and (2) dominance in the exercise of interpersonal authority. Sadistic agents are the opposite of masochistic patients, behaving in a domineering, denigrating, and controlling fashion toward the humiliated dependent members of their family or social circle.

The sadistic agent is a vain braggart who orders others around in a very authoritarian manner. Such people usually have more education, money, or social status than those close to them, and they perceive themselves as more intelligent and superior to others. Kohut's (1971) narcissistic personality, which was described as grandiose, omnipotent, and ambitious, coincides with our description of the sadistic agent. Affectively, the agent's greatest fear is humiliation and loss of power (Gear, Hill & Liendo, 1981).

A bitter picture of a true sadistic agent is given by Aram Saroyan (1982) when describing his relationship with his father.

> My father never liked me or my sister, and he never liked our mother either, after an initial infatuation, and in fact, he never liked anyone at all after an hour or two, no, no one except a stooge, someone he could depend on to be a lackey, a nitwit he could make fun of behind his back, someone he could control completely by whatever means he could make work—fear, intimidation or, because he was a famous and admired man, blind worshipfulness. . . . He wanted me to be a failure like Chesley, so he could stand at my funeral, the big, wonderful, disappointed father. (p. 42)

The Clinical Interview

Sadistic agents perceive the therapist as a powerless, impotent employee whom they try to dominate all the while idealizing themselves as powerful, omnipotent authorities. For instance, the sadistic agent will start blaming or denigrating the therapist if the latter remains silent for a while: the therapist's silence seems to mean stupidity, cruelty, etc.

On the other hand, we therapists are made to feel that we must act like soft, submissive, humiliated, impotent servants;

otherwise such clients will think that we are scheming or plotting to put them down because we are not following their directions. Thus, paradoxically, our client will respect us only if we show self-confidence and assertiveness; but if we do, our client will not tolerate it.

In other words, such clients seem to be demanding the right to take care of and command the therapist. They seem to want to be an authoritarian, tough, cruel parent, able to cope not only with their own socioeconomic reality but with that of the therapist, because they are strong and astute while the therapist is supposed to be weak and naive. We therapists thus find ourselves being doubtful, indecisive, and self-deprecating, even if this is not our usual style.

Family of Origin

As a general rule the sadistic agent comes from the same type of family as the masochistic patient: an authoritarian family comprising a brutal, cruel, feudal leader and obedient, mistreated, dependent followers.

The sadistic agent identifies with the family despot, usually the parent of the opposite sex, while the same-sex parent becomes the alter ego. For example, if the mother is the sadistic agent, the father and the daughters will be the masochistic patients, while the sons will model themselves on their mother. The problem is more complicated when the father is the sadistic agent; in that case the daughters become sadistic agents only if the culture allows women to take over socioeconomic control. Otherwise they will merely be sadistic patients or aggressive, restricting insufficients. If the mother is a sadistic patient or insufficient, she may teach her son the interpersonal, social, and economic skills that will enable him to be a controlling, domineering master of others. The mother, as a spoiled princess, thus teaches her son how to be a king, a primitive type of feudal or entrepreneurial leader, an "empire builder" who knows how to control and dominate his loyal subjects (Leslie, 1979).

Adult Social and Family Roles

A man who is a sadistic agent in his family context may be obliged to take a masochistic-patient role vis-a-vis his employer because of the latter's greater socioeconomic power. Because of sex-role stereotypes, the man may be expected to be a sadistic agent in his home, and the woman a masochistic patient (Sturges, 1967). This type of social structure frequently results in the formation of pseudoagents who control the economic resources and abuse the authority role but do not have the real leadership of the family or the ability to make sensible decisions. Hence, rigid sex-role expectations often deprive the society and the family of access to the most appropriate or effective family leader.

Object Relations and Clinical Traits

Sadistic agents act as if they were always facing a masochistic patient—and most of their significant others (spouse, partners, friends) do, in fact, belong to this type.

Sadistic agents usually make others dependent on them by means of a crippling economic overprotectiveness. They are themselves pathologically independent, having a mentality most commonly associated with the self-employed petit enterpreneur. They are uncomfortable with the bureaucratic structures of industrial society. Bureaucracy makes them feel claustrophobic, controlled, and impotent because it interferes with their ability to exploit and control others. Sometimes such people are able to preserve a degree of creativity, not unlike the robber barons and other entrepreneurial renegades of the early industrial period.

Sadistic agents are extremely poor at delegating responsibility, treating others like incapable children. Indeed, they make the "real world" seem extremely complex, disagreeable, or dishonest, thus inducing those close to them to avoid adult responsibility and idealize their "protector." They pay a heavy price for this protection: sadistic agents preserve their power and their charisma by blaming others for any mistakes and demanding complete, blind submissiveness. Any thrusts toward independence on the part of their dependents bring swift retribution in the form of accusations of ingratitude and infidelity, threats of economic and emotional abandonment, etc. The sadistic agent is an infantilizer par excellence; masochism and dependence are always rewarded (Deutsch, 1938).

The following interaction shows how Russ, a devaluing sadistic agent, undermines the efforts of Diane, his devalued masochistic-patient wife, to understand socioeconomic issues:

DIANE: I was afraid that something had happened to you. I was expecting you earlier.

RUSS: My God! You are always exaggerating things. There was something important at the office that I had to decide, that's all.

DIANE: What happened? Any trouble there?

RUSS: *(Interrupting)* Not really. Don't worry. I can take care of it.

DIANE: Oh, but now I really want to know.

RUSS: *(Interrupting)* I see. This must be something that your damned therapist is trying to put into your stupid little mind. You should tell him that what he must try to teach you—if he can deal with you at all—is to stop crying and getting anxious without reason instead of teaching you to nag me. This is not your business! Do you understand?!

DIANE: *(Disoriented)* I understood from my therapist that it was important that I start facing adult responsibilities.

RUSS: *(Angry)* Maybe it's time that I talk with your therapist.

DIANE: *(Frightened)* Don't do that, please.

RUSS: It seems to me that he is making a damned mess here. We were better off before. Look, baby, let "Daddy" handle the business!

In the work world sadistic agents often appear to be pragmatic, efficient leaders. They are frequently astute about financial matters, responsible, reliable, and tenacious in a crisis, but utterly resistant to bureaucratic fetters and regulations (Sewell & Hauser, 1975). They don't make good team workers, for example.

They do have a charismatic effect on those around them,

however, often becoming the central focus of their dependents' emotional lives. They fascinate and infatuate and inject special meaning into the lives of those close to them (Freud, 1914).

No one remains neutral in the company of sadistic agents. To a greater or lesser degree, they attack the memory, thoughts, actions, and very perceptions of their dependents in such a way that the dependents come to feel responsible for any social or economic setbacks. Sadistic agents can be ruthless "crazy people makers." Of the six basic client types they are the most psychoticizing because they possess the greatest degree of interpersonal and socioeconomic power. When analyzing the psychotic breakdown of a masochistic patient, the therapist may be amazed at the degree of relentless and ruthless cruelty exercized by the sadistic agent (Anderson, 1974).

The following is an interaction between Pearl, a ruthless blaming sadistic-agent mother, and Ethel, a blamed masochistic-patient daughter:

PEARL: Did my eldest illiterate manage to cook something edible?

ETHEL: Don't treat me like that Mommy! Sometimes I'm able to cook well!

PEARL: Who do you think you are talking to me like that! How dare you tell me what to do and what to say.

ETHEL: I didn't mean to offend you!

PEARL: If you are so mean to your mother, I don't think you'll ever manage to get married. No sense of humor!

ETHEL: But Bob asked me to marry him . . .

PEARL: Maybe he's so stupid that he likes parasites. A genius at mistakes!

Sadistic agents will jealously guard both their emotional and their economic control over their dependents. They will rarely recognize the good judgment or cleverness of others, instead subtly or openly putting them down, censoring any outside comments about their own failures, restricting contacts with the "outside world," etc. (Kiraly, 1975). For instance, a sadistic-agent husband may make fun of his wife's attempts to turn her craftwork into a business. He may become "sick" or have to "work late" on the night that he is to baby-sit so that his wife can attend a meeting. If she decides to go to a course, he may flatly refuse to "allow" it. If she seeks a divorce, he may accuse her of "desertion" and threaten to abandon the children altogether, leaving her with the full economic and emotional responsibility. Often he will carry through on this threat, particularly if he has another masochistic-patient lover waiting in the wings.

Because of their overwhelming sense of omnipotence, sadistic agents cannot tolerate people who do not idealize or submit to them (Potter, 1947). They distrust others completely, regarding them as weak, naive, or dishonest. Their psychological survival depends entirely on their ability to control socioeconomic reality. Hence sadistic agents can tolerate an end to a partner's masochism much better than they tolerate their partner's economic independence. If a sadistic agent loses his or her job or becomes otherwise socioeconomically dependent, true panic may set in because of the perceived degradation of being dependent. Agents cannot trust anybody else for survival and may even commit suicide if they suddenly lose their social and interpersonal power (Ferreira, 1963).

Defense Mechanisms

The sadistic agent employs certain typical interpersonal and intrapsychic defense mechanisms in order to build up and maintain the sadistic controlling structure.

Interpersonal defenses. Sadistic agents

1. Compulsively and unconsciously select masochistic patients—and reject nonmasochistic patients—as significant others (selection of complementary partner)
2. Induce others to behave in a dependent and obedient fashion (induction of complementary behavior)
3. Systematically avoid all discussion of their exploitive economic monopoly over those who are close to them (displacement by trivialization or personalization)
4. Stand reality on its head by insisting that they—not their

partners—are the ones who are persecuted, exploited, and blamed (inversion of direction and sequence of sadomasochism)
5. Repeatedly insist on the mistreatment they receive from others in the same stereotyped way (narrowing)

Intrapsychic defenses. Sadistic agentism is played out as follows:

1. Unconsciously, sadistic agents view themselves as (controlling-domineering) parent-masters and others as (dependent-submissive) child-servants, while consciously they view themselves as (controlling-submissive) parent-servants and others as (dependent-domineering) child-masters.
2. They disavow their actual socioeconomic monopoly and exclusion of others and deny their interpersonal authoritarianism by maintaining that they are the ones who are persecuted.
3. They perceive others as sadists and themselves as masochists, idealizing themselves and blaming others.
4. They always perceive others as mistreating them in the same way.

Misqualification and Reality Testing

Sadistic agents belong to two main groups, which can be further divided into subtypes. Those in the first group tend to idealize themselves and devaluate their partners. They are generally compulsive hypomanic persons who are dyadically related to self-devaluing, idealizing masochistic patients. Those in the second group attribute moral entitlement to themselves and blame their partners. They are usually compulsive paranoid persons, dyadically related to self-blaming, entitling masochistic patients.

Sadistic agents' perception of interpersonal reality is impaired, obviously in their favor. Their perception of socioeconomic reality is less distorted, but it is still mutilated and selective (Gear & Liendo, 1975).

Because sadistic agents attack both the interpersonal and the socioeconomic reality testing of their masochistic-patient partners, they tend to be psychoticizers. When their attack is massive, relentless, and ruthless, they can produce either schizophrenic or melancholic breakdowns in their submissive abused dependents.

It is the sadistic agent's total control in all spheres of reality—both interpersonal and socioeconomic—that creates the conditions for psychoticizing (Savage, 1881). Sadists have the authority to define the relationship. They therefore impose their own vision of the world on the masochists, who are receptive to their definition. They also have the authority to censor, that is, to forbid discussion or comment on, their definition. Agents have the power to bind the partners in the situation and to cut off escape from the attack. They also have the power to isolate patients from corrective experiences. Agents can reinforce the attacks, creating the impression that there is a hostile majority (Asch, 1952).

Although sadistic agents are not easily psychoticized, they are also not easily brought to a healthier shared definition of reality. They powerfully resist any suggestion to change and their defenses are more impregnable than those of the other types of client. Though not psychoticized, they are neuroticized by their own misuse of power and by the unconscious complicity of their submissive dependent others. They are trapped in an inverted perception of interpersonal mistreatment (sadomasochism) and a narrow conception of socioeconomic relations (agent-patientism).

This is a typical psychoticizing transaction between a blaming paranoid sadistic agent (Claudia) and a blamed schizoid masochistic patient (Randy).

CLAUDIA: Did you hear voices?
RANDY: (Vacillating) No, I didn't.
CLAUDIA: (Surprised) You didn't hear me either?
RANDY: (Confused) Oh yes, I heard you. But I thought that you were asking if I heard voices that didn't exist.
CLAUDIA: (Angry) You always think in a twisted way! Trying to drive me crazy!
RANDY: (Perplexed) I'm so confused and I guess I'm not sure what I'm talking about.

Complementarity in the
——————— Authoritarian Dyad ———————

The Problem

Those involved in an authoritarian dyad share a common understanding of the way the world functions and the means of achieving certain goals and affect states. For the masochistic patient the goal is survival, which is achieved through total dependence on the protection of the sadistic agent. The sadistic agent, in turn, maintains control over the dyad's reality (that is, provides "protection") in exchange for the masochistic patient's surrender of all hedonistic pleasure and cognitive autonomy.

Unfortunately, this mutual dependence provides only a temporary solution to the problem of survival and pleasure. In their pursuit of survival, masochistic patients condemn themselves to permanent insecurity (Pulver & Brunt, 1961). The more they submit to the full control of another, the greater their sense of insecurity. Their survival is thus totally dependent on the whims of the other and, therefore, never guaranteed. It must be eternally pursued and paid for. Only by not submitting and by taking back control can these masochistic patients guarantee their survial. This is precisely what is forbidden to them. The sadistic agent's "solution" to the problem of pleasure precludes all possibility of achieving true gratification, namely, the sharing of pleasure with an equal. Such people perceive life as a win-or-lose game and know nothing of the value of cooperation. They are limited to short-term gains through power plays and abuse. Paradoxically, then, maximum pleasure will never be theirs.

Cognitive Structure

Just as masochistic patients are convinced of their impotence, sadistic agents are convinced of their omnipotence. This distorted perception of power is the result of an overgeneralization of a frequently repeated early learned experience of the world. The early world was divided bipolarly into powerful exploiters with all entitlement and powerless exploited with no entitlement.

Attitude toward risk. Masochistic patients are risk-sensitive. Fear, vacillation, and doubt make decisions difficult for them. They readily accept decisions made by others because they do not feel competent to decide for themselves. They tend to be somewhat paralyzed by their own thoughts and emotions even if, objectively, the risk factor is relatively unimportant. Sadistic agents, on the other hand, are overly convinced by their own arguments and do not measure risk well because they misjudge their actual ability to control external reality. They tend to minimize risk—especially if it comes from factors outside their control. Their ability to manipulate the perceptions of others bolsters their sense of omnipotence, unfortunately, thus further distorting their perception of risk.

Loss-gain strategy. If freed to make decisions, masochistic patients do so with the objective of avoiding loss. In general, though, they leave decisions to others. The sadistic agents are the decision makers. Because of their deep sense of self-confidence, they tend to minimize risks and idealize gains.

Error sensitivity. An important factor in actualizing systems and modifying theoretical contructs of the world and interpersonal relationships is the ability to recognize and evaluate failure or errors. The sadistic agents deny their own errors and therefore may persist in strategies that fail, all the while blaming the failures on others, fortuitous circumstances, etc. (Festinger, 1957). Masochistic patients attribute reality failure to their own inadequacies or to some error of their protectors. However, even if they correctly perceive the source of the problem, they wait for the other to change the strategy. Success and failure are in the hands of the other.

Breaking the Dyad

Of the two partners in the authoritarian dyad, the masochistic patient is more accessible to therapeutic intervention. The therapist is perceived as an authority figure and hence a source of reality control and "protection." Masochistic patients have, in all probability, learned to be more introspective than their partners—this because of their survival need to serve and second-guess their partners. Sadistic agents, on the other hand, rarely allow self-doubt to penetrate their well-constructed armor of omnipotence and rigid, authoritarian control.

An Authoritarian Dyad Asks for Consultation

The Partners

Jane is a 23-year-old white housewife referred for treatment by her personal physician, who was consulted because of weight loss and stomach pains. In taking the history he noted that Jane was under the stress of a possible divorce. Her first and only child was 13 months old.

Tom, her 28-year-old white executive husband, made the first contact with the therapist by telephone. He made the appointment and asked about the fee, which he sent with his wife in a sealed envelope.

He made it clear that something must be done about his wife, stating that if she did not improve, he would have to divorce her since, he could not "stand much more of this kind of life."

Jane, an unattractively dressed woman, stated that "apart from a miracle, there is no hope for me." She felt to blame for the inminent break-up of their marriage. "I have no interest in sex. You know, in my religion they taught me that I must submit to my husband's needs, and I don't ever do that. There is no pleasure in it for him."

The history revealed that there was no foreplay, that Jane was insulted and humiliated during the act, and that her husband was "rough" and gave no importance to her needs. Jane, however, attributed no relevance to these facts, viewing herself exclusively as a "frustrator." She justified his rejecting and unpleasant sexual behavior as a sign of his manhood, while she was a failure as a woman.

Typical excerpts from interviews with Jane and telephone communications with Tom follow:

JANE: I feel so badly. Some visitors came last night. I didn't have the energy to fix anything yesterday. They liked the pastries, and Tom ordered me to make some. When they asked me if I had made them, I did a bad thing. I boastfully said yes. Then Tom laughed and said, "Pastries! What pastries could my wife make? She bought them this afternoon—and that is an accomplishment. At least she went to the bakery." I felt so awful but he is right. He didn't acknowledge my making the pastries so that I wouldn't indulge myself.

TOM: (By phone) Did you get the money I sent you? I don't see any improvement in her—the same boring unattractive person. How much longer, Doctor?

JANE: Doctor, I did what you said. I fixed myself up, but I look so awful because I'm so thin. He told me, too. He said "My God. You've lost more weight! Can't you hide that in some way? Use a blousy dress, do something clever at least once!" I think that definitively I have an uncurable lack of femininity!

Working Diagnosis

Tom and Jane form an authoritarian dyad, where Tom is a frustrating, blaming, and devaluing domineering-controlling psychoticizing sadistic agent, and Jane is a frustrated, blamed, and devalued submissive-dependent psychoticized masochistic patient.

In the socioeconomic sphere, Tom is the agent because the locus of socioeconomic control is in him and is perceived by him and Jane as being in him. Jane is the patient because she does not entertain the possibility of having some degree of control over her life.

1.   Tom makes the major decisions, and Jane accepts them.
     • Jane's entrance into treatment is suggested by her physician and decided by her husband.
     • The therapeutic goals are set by Tom.
     • Her appointment time is fixed by her husband.
2.   Tom controls information.

- The envelope with payment is sealed.
- Tom does not reveal the information about the pastries to the friend.
- Tom calls the therapist with his comments on Jane's progress.

3. Tom controls resources and believes the locus of control over his future is within himself, whereas Jane feels that hers is in someone else's hands.
   - Jane had no plan for separation.
   - She knows nothing about the economic future of the family.
   - She feels that improvement would come as a miracle.
   - Tom is the sole breadwinner.

4. Tom represents the couple in their relations with the outside world.
   - He is the one who goes out to work.
   - He chooses the family friends.
   - He defines the nature of these outside relationships.
   - He makes the therapeutic contact.

In the interpersonal sphere, Tom is the sadist and Jane the masochist.

1. In interpersonal authority Tom commands and Jane obeys.
   - The physician told Jane to go to the psychiatrist.
   - Tom ordered Jane to make some pastries.
   - Jane understood—and tried to obey—when the psychiatrist suggested she fix herself up.
   - Tom ordered Jane to use a blousy dress to hide her loss of weight.

2. In interpersonal qualifications Tom is principally devaluing and Jane is both self-devaluing and self-blaming, while overvaluing others.
   - In the pastry incident, Tom publicly humiliated Jane and she accepted it, feeling that he was justified.
   - Her efforts at fixing herself up resulted in greater devaluation on Tom's part. This was fully accepted by her.
   - Implicit in his conversation with the therapist is a dissatis-

faction with therapeutic progress. The therapist is judged and found wanting.

- She, on the other hand, idealizes her husband and the therapist; they are trying to educate a very stupid student.

3. In interpersonal satisfaction and frustration (victim-victimizer), Tom blames the problem on Jane, the therapist, etc. and sees himself as suffering the frustrating consequences of their behavior. That is, he sees himself as the frustrated satisfier of Jane, the therapist, etc., whom he sees as his satisfied frustrators.

- Tom states that he "couldn't stand much more of this kind of (frustrating) life.
- Tom sees no improvement (he is frustrated), while he places all responsibility for improvement on the therapist and his wife.
- Jane feels that she does not meet her husband's sexual needs and is totally responsible for his frustration, while in fact he is clumsy in his approaches and frustrates her sexually. He claims to be the victim of little sexual gratification from an unattractive woman.
- Tom says that he is the victim of a lazy wife who doesn't make pastries for the visitors, while in fact she does. He humiliates (victimizes) her unnecessarily (and in bad faith) with his visitors.
- He says that he is frustrated by her nonimprovement, while he frustrates her in her small attempts at improvement.

With respect to reality testing, Tom is psychoticizing and Jane is psychoticized.

1. Tom denies her reality (making the pastries).
2. Tom creates a negative socioeconomic consensus for Jane.

3

The Demagogic
——Dyad——

The demagogic dyad consists of a masochistic agent and a sadistic patient. Unlike the authoritarian dyad, this couple minimizes the importance of the agent's socioeconomic dominance. Masochistic agents play down their achievements, attributing them to chance or lucky opportunities. Sadistic patients, though fully aware of their own socioeconomic dependence, exploit their partners' delusions about romantic love and desire to be valued for their own "intrinsic" worth. Highly skilled at manipulating their masochistic partner's feelings, sadistic patients define themselves as the true possessors and givers of love and morality. Masochistic agents then find themselves in the uncomfortable position of being used rather than loved.

The demagogic dyad strikes the following bargain. In order to avoid what they fear most—loneliness—masochistic agents exchange hedonistic and moral pleasure for company. They avoid unpleasure, rather than actively seeking pleasure. In exchange for their valued company, sadistic patients demand all pleasure from their partners. They do not accept the limitations of reality or the frustrations of the reality principle. The socioeconomic reality principle is denied; romanticism reigns supreme.

————————————— The Masochistic Agent —————————

The two basic clinical traits of a masochistic agent are (1) control
of socioeconomic reality and (2) submission to the interpersonal
authority of the partner. Such people are both controlling and
submissive; they act like spoiling caretakers of spoiled dependents.
Masochistic agents seem to be concerned, modest, sensible, warm
people who are saddled with the care of denigrating, demanding,
unrealistic, childish others. The agents usually have higher educational, occupational, and monetary status than their charges.
Nevertheless, they feel worthless by comparison. Consequently,
their anxiety stems from their sense of inferiority and loneliness.
They fear that they will be abandoned unless they buy the
affections of others; they usually sell themselves very cheaply.

The Clinical Interview

Masochistic agents perceive the therapist as a socially powerless but badly needed instrument whose function is to assist them in
regaining control over their problematic dependent others. Masochistic agents really don't trust therapy, even though they may be
very submissive and modest in their outward behavior. In truth,
they think it will be possible to manipulate the therapist to further
their own goals (or to be manipulated by the therapist to further
his or her own goals).

For instance, masochistic agents customarily talk constantly
about their spoiled charges, while avoiding all discussion of their
own feelings. They seem to resemble "invisible" clients who are
only reporting the objective "facts" about those they live with. In
other words, the clinical interview becomes transformed into a
supervisory interview, in which the therapist guides the masochistic agent in the treatment of the "real" clients, the agent's
significant others. However, when there has been a real crisis in
the relationship, masochistic agents are willing to discuss their
depression, feelings of inferiority, and fear of loneliness.

In any event, such clients are very considerate of the therapist's needs. They may offer to rearrange their entire schedule just
to suit the therapist. If the therapist does not behave like a

demanding, spoiled child, they may appear disappointed. But at the same time, paradoxically, the therapist must come across as a cautious, sensible, reflective, and caring adult when discussing the masochistic agent's treatment of sadistic dependents because these clients perceive themselves as cotherapists who are merely being assisted by the therapist. Unless we exercise caution, we therapists may find ourselves acting in an authoritarian and demanding fashion, while simultaneously leaving the strategy of the treatment in the hands of our client. And underneath our client's apparent acquiescence to our suggestions is great resistance to the treatment; masochistic agents are far more ready to "help" others—the therapist included—than to let others help them to make fundamental changes. What they least tolerate is the dependent patient role.

Family of Origin

As a rule masochistic agents come from families in which competition is overregulated, and authority is not exercised by the member who is in charge of economic survival (Toffler, 1981). Whereas the authoritarian families of the sadistic agent and the masochistic patient were complementary with respect to economic control and interpersonal authority, the demagogic families of the masochistic agent and the sadistic patient place control in one member and authority in the other; that is, the socioeconomically strong "allows the weak to feel and behave as if he were the strong" (Watzlawick, Beavin & Jackson, 1967).

In this type of "welfare family," the person who earns the money has no authority or respect. The children are spoiled and the breadwinner is unable to set healthy limits. Instead, the adult in charge controls through manipulation, that is, by letting the dependents think they are in command, while in actual fact they are merely doing exactly what the demagogic "weak" leader had unconsciously or consciously suggested that they do.

Generally, the masochistic agent's same-sex parent is a domineering, financially dependent follower, while the opposite-sex parent, the breadwinner, is an obedient, submissive leader. For example, if the father is spoiled, demanding, and dependent (a sadistic patient), the mother and the sons would be spoiling caretakers, and the daughter a spoiled childish princess.

Consequently, masochistic agents learn how to behave as inferior, demagogic, spoiling caretakers, who do not feel intrinsically lovable but must buy the love of others. They are never allowed either to depend on or have authority over their same-sex parent. Instead, they learn from the opposite-sex parent to hide their open authority and aggression while allowing others to depend on them economically. For example, the mother of the male masochistic agent asks him to take care of and submit to his father simultaneously. Thus, the son becomes the socioeconomic "father" of his father, while feeling the need for his father's protection and affection. The daughter needs the love and approval of the mother, who may be both demanding and financially dependent.

Adult Social and Family Roles

As has been stated, the social role permitted to the client in the larger society may not be the social role that he or she fills in the family. Masochistic agents may be employed by other masochistic agents. At work, therefore, they may function as sadistic patients, manipulating and behaving in a spoiled fashion and demanding special benefits. This is a frequent perversion in established democracies. Politicians may promise benefits which are not earned or available, in order to get the vote and appear more "lovable" and "better" than the opposition. In other words, politicians buy votes demagogically. Pleasure and gratification divorce themselves from the reality principle, and the society becomes the supermasochistic agent to the unrealistic sadistic patient that it has encouraged and developed.

Object Relations and Clinical Traits

In accordance with their family experience, masochistic agents act as if they were always facing a sadistic-patient type of person, and their spouse, partners, and friends usually belong to this category. Masochistic agents generally depend affectively on financially dependent persons.

Masochistic agents seem to be very soft, tactful, warm, overprotective people. They are "pushers"—subtle, effective dependency makers who tend to monopolize financial control and exclude others from decisions and responsibilities.

On the job they are usually very skilled in dealing with meetings, boards, regulations, etc. They thrive on bureaucracy. They tend to overidentify with the organization. In fact, they are successful belongers, good when working for institutions but not on their own. They become extremely anxious if they cease to be a part of a well-known and prestigious organization (Schachter, 1959).

They are usually overqualified for their job but lack the self-confidence to climb further up the bureaucratic ladder or take real risks (Blau, 1955). Considering the quality and quantity of work they do and the responsibilities they assume, they are underpaid. Their dependents usually reproach them for this, asserting that the organization is exploiting them; but such reproaches fall on deaf ears because of the masochistic agent's tremendous need for acceptance by the organization. In this sense masochistic agents are much less ambitious and more cautious than sadistic agents. While they are fully capable of making decisions and assuming responsibility, they need the framework of a "protective" organization. Paradoxically, many times the survival of the company depends on their managerial abilities—just as their same-sex parent survived only because of the masochistic agent's financial protection.

But even if they are dependent on the organization, they are the undisputed leaders of their social microgroup: they have larger incomes, more education, and better jobs. However, just as the sadistic agent needs the help of the masochistic patient when dealing with bureaucratic issues, the masochistic agent sometimes needs the support or initiative of the sadistic patient when dealing with economic decisions related to his or her own interests.

Although they may coolly decide how the organization should invest $5 million, they are extremely insecure when they have to invest $100,000 of their own money to buy a house. The decision is finally made only after an outburst of rage or desperation on the part of their sadistic dependents (Jackson, 1959).

Masochistic agents never appreciate or praise any of their dependents' efforts to achieve economic independence. On the contrary, this is the only time when they lose their temper and start blaming their dependents for being ungrateful.

They feel uncomfortable when someone gives them a present, even though they are constantly giving wonderful gifts to others. In fact, because they think they are unworthy of any gift, they often become sad or angry. "Stop being so damned generous," one young man told his girlfriend when she gave him a birthday gift. It is very clear that this was a projection of his own "damned" generosity. Because he was actually a compulsive altruist, a compulsive spoiler, he was capable of spoiling a child or a pet within just a few days.

Consequently, masochistic agents turn others into selfish cripples by creating an artificial world where the living is easy as long as they remain utterly dependent. For this reason they always praise or reward the childish attitudes of those close to them and seem immensely amused and touched by them. The agent infantilizes in a subtle, persistent way; for example, when someone in the family is sick, the agent relishes the role of a martyred and extremely patient nurse (Mahler, 1952).

The following transaction shows how Sam, a blamed and devalued masochistic agent, cripples Grace, his blaming and devaluing histrionic sadistic patient wife, through overprotection. He tolerates her spoiled behavior and unreasonable demands and relieves her of her adult responsibilities.

GRACE: *(Crying and screaming)* I don't know what to do! I'm a total failure as a mother. Even if I sacrifice myself beyond description, the children don't want to play with me.
SAM: *(Trying to console)* Don't worry, my darling. Maybe it's

because they've hardly seen you at all during the last few days, only because of your ballet classes, the hairdresser, and the bridge competition.

GRACE: Are you trying to imply that I'm selfish? Of course, always justifying the children and accusing me . . .

SAM: *(Justifying himself)* Oh, no! Please don't get me wrong! What I'm trying to say is that they are just children. Maybe they didn't pay enough attention to you because they were thinking about playing with their friends. Who knows? But they certainly love you very much.

GRACE: *(Crying)* Maybe, but they are very selfish children. Only thinking of themselves.

SAM: *(Kind and tender)* OK. OK. I'll tell them right away to come and try to play with their mother. They are good children, but maybe they don't realize how sensitive you are, how delicate your feelings are.

GRACE: *(Angry again)* Maybe it's because they prefer to stay with their "dear Daddy"! You're always spoiling them so much. *(Crying)*

SAM: *(Worried)* Please don't cry. You know that I love you more than anything in this world. Maybe I've been thinking too much of the children and of business lately.

A remarkable trait of the masochistic agent is the ease with which he or she abandons an adult interest to take care of some childish mistake or behavior of a dependent other. This trait is particularly apparent when the masochistic agent is dealing with creative, nonbureaucratic work. Because they are so bureaucratized and ritualized, they suffer greatly when they have to do creative work. Consequently, the childish troubles of the dependent others serve as a means of escape. He cannot write because he has his family; she cannot think because they need her. Thus, although they complain that their obligations prevent them from doing more creative, less sterile work, in fact, they feel noncreative and impotent and are merely using their dependents' needs as an excuse.

Unconsciously, masochistic agents fear abandonment, and for this reason they encourage their dependents to act like spoiled, unrealistic, aggressive "brats," thus assuring that they will be rejected by society and never leave. This is especially true of the agent's actual children: the agent spoils them and leaves the role of the tough "sergeant" to the other parent. The agent constantly betrays his or her spouse's attempts to set reasonable limits and instead establishes an alliance with the children behind the other parent's back; in that way the spouse is the bad parent, and the agent is the good parent. Because of the agent's ability to modify reality, it is easier to spoil than to educate the children. This ability, which is linked to the agent's feelings of inferiority, prevents the emergence of creative solutions and also results in extremely conservative attitudes, which belie an outwardly permissive appearance. If the spouse attempts to discipline their children, or if the children begin to develop some economic independence, the agent sabotages these attempts in a passive-aggressive manner, for example, by pushing them toward trivial, domestic issues or tempting them with regressive propositions, and so forth. This is at times very evident, and children habitually complain of being exhausted and depressed by the agent's attempts to castrate and cripple them in this sweet, soft manner.

Masochistic agents present the "real world" of work as something ugly, dirty, and extremely difficult to handle—to the point where the dependents become phobic toward it. Through these manipulations, the dependents disqualify themselves as socioeconomic cripples and overqualify the agent as their socioeconomic "tutor." Unlike the sadistic agent, however, the masochistic agent is usually honest and does not exploit his or her dependents.

Masochistic agents ignore, deny, or rationalize all attempts to make them confront their role in maintaining the economic dependence of their significant others—even though they sometimes complain about their responsibilities to others. Indirectly, they attack the reputation and prestige of their dependents in order to isolate them economically and make them even more dependent (Wynne, Rychoff, Day & Mirsch, 1958). Dependents may even be induced to denigrate themselves and attack their own prestige. In brief, the agent unconsciously attacks the objective status of close family and friends, even while consciously trying to help them upgrade their socioeconomic status (Kadushin, 1966).

Because of their inferior subjective status, masochistic agents tend to idealize the love worth of their dependent others while putting themselves down. This is a very vicious circle. Although they want to be loved by a worthy person who will elevate their own opinion of themselves, they don't believe they can achieve such a goal because their own parents convinced them they were not lovable. Consequently, they look for an idealized, artificially overvalued person who will depend on them financially and socially.

But this idealized other is usually a dependent sadist, who further devalues the masochistic agent by making it clear that the agent's only worth lies in the unrestricted offer of money or social protection. In this way, the vicious circle is closed because the masochistic agent feels progressively less and less lovable, and the only alternative is to control and overprotect the sadistic-dependent others in a crippling way. Hence, the agent becomes an addict to the dependent cruelty of the significant others, who exploit this addiction to the fullest, knowing that despite their economic dependence they have complete affective control: the agent cannot make it emotionally without them. If the agent does stop being overprotective or denounces the dependents' sadism, they may threaten suicide or homicide or other types of destruction, such as attacking the agent's social prestige (Watzlawick, 1978).

If the sadistic-patient partner stopped being sadistic, this would precipitate a minor affective crisis, possibly causing the agent to seek other spoiled protégés. But a far more serious crisis would ensue if the other partner finally ceased to be dependent. The situation would become intolerable if the agent's objective status were lowered, for example, through job loss or a decrease in social standing.

Defense Mechanisms

The masochistic agent applies typical interpersonal and intrapsychic defense mechanisms in order to avoid feelings of unpleasure or devastating loss of control.

Interpersonal defenses.   Masochistic agents

1. Compulsively and unconsciously select sadistic patients—and reject nonsadistic patients—as significant others (selection of complementary partner)
2. Induce others to behave in a dependent and obedient fashion (induction of complementary behavior)
3. Systematically avoid all discussion of their infantilizing, crippling economic control over those who are dear to them by compulsively talking only about irrelevant issues or devaluing their self-worth (displacement by trivialization or personalization)
4. Insist repeatedly that they—and not their partners—are the initiators and perpetrators of their sadomasochistic interactions (inversion of direction and sequence of sadomasochism)
5. Repeatedly insist on their sadistic mistreatment of others in the same stereotyped way (narrowing)

Intrapsychic defenses.   Intrapsychically, masochistic agentism is played out as follows:

1. Unconsciously, masochistic patients view themselves as (controlling-submissive) parent-servants and others as (dependent-domineering) child-masters, while consciously they view themselves as (controlling-domineering) parent-masters and others as (dependent-submissive) child-servants.
2. They take as "natural" their actual socioeconomic monopoly over and exclusion of others and deny their interpersonal submissiveness by maintaining that they are the ones who force others to submit.
3. They perceive others as masochists and themselves as sadists, idealizing others and blaming and/or devaluing themselves.
4. They always perceive themselves as mistreating others in the same way.

Misqualification and Reality Testing

With respect to status qualification, masochistic agents tend to behave in two principal ways. The depressive masochistic agents blame and devalue themselves, while they idealize and

attribute moral entitlement to their partners (Webster & Sobieszek, 1974), who usually are blaming and devaluing hypochondriac, histrionic, and psychopathic sadistic patients.

On the other hand, the hypomanic masochistic agents tend to
subtly devalue their partners (and idealize themselves). They end
up blaming themselves for this behavior. That is, even if the
hypomanic masochistic agents devalue others, they finally blame
themselves and attribute moral entitlement to devalued but blaming paranoid, explosive or schizophrenic sadistic patients.

Depressive masochistic agents can fall into acute psychotic
reactions when their blaming and devaluing dependents either
launch a devastating attack on their interpersonal reality testing or
suddenly replace them with another spoiling caretaker (Jacobson,
1968). At the same time, depressive masochistic agents are the
typical producers of the borderline syndrome in others. They are
borderliners because, through overprotection, they strongly and
systematically attack others' socioeconomic reality testing. They
are strong agents of mental illness because they specifically stimu-
late others' omnipotence by sparing them from the negative
consequences of their impulsive actions (Giovacchini, Kernberg,
Masterson & Searles, 1980).

The following transaction shows how a blamed and devalued
depressive masochistic agent (Linda) is psychoticized by a spoiled
blaming and devaluing psychopathic sadistic patient (Peter), who
is in turn borderlined by the masochistic agent's overprotection.

LINDA: (*Concerned and crying*) You did it again! You told me you
were going to Buffalo for business, but I called you there and
nobody knew anything about it.

PETER: (*Angry*) You are always controlling me as if I were a
delinquent! When will you stop nagging at me!?

LINDA: (*Frightened*) Yes, but I'm sure that you went to Las Vegas
and spent all our money there. You do it every month. I know you
do!

PETER: (*Still angry*) What do you want from me?! If you want to be
married to a true man, you can't treat him like a child. A man has
the right to enjoy life from time to time.

LINDA: (*Crying*) But we have no money left! We keep paying your debts, and as soon as we pay them they give you credit again. You run to Las Vegas to your destruction, to your utter destruction.

PETER: *(Proud)* That's not true! Sometimes I win, and the money I lose is mine alone, not yours. I saved it.

LINDA: *(Worried)* But I talked to your friend Jimmy, and he told me that you borrowed the money from him.

PETER: *(Furious)* So! you keep controlling me, giving my friends the impression that I'm a delinquent.

LINDA: *(Sad)* No, it was Jimmy who called me and asked me for the money back. I didn't call him. Why do you keep lying to me?

PETER: *(Very angry)* Because I care for your feelings! I don't want to make you sad. I know you hate my going to Las Vegas, but you're the one who doesn't care a bit for my maturity, for my feelings. You want to make a docile pet out of me, a prisoner. But I warn you! I'll fight for my freedom even if I have to leave you! And if it comes down to it, I will!

On the other hand, hypomanic masochistic agents could be either neuroticizers or even psychoticizers because they attack the others' socioeconomic reality testing through overprotection and interpersonal reality testing through subtle devaluations. They can produce in others neurotic or psychotic depressive paranoid, dissociative explosive, or paranoid schizophrenic breakdowns.

The following transaction shows how a blamed but devaluing masochistic agent (Carol) psychoticizes a dissociative explosive, blaming but devalued sadistic patient (Norm):

NORM: I'm very glad I started body building. I was looking like a woman. That was awful, don't you think?

CAROL: *(Smiling)* Certainly, yes, it is always better to look like an old man than like an old woman.

NORM: *(Astonished and extremely angry)* What did you say? What did you say? Are you crazy? That I look like an old man? *(Shouting)* You're always attacking me every time I try to improve myself.

CAROL: *(Very calm, as if dealing with an unpredictable lunatic)* I didn't mean that at all! I'm just agreeing with you. I'm saying that society is very unjust and tends to accept the looks of an old man better than the looks of an old woman. Eventually when I talked about an old man I was referring to myself . . .

NORM: *(Confused but still angry)* You have a very poisonous tongue. When I was happy you called me an old man, and now that I'm miserable, you try to be tender with me.

CAROL: *(Patiently and tenderly)* Sometimes I wonder if you don't have some specific difficulty in enjoying life. You were so unhappy during your childhood.

NORM: *(Moved)* Well, this is true. I realize that sometimes I am oversensitive.

CAROL: *(Smiling tenderly)* Now you are coming back to your senses. You must forgive me. Sometimes I forget how fragile you are . . . *(Ironically)* "Old Man."

NORM: *(Confused and very anxious)* I never know whether you are joking or insulting me.

The Sadistic Patient

The two basic traits of a sadistic patient are (1) avoidance of socioeconomic control and (2) dominance in the exercise of interpersonal authority. In other words, sadistic patients are controlled but domineering, the spoiled dependents of spoiling caretakers. They are usually egocentric, theatrical, and demanding. They order others, in an authoritarian and seductive way, to take care of their every whim and unrealistic demand. Although they may be lower down on the socioeconomic ladder, they feel superior—smarter, wittier, holier—to their masochistic-agent partner. Kernberg's (1975) description of borderline patients who are emotionally labile, irresponsible, seductive, manipulating, and exploiting coincides roughly with certain types of sadistic patients. Their greatest anxiety stems from the loss of feelings of omnipotence and a confrontation with catastrophic, intolerable feelings of impotent frustration. These characteristics make them avoid painful confrontations with reality by abusing drugs and alcohol (Loberg, Marlat, & Nathan, 1980).

The Clinical Interview

In most cases, sadistic patients are sent into therapy by their partners because their destructive behavior is getting out of control. The therapist is included in the picture as an emergency force who may be able to neutralize and disarm explosive situations and further a more civilized type of interpersonal negotiation between the two partners in this pathological dyad. Hence sadistic patients really do not trust the therapy. Instead, they perceive the therapist as a tolerant instrument to be used either to satisfy all their omnipotent, unrealistic wishes or to influence their over-protective masochistic-agent partners. Their behavior toward the therapist can be very seductive.

Very early in the interview, the therapist experiences an overwhelming feeling of responsibility; this stems from the remarkable ability of sadistic patients to live as a parasite on others and to make others feel responsible for their own careless and destructive behavior. Such clients convey to the therapist that they are entitled to protection and infinite patience in exchange for little more than their—at times charming—company. If the therapist is less than pleasant and compliant, this charm can very quickly be turned into threatening anger; the therapist may then be facing a very volatile and dangerous balance of charm, blackmail, and terror (Kernberg, 1967).

In fact, it is quite difficult to establish a regular schedule with such clients. From the beginning they demand very special conditions, and if the therapist does not accept these conditions, such clients will make all manner of dire threats—to quit the treatment, commit suicide, or carry out some other destructive behavior (Emerson, 1962).

In such circumstances we therapists face a very hard negotiator, who may alternately fascinate or terrify us and push us into accepting counterproductive conditions for the treatment. We may find ourselves being warm, overpermissive, obedient, or protective to an unhealthy extent. The whole meaning of treatment may be subtly but profoundly distorted. Sooner or later, it will be necessary to make an "adult" contract with our client's partner in order to consolidate the therapy (Gamson, 1968).

Family of Origin

As a rule the sadistic patient comes from the same type of family as the masochistic agent, in which one parent is the breadwinner and the other parent—the nonbreadwinner—exercises authority. The parents are overly tolerant, weak, and unable to satisfy the omnipotent unrealistic demands of their children, who are spoiled and irresponsible (Perez, 1979).

Sadistic patients are in a paradoxical situation. Although they may be idealized by other family members, they have never been trained for independence (Gear, Hill & Liendo, 1981). This idealization then becomes a trap, a prison, and they lack the necessary discipline and training to improve their objective status and break free. Usually, the family group sets very high intellectual, artistic, or financial standards and implicitly expects nothing less than genius from the sadistic patient—a totally unrealistic and impossible goal. For this reason sadistic patients usually feel overwhelmed at the slightest hint of failure. Though spoiled, they are also unrealistically perfectionistic. Such people flee from all confrontations with socioeconomic reality because of the internal contradiction in their lives: they are not geniuses if they have to learn from others, but they cannot become geniuses without learning from others.

As with the masochistic agent, the sadistic patient usually identifies with the parent of the opposite sex and rejects the role model of the same-sex parent. For example, if the father is a spoiling caretaker, the mother and the sons will be spoiled dependents (sadistic patients) and the daughter will become a masochistic agent.

Adult Social and Family Roles

Sadistic patients have great difficulty in changing, since they lack both the skills, initiative, and reasoning capacity of an agent and the masochist's ability to tolerate frustration. Therefore they tend to retain their socioeconomic position or escalate their sadistic actions. If this fails, they find new partners (Bales & Slater, 1955). Alternately, they may force all those close to them to relate as masochistic agents. For example, a hypochondriacal mother will force her less powerful son into nursing her, as would a masochistic "agent." When it is possible to do so, the son will resume his preferred position, that of sadistic patient.

Object Relations and Clinical Traits

Sadistic patients act as if they were always facing a masochistic agent—which their spouse and most of their friends are. They have special skills which enable them to manipulate those close to them, to be the "power behind the throne." But they are heavily dependent on the real power broker, the masochistic agent (Fox, Payne, Priest & Phillber, 1977).

They usually hate institutions; they cannot tolerate the predictability, stability, and discipline of bureaucracies. Frequently, they drop out of school or move from job to job. They have no staying power, and their unrealistic attitude toward their own abilities makes them quit easily.

The masochistic agent serves as a ready scapegoat for failing to provide the right conditions in which the sadistic agent's true talents can shine forth. The conditions can *never* be satisfactory because if they are, then the sadistic patient would be forced to confront his or her own failure to produce works of genius. If conditions are optimal and our client is unable to give the required extraordinary performance, he or she may attempt suicide.

Sadistic patients also react very badly when left with adult responsibilities: they behave more irresponsibly than usual. However, sometimes when their partner is indecisive about a reality decision, sadistic patients may explode in frustration and rage, thus "pressuring" the masochistic agent into a decision. Such indecisiveness threatens the patient's need for security and dependence.

Sadistic patients treat all discussions about money or politics as trivial, either ignoring or disrupting serious discussions. Such people can be sweet, warm, and charming one moment and nasty, cold, and bitter the next, alternately rewarding and punishing those upon whom they depend for survival. Their style is often characterized by flamboyant histrionics (Reid, 1980).

Just like a sick person who cannot manage without a full-time nurse, the more spoiled, omnipotent, and unrealistic these sadistic patients become, the more they will fail in reality control, be rejected by society, and be forced to depend on the masochistic agents in their lives. The vicious circle is self-perpetuating. And they delude themselves further by accepting the agent's assessment of the "real world" as ugly, dirty, and very difficult. In fact, they think they are very smart to allow others to take care of them. They fail to realize that this is the cleverness of a slave.

Sadistic patients, like sadistic agents, idealize themselves; they see themselves as adorable, altruistic, sensible, and witty and consider their caretakers to be selfish, dumb, crazy, and unlovable (Bem, 1967). Deep down, they despise their caretakers, who take away their autonomy and adulthood precisely by giving them all that they demand. They are not as economically naive as the masochistic patient: their first priority is to maintain their omnipotence, but they also know that their economic welfare depends on their ability to seduce and dominate those who control the purse strings (Bander & Grinder, 1975).

Sadistic patients may suffer an affective crisis if their overprotective others stop being masochistic: they would be unhappy and would possibly look for a new spoiling caretaker. But a far more serious crisis is precipitated if the masochistic agent stops being overprotective or if our client ceases to be a charming, manipulative dependent: such people do not tolerate aging, for instance, because they lose the capacity of using their body as an instrument of seduction.

Defense Mechanisms

Interpersonal defenses.   Sadistic patients

1. Compulsively and unconsciously select masochistic agents—and reject nonmasochistic agents—as significant others (selection of complementary partners)
2. Induce others to protect and submit to them (induction of complementary behavior)
3. Systematically avoid all discussion of their socioeconomic self-exclusion, and dependence on others who infantilize and cripple them, by compulsively talking about irrelevant issues or devaluing others' worth (displacement by trivialization or personalization)

4. Insist repeatedly that they—and not their partners—are the ones who are put down, persecuted, blamed, and otherwise victimized by others' sadomasochistic games (inversion of direction and sequence of sadomasochism)
5. Repeatedly insist on the mistreatment they receive from others in the same stereotyped way (narrowing)

Intrapsychic defenses.   Sadistic patientism is played out as follows:

1. Unconsciously, sadistic patients view themselves as (dependent-domineering) child-masters and others as (controlling-submissive) parent-servants, while consciously they view themselves as (dependent-submissive) child-servants and others as (controlling-domineering) parent-masters.
2. They take as "natural" their actual socioeconomic dependence and self-exclusion and deny their interpersonal dominance and manipulation by maintaining that they are the ones who are persecuted.
3. They perceive themselves as masochists and others as sadists, idealizing themselves and blaming and/or devaluing others.
4. They always perceive themselves as mistreated by others in the same way.

Misqualification and Reality Testing

Complementing masochistic agents, sadistic patients tend to behave in two different ways with respect to status qualification. There are sadistic patients who blame and devalue depressive masochistic agents and who idealize and entitle themselves: they can be either histrionics, hypochondriacs, or psychopaths (Jacobson, 1959).

On the other hand, there are sadistic patients who blame but are devalued by hypomanic masochistic agents. They entitle but devalue themselves: they can be either depressive paranoids, dissociative explosives, or paranoid schizophrenics (Jacobson, 1966).

Blaming and devaluing sadistic patients can produce acute

psychotic reactions in their depressive masochistic agents by attacking their interpersonal reality testing or by suddenly abandoning them. At the same time they are extremely prone to be borderlined by these masochistic agents who attack their socioeconomic reality testing; the borderlined are constantly sheltered from having to face the negative consequences of their counterproductive irresponsible actions (Kernberg, 1975).

Unlike the psychoticized subjects, who are practically out of touch with socioeconomic reality and perceive only the relevance of sadomasochism, the borderlined are very much materialists who make their decisions in terms of manipulating the masochistic agents into solving their socioeconomic problems (Grinker, 1973).

The following transaction shows how Ralph, a very dependent blaming and devaluing psychopathic sadistic patient, neuroticizes Liz, an extremely overprotective depressive masochistic agent, who, in turn, borderlines him:

Liz: Did you put in your application at the university?
RALPH: (Defiant) No! What do you think, that I'm your servant?
Liz: But it was extremely important that you put in your application today.
RALPH: You know that I can't stand those people at the admissions office. They're arrogant and unkind.
Liz: (Concerned) I understand your feelings, but it is your letter of application to the university. You can't miss this last opportunity.
RALPH: (Angry) My application, my foot! You're the one who wants me to continue studying, not me.
Liz: (Begging) But you can't go on sleeping, watching television, and using drugs all your life! I already did all the necessary preliminary steps for you to get in. This was the only thing that I couldn't do for you. Oh my God! What should we do?
RALPH: I couldn't care less. This is your problem. If you want me to obey you, you should at least clear the way for me.
Liz: (Thinking) Well, maybe we can ask Dr. Wilson to give me a certificate stating that you are too sick to go in person. In this way, maybe they will allow me to put in the application myself, and you can be spared the experience of dealing with these people at the

admissions office. They might give you a wrong idea of what the university is like.

On the other hand, blaming but devalued sadistic patients can be psychoticized by the combined attack on their social and interpersonal reality by their devaluing and overprotecting hypomanic masochistic agents. (Freud, 1924).

The following transaction shows how Joe, a spoiling but ironic hypomanic masochistic agent, sets the trap to produce an angry outburst in Anita, a dissociative explosive sadistic patient:

JOE: Good news! My boss told me that we are going for a whole week to Florida for a convention. Isn't that something? In the middle of winter! Can you imagine the sun, the beach?

ANITA: Oh! I'm so happy! I really need a vacation! I was feeling so depressed around here, tired of all the relatives picking on me. I'm especially sick of your sister Peggy! She enjoys putting me down. She purposely excludes me all the time.

JOE: (*With a disappointed face and surprised tone*) Ah! Are you coming too?

ANITA: (*Very angry*) How dare you ask me that! Of course I'm going. I'm your wife, after all! You're so damned selfish! You're just like your sister!

JOE: (*Interrupting her in a very soft tender tone*) Don't misinterpret me, sweetheart. You got me wrong. What I was asking you was if you really wanted to come with me. I didn't know, I thought that maybe you were tired. (*Changing to an ironic tone*) Maybe you don't want to go on vacation with your stupid selfish husband . . .

ANITA: (*Still very angry*) You know perfectly well what I am talking about. First, you tried to exclude me, to get rid of me, and now you are playing innocent and making fun of me as if I were an idiot.

JOE: (*Still ironically*) If you say so. No, I'm joking again.

Complementarity in the
——————— Demagogic Dyad ———————

The Problem

The goal for the masochistic agent is the avoidance of unpleasure, and for the sadistic patient the seeking of pleasure. Unlike the masochistic patient, the masochistic agent has enough basic skills and competence to guarantee survival But masochistic agents are victims of their own devalued self-image; they perceive themselves as unlovable and in constant danger of abandonment. Their sadistic partners encourage this devalued self-image, since threat of abandonment is their only weapon—the only hook by which they keep the masochistic partner attached. Hence, any effort on the part of the masochistic partner to seek pleasure is branded as "selfish" and "egotistical." Sadistic patients present themselves as the embodiment of lovability. They promise love and moral approval, or at least the absence of overt disapproval, in exchange for material and moral pleasures. Thus they acquire entitlement to pleasure despite their lack of achievement or productivity. Their wish is the other's command.

Masochistic agents are obsessed with a desire to confirm their goodness and lovability, and this is precisely what their partners exploit. To achieve a true sense of self-worth and value, they have to reject the manipulative coercion of their partners—and live with the real possibility of abandonment. Because they have bought the affections of others, they can never feel secure in their partner's love.

On the other hand, pleasure-oriented sadistic patients will never achieve the maximum degree or quality of pleasure as long as they persist in remaining dependent and exploiting others. The paradox is that what they claim to have—love—is what they can never truly give; hence they are denied the meaningful pleasure of a truly equal relationship.

Cognitive Structure

Just as masochistic agents are convinced of their unlovability, sadistic patients are overly convinced of their own lovability (Green & Taylor, 1969). This distorted sense of values results from an overgeneralization of an oft-repeated early experience of the world, which was divided into the lovable, worthy, and self-valuing and the unlovable, unworthy, and self-devaluing. The right to certain benefits was exchanged for the promise of love (Crown & Marlow, 1964). Any attempt to exercise such rights by the masochistic agent was qualified as morally bad and he or she was threatened by withdrawal of love.

Attitude toward risk. Masochistic agents may be indecisive, but not so much because of the risk as because of the fear of losing the company of the sadistic patient. When not under emotional pressure, they are less omnipotent and more accurate in their assessment of risk than sadistic agents. Those who are chronically depressed may exaggerate the risk or be afraid to take action.

Sadistic patients want pleasure so much and are so little influenced by the reality principle that they may not measure risk well. Those who tend toward impulsiveness and histrionics, for example, may not calculate risk at all well because they do not realize the future consequences of their acts. They obtain immediate pleasure and are too bound to the here and now to examine risk probabilities based on past experience. They do not analyze or contextualize well.

Loss-gain strategy. If left to themselves, masochistic agents would probably make decisions to avoid loss. If of the manic type, they would be more concerned with a gain orientation. On their own, their attitude toward loss and gain would probably be realistic; however, when coupled with the sadistic patient, masochistic agents promise gain, and struggle toward gain, even in unrealistic circumstances.

Error sensitivity. Sadistic patients are protected from the consequences of errors in thinking or behavior by their masochistic-agent others. Their omnipotence therefore is fomented by this protection, and they do not even receive information that a significant error has been committed in the socioeconomic sphere (Bruner, 1973).

Masochistic agents are sensitive to their own errors in the socioeconomic arena but tend to blame themselves for the errors of others. They do think about problems and about others but seldom put themselves in the equation (Bion, 1957).

Breaking the Dyad

Masochistic agents are generally very firmly bound in their pathology. They are convinced that it is a privilege to have such a desirable and challenging partner to look after. They concentrate on the other and how to improve or indulge the other and they do not take very seriously what is being done to them. They give very little importance to their own inner world and concentrate their attention on their sadistic-patient partners. This is the chief difficulty in the therapeutic process with masochistic agents.

Sadistic patients, on the other hand, present the difficulty of having to leave their omnipotence and instrument themselves for the handling of their own socioeconomic reality problems; generally they are not disposed to tolerate the frustration that this implies (Grinker, Werble & Dryer, 1968). It is easier to find another masochistic agent than confront socioeconomic reality. They show an interest in themselves and talk about their inner world but they do not change their behavior very readily (Gunderson & Singer, 1975).

When the couple relationship breaks up, it does so usually because the sadistic patient seduces a more spoiling masochistic agent. But sometimes the sadistic patient is seduced by a still more manipulative sadistic patient: in this case, either a ménage à trois is installed or the seduced sadistic patient goes through a brief performance as a pseudomasochistic agent before breaking down and coming back to his or her old performance.

Masochistic agents tend to have great staying power. They attempt to better and to "save" their dependent partners and leave them with great difficulty.

Sand and Chopin: A Demagogic
——————— Dyad ———————

The Partners

Perhaps one of the clearest and best known examples of a romantic demagogic dyad was the liaison of the talented writer George Sand and the musical genius Frederic Chopin. The relationship is described by William Atwood in *The Lioness and the Little One*. She was the masochistic agent, an overprotective "lioness" and he the sadistic patient, a spoiled "little one."

Sand learned her role as a compulsive helper in her relationship with her demanding and dependent mother who was, interestingly enough, of Polish origin, as was Chopin.

This overprotective relation with her mother is described by Sand in the following:

> I have lost my dear little mother! . . . Poor little woman! Clever, intelligent, artistic, petulant, generous, slightly unstable and selfish. . . . She caused me much suffering and my greatest problems were due to her . . . I never had a mother or a sister to dry my tears. (p. 40)

From this early experience, Sand developed her fascination with and compulsive need to sacrifice herself for apparently helpless others. "I need to suffer for someone. I need to nourish that maternal solicitude whose nature is to look after a tired and suffering being" (p. 7). When Chopin wrote to his friend, Mme. Hanska, he emphasized these maternal qualities. "She is very unhappy and working as a horse. . . . She is not a lovable woman . . . but she is great, generous, devoted . . . an excellent mother" (p. 46).

Chopin learned his complementary spoiled dependent role from his father, an energetic industrious man, of French origin as was Sand. Chopin's mother was, on the other hand, of aristocratic origin and also, like Chopin, protected, quiet, and devout. An example of Chopin's desperate economic dependence is found in his excessive reaction while awaiting funds from his father. He suffered agitation, a sense of desperate futility, became homesick and almost lost his mind, engaging in incoherent talk and behavior. He identifies himself with his mother, indirectly protesting his father's delay in sending funds, saying: "Mother! Sweet suffering Mother! Alone! Alone! Ah, no one can imagine my misery!" (p. 64).

Although specifically cautioned and admonished by his parents to save his money, Chopin could not resist the temptation to take exquisite care of himself, buy expensive and elaborate clothing and generally play the "dandy."

Both Sand and Chopin thought of their relationship more as that of a nourishing, healing mother with her needy son than that of a wifemistress with a mature husband. This is reflected in Mme. Sand's words: "Chopin, for whose genius and character I felt the tenderest affection, said to me several times that if he were in Maurice's [Sand's son] place he would soon be cured himself" (p. 73). It is also reflected by Chopin: "My health is improving day by day . . . all the indefatigable attentions of my angel [Mme. Sand] are putting me back on my feet again" (p. 128). This relationship was apparent even to close friends to the point that Liszt comments: "She was like those sturdily healthy mothers that seem to transfer magnetically some of their strength to children."

Upon recovering somewhat from his illness, Chopin had no difficulty asking favors of his totally devoted friends Fontana and Grzymala as is exemplified in the following admonition to Fontana: "Now don't go to sleep on the job. Love me and write. Forgive me for burdening you with commissions but I believe that you are happy to do what I ask you" (p. 130).

Sand's idealization of his weakness and his impractical nature is revealed when Sand writes:

> This Chopin is an angel. I am afraid he has been too delicately constituted; he is too exquisite, too perfect to survive long in our coarse, crude, earthy life. He himself really doesn't know on what planet he is living, and has no awareness of life as we conceive and experience it. (p. 133)

Again, through Prince Karol (the principal male character of Sand's novel *Lucrezia Floriani*) Sand confides:

> He had no conception at all of reality . . . devoured by a dream of

the ideal . . . did not accept anything of reality. This was his vice and his virtue, his source of greatness and of misery. (p. 205)

Liszt describes Chopin's complete comfort with the position of entitled beneficiary:

Happily complacent in outward appearance, he so completely hid the injury to his rightful pride that its existence was scarcely suspected. . . . A cold, disdain, indeed even an insurmountable aversion. (p. 150)

Atwood poetically describes the dependent, protected mother-child relationship of this helpless child-invalid and this solicitous devoted mother.

Frédéric had entered her life as a lover, and lived in her house as a "guest," and was to develop in her affection as a "second son," but under no circumstances would she ever allow him to entertain the notion that he might be "head" of her family. (p. 160)

With time, Sand completely took the role of Chopin's mother and her behavior toward him became identical to that of her Lucrezia toward Prince Karol. What she says about Prince Karol is totally applicable to Chopin's passion toward her:

Had but one real passion in his whole life: filial love. (p. 208)

Working Diagnosis

Sand and Chopin form a demagogic dyad, where Sand is a frustrated, satisfying, blamed, and devalued submissive controlling borderlining masochistic agent and Chopin is a satisfied, frustrating, blaming, and devaluing domineering, dependent borderlined sadistic patient.

In the socioeconomic sphere, Sand is the agent because the locus of socioeconomic control is in her and is perceived by her and Chopin as being in her. Chopin is the patient because he does not entertain even the possibility of having some degree of control over his life.

1. Sand socioeconomically controls Chopin, who depends on her.

- Chopin is a helpless child looking for a mother (in fact, for his strong, overprotective father).
- Sand was looking for a son (in fact, for her little, spoiled mother).
- Sand is a very strong, healthy mother who works like a horse.
- Chopin's father was sending him funds, while Sand had to take care of her own little mother.
- Chopin says that he would be cured "if he were in Maurice's place."
- Sand has always preferred the role of mother to that of mistress.
- Nothing could be better for Chopin that this overprotective maternal attitude of Sand.
- Chopin kept asking personal favors from his devoted, loyal, long-suffering (masochistic-agent) friends.
- Chopin was out of touch with reality; he seems too delicate, too exquisite to face it.
- Chopin does not know on what planet he is living.
- Under no circumstances will Sand ever allow Chopin to play the role of "head" of the family.
- The true passion of both Sand and Chopin was "filial love." That is, the overprotective parent-spoiled child relationship.
- Chopin was like an invalid, a helpless charge, practically a child.
- Sand had the need to look after a tired and suffering human being.
2. Sand made all major decisions.
    - When Chopin was seriously ill with tuberculosis, she decided to take him to Valdemosa, Spain, to help him get cured.
3. Sand represents the couple in their relations with the outside world.
    - Chopin hated appearing in public or dealing with managers. Sand "protected" him from the public.
    - Chopin could create when he was isolated and protected by Sand.

In the interpersonal sphere, Chopin is the sadist and Sand the masochist.

1. In interpersonal authority, Chopin is the one who commands and Sand the one who obeys.
    - Sand's mothers' was harsh and domineering.
    - Sand is totally devoted to Chopin's minor commands.
    - Chopin commands his faithful friends "not to sleep on the job" he selfishly assigned to them.
2. In interpersonal qualifications, Chopin is devaluing, and Sand is usually devalued and blamed while overvaluing and entitling Chopin.
    - Chopin considers himself an aristocrat, with a rightful pride, a cold disdain, and even an aversion to others.
    - Even if Chopin appreciated Sand's eyes, he secretly considered that she was neither beautiful nor elegant.
    - Sand considered that, in short, she was not lovable.
    - Sand idealized Chopin as being an angel, a perfect and exquisite genius.
    - Chopin considered it logical to equip himself with all luxuries, even if he had little money.
    - Chopin keeps blaming and insulting his publishers and despising his audiences.
3. In interpersonal satisfaction and frustration (victim-victimizer), Chopin considers himself a suffering victim even if he exploits others, while Sand feels the other way around.
    - Sand describes as a "poor little woman" her harsh, selfish, unfeeling mother who "never dried her tears."
    - Sand says that she needs "to suffer for someone . . . to look after a tired and suffering being."
    - Sand gives Chopin "her indefatigable attention."
    - Chopin complains about how lonely he is, that "no one can imagine my misery!"
    - Chopin plays the dandy: his wardrobe was elaborate, expensive, and impeccably elegant.
    - Chopin blames his publishers while frustrating them.
    - Chopin says that his friends were "happy" to do what he asks them.

With respect to reality testing, Sand is borderlining and Chopin is borderlined.

1. Chopin equipped himself with all luxuries, in spite of his parents' advice to save money.
2. Chopin is so delicately constituted that it is difficult for him to survive long in our "coarse, crude, earthy life."
3. Chopin "doesn't know on what planet he is living, and has no awareness of life as we conceive and experience it."
4. Chopin "has no conception at all of reality"; devoured by a dream of the ideal he "did not accept anything of reality."
5. When Chopin tried to change his role and protect Solange (Sand's daughter), Sand becomes extremely disappointed and ended their relationship. Chopin was unable to survive without her protection and died. Sand, who tolerated any kind of childish, spoiled behavior from Chopin, couldn't stand a minor movement toward socioeconomic autonomy and control on his part.

4

The
Undercommitted
——————Dyad——————

Christopher Lasch's (1979) book, *The Culture of Narcissism: American Life in an Age of Diminishing Expectations,* seems to describe a sociopathological change from a "culture of borderlinism"—derived from a society of abundance—to a "culture of insufficientism"—derived from a society going through an economic crisis. We see this in the undercommitted dyad, which consists of a sadistic and a masochistic insufficient. Neither partner has direct economic power over the other or sufficient manipulative skills to control the dyad's economic resources. Both fear real commitment and closeness. The bargain, therefore, is one of limited commitment to common socioeconomic goals. Finances are discussed, but the relationship is constantly measured in terms of obligations and contributions. This relationship is strictly fifty-fifty, an economic bargain that is egalitarian in the narrowest sense of the word. The sadistic partner refuses to be generous; the masochistic partner is afraid to be.

──────── The Masochistic Insufficient ────────

The three basic clinical traits of a masochistic insufficient are (1) restricted control of socioeconomic reality, (2) submission to the interpersonal authority of the partner, and (3) inability to tolerate closeness and consequent phobic withdrawal from others. Escape is possible because masochistic insufficients are able to survive economically on their own. Nevertheless, such people tend to be dominated by others, at least for a time, and then slip away when the domination becomes intolerable. They are pleasant runaways who have limited socioeconomic resources—sufficient for their own needs but not for those of their sadistic partner. They can barely take care of themselves, and even if they are equal to their partners in socioeconomic status, they feel that they are worthless by comparison.

Their main anxiety stems from their fear of being invaded and abused by the sadistic partner. This anxiety leads to a compulsion to escape, and thus they are constantly plagued by feelings of loneliness, feelings which drive them back to their overly aggressive, tenacious partners. Thus the vicious cycle starts again (Patchen, 1970).

The Clinical Interview

Usually masochistic insufficients perceive the therapist as a very needed but feared companion who will help them in their efforts to control and work through their anxiety and their difficulties in forming stable, constructive, and satisfying relationships. They expect the therapist to serve as an nonintrusive antianxiety agent (Searles, 1973).

They frequently talk about their problem in saying no and in setting limits on others' demands. They may also complain of the sudden emergence of terrifying anxiety in certain contexts— which are systematically avoided thereafter. Usually these clients are unable to link such anxiety attacks to specific interpersonal episodes. They may live in their parents' home, somewhat apart from them but not totally. They do not tolerate family tensions well but are unable to be completely independent of them or to form a satisfactory relationship outside the family. So they keep going back and forth, to and from, their family (Gamson, 1968).

Something similar happens with the therapeutic relationship. They won't be able to come often enough because of their scarce economic resources; and they won't ask their family for help because they don't want to be controlled. Or they will not be able to arrange a convenient schedule because they are "unable" to rearrange some other, usually trivial, activities. Unless we therapists recognize the masochistic insufficient's fear of commitment and closeness, we may find ourselves acting in an invasive and possessive manner. But if we try to corner our client into making a solid commitment to the therapy, we will only drive our client into escape (Langs, 1975).

Family of Origin

Usually, masochistic insufficients come from emotionally miserly, conservative, narrow-minded families. Money is scarce; family members are savers, not investors or traders. Economic decisions and leadership are usually shared by both parents, who have limited abilities to increase and to improve their resources. Sometimes this scarcity is idealized as some kind of middle-class wisdom.

The following transaction shows a socioeconomically restrictive relationship between a blaming and devaluing sadistic-insufficient father (Walter) and a blamed and devalued restricted masochistic-insufficient son (Martin):

MARTIN: Do you think that it would be wise for me to accept a new position at the corporation? It's true that it means more responsibilities, but it also seems more exciting. I can get more money. I can be with more interesting people and learn new skills.
WALTER: *(Suspicious)* How much is the raise?
MARTIN: *(Vascillating)* Well, not that much, really. But that's not the point.
WALTER: *(Sarcastically)* That is *the* point, my boy! If they're not giving you more money but are giving you more responsibilities, that means that they are trying to take advantage of you. That's a trap.

MARTIN: *(Doubting)* Really? But maybe it's just that the guy who was working there had to move to another city and couldn't hold the position any longer.

WALTER: That's what they're telling you. Why did he move to another city?

MARTIN: *(Relieved)* Because he went to work in a new family business.

WALTER: *(Still suspicious)* I wouldn't be so sure of that.

MARTIN: *(Trying to convince him)* In any case, in this new position there are more opportunities, more future. Actually I'm on a plateau. My current position doesn't go any further.

WALTER: *(Very sure)* Oh yes! But it's always better to be in control. "The one who wants to grasp too much ends by grasping nothing." It's better to have a bird in the hand than two in the bush, you know.

MARTIN: *(Demoralized)* But I'm pretty sure that this is not too much for me. I won't be out of my depth. I'm prepared for the position. I have the skills, the knowledge.

WALTER: *(Patronizing)* Don't overestimate yourself, my boy. It could be very dangerous. A man must know his limitations. It's always better to be less ambitious but happier and more secure. As you know, blind ambition can kill you. Also, you must think of your family. You can't be so selfish to be thinking only of your future.

MARTIN: *(Convinced and depressed)* Maybe. I should think things over. Maybe I was fascinated by the idea of being in the spotlight. Maybe it would be better to tell them I prefer to remain just where I am. I'd like to preserve my freedom, my family life. Maybe I'll feel trapped there having to face more responsibilities.

   The parent of the opposite sex is either a masochistic agent or a masochistic insufficient who probably works as a bureaucratic employee. But the same-sex parent is either a sadistic patient or a sadistic insufficient who is probably self-employed. This parent's rigidity and argumentative nature tend to cancel out any possibility of economic success, despite other personal abilities (Rappaport & Wallsten, 1972).

Both parents emphasize caution, conformity, and modest ambition. Both idealize modesty and the ability to make do with scarce resources. Neither one ever values the ability to expand and to invest abundant resources (Meier & Johnson, 1977). Also, at some point the masochistic insufficient frequently discovers some awful secret about the parental relationship: for example, that one parent did not divorce the other "because of the children" or, more covertly, because of their own insecurity and lack of self-confidence. Thus the opposite-sex parent—the one who was always nice to our client and with whom our client identifies—is revealed as a coward.

The same-sex parent of the masochistic insufficient is bossy and intrusive with equal objective status and superior subjective status to the opposite-sex parent. The opposite-sex parent encourages the masochistic insufficient to be economically independent—though only modestly so—and submissive to others.

Adult Social and Family Roles

Masochistic insufficients tend to live in a society which espouses the philosophy of individualism rather than communally shared goals. They do not as a rule have large families and do not become very involved with family members. Their major defense, even here, is distance (Toffler, 1981).

At work, they are often bureaucratic employees but not strongly committed. They tend to change jobs rather than change the type of relationships.

Object Relations and Clinical Traits

In accordance with their family experience, masochistic insufficients act as if they were always facing a sadistic insufficient—the category that their spouse, partners, and friends usually belong to. Masochistic insufficients appear to be very nice, agreeable, flexible, pleasant people who usually take full socioeconomic responsibility for themselves but not for others. They are effective but mediocre employees who stick firmly to the rules, never doing more or less than they have to (Johnson, 1973).

Consequently, they tend to remain in much the same work niche over time, neither gaining nor losing ground. They have a civil-service mentality. As long as the rules remain the same, such people do all right in large institutions. They never "think big" and always proceed with caution. They become extremely anxious if they lose the protection of institutional rules; they may even quit their job (Etzioni, 1961).

Masochistic insufficients are very proud do-it-yourselfers. In this way they preserve the illusion of independence. They save rather than spend, even if inflation makes this an unwise financial move. They usually contribute somewhat to their parents' support. This is in keeping with their general tendency to allow others to rely on them in a very limited way. If others demand too much socioeconomic support, these clients feel overwhelmed by the responsibility or controlled and invaded (Parkinson, 1957). Consequently, those close to masochistic insufficients feel unable to rely on them, even in unimportant matters. Those who try to depend heavily on them or exercise excessive control are punished. Cautious distance is rewarded.

Whenever somebody tries to openly discuss the negative consequences and irrationality of their overly cautious approach to socioeconomic reality, they tend to switch the subject and start blaming themselves for their lack of success. This area is usually excluded from consciousness, although other minor socioeconomic matters can be freely discussed.

Sadistic partners are idealized as being more sincere, clever, sensible, and altruistic; masochistic insufficients are usually perfectionists who expect excellence even in small, insignificant details. This idealization follows a very typical, repetitive sequence: the masochistic insufficient starts by trying to please the other but then gradually switches to devaluing and escaping from the other until the relationship is finally interrupted. Such clients are specialists in seducing others and then slipping away. They invite others to "own" them—to invade, imprison, and control them. When they proceed to do so—to mistreat and eventually humiliate them—our clients simply run away. Having escaped from this intolerable, claustrophobic relationship, they feel momentarily liberated. But then they become depressed, rejected, and devalued and start the whole cycle anew (Elon, 1974).

Masochistic insufficients are able to establish close affective relationships, but only for short periods of time. When these relationships achieve some degree of closeness and intimacy, they escape or, at best, establish a chronically unstable relationship, characterized by alternating periods of closeness and separation. Ultimately, the only people who remain close to masochistic insufficients are sadistic insufficients. They are the only ones able to tolerate such an on again-off again relationship. We are all familiar with the couple who go together for years but never quite get married, or the put-upon mistress and the married man who will never get divorced. Many never marry, or if they do, they may protect their "privacy" by leading a double life—carrying on secret and, not uncommonly, homosexual affairs (Bonacich, 1976).

Another remarkable characteristic of masochistic insufficients is that at some time they may become infatuated with another masochistic insufficient. A curious chain is established: a sadistic insufficient is pursuing the masochistic insufficient, who, in turn, is pursuing another masochist, who is an even greater runaway than the first one. Hysteric masochistic insufficients tend to be subtle and pervasive jealousy makers: they constantly exclude others without realizing it.

A minor affective crisis may be precipitated if the partner stops being sadistic. The masochist would be unhappy and disoriented and would possibly look for other sadists. A more serious affective crisis would occur if the sadistic partner became dependent and started behaving like a masochistic patient. This would cause an explosion of claustrophobic anxiety. Finally, if the partner became a sadistic patient—spoiled, demanding, and dependent—the masochist could be totally overwhelmed by this parental responsibility and possibly have a psychotic breakdown.

Defense Mechanisms

The masochistic insufficient uses very typical interpersonal and intrapsychic defense mechanisms in order to avoid claustrophobic anxiety or feelings of affective rejection.

Interpersonal defenses.   Masochistic insufficients

1. Compulsively and unconsciously select sadistic insufficients—and reject nonsadistic insufficients—as significant others (selection of complementary partner)
2. Induce others to invade and dominate them and then avoid and escape from their intrusions (induction of complementary behavior)
3. Systematically avoid talking about their rigid, narrow-minded management of socioeconomic reality by compulsively disqualifying themselves or talking about irrelevant issues (displacement by personalization or trivialization)
4. Insist that they—not their partners—are the sadists who initiate the sadomasochistic games (inversion of direction and sequence of sadomasochism)
5. Repeatedly insist on their sadistic mistreatment of others in the same stereotyped way (narrowing)

Intrapsychic defenses.   Masochistic insufficiency is played out as follows:

1. Unconsciously, masochistic insufficients see themselves as (restricted-submissive) adolescent-servants and others as (restricting-domineering) elderly-masters, while consciously they view themselves as (restricted-domineering) adolescent-masters and others as (restricting-submissive) elderly-servants.
2. They take as natural their irrationally restricted socioeconomic reality and deny their interpersonal submissiveness by maintaining that they are the ones who force others to submit.
3. They perceive others as masochists and themselves as sadists, idealizing others and blaming themselves.
4. They always perceive themselves as mistreating others in the same stereotyped way.

Misqualification and Reality Testing

There are two types of masochistic insufficients: those who are avoidant depressive and blame and devalue themselves while idealizing and morally entitling the intrusive and restricting hypomanic sadistic insufficients to whom they are linked; or those who are avoidant hysterical and blame but idealize themselves while morally entitling but devaluing the intrusive paranoid sadistic insufficients to whom they are linked.

Blamed and devalued masochistic insufficients are usually neuroticized, because their blaming and devaluing sadistic insufficients not only attack their perception of interpersonal reality but also restrict their perception of socioeconomic reality.

The following transaction shows how an intrusive hypomanic sadistic insufficient (Barry) neuroticizes an avoidant depressive masochistic insufficient (Ella) by blaming and devaluing until the latter runs away:

BARRY: Hey! I want to borrow that book we were talking about the other day.

ELLA: (Kindly) But of course! Just remind me which one.

BARRY: (Making fun) You know, *How to Make Friends and Influence People*.

ELLA: (Justifying herself) Oh, I'm really sorry, but I think I already gave it to someone else. However, if you're in a hurry, they're selling it in the bookstore on the next block. It's really cheap.

BARRY: (Sarcastically) I see. Just as I feared. You're so selfish that you don't want to lend it to me, even for a few days.

ELLA: (Worried) Oh, no! It isn't that. I don't want to . . . it's that I can't . . . one of my friends, who is out of town now, has it.

BARRY: (Sarcastically) One of your friends, you said? Who can be so hard up or so naive as to be "your" friend? My God! There are people for everyone. Now I need the book more than ever. To make real friends who are not like you!

ELLA: (Depressed, with tears) Maybe you're right. Maybe this is why I am so lonely.

BARRY: (Sarcastically) Oh, my dear! You're not working on me with your crocodile tears.

ELLA: (Preparing to leave) Oh, please! Stop making fun of me, teasing me. I know I have my faults, but enough is enough. I can't stand you any longer. Goodbye!

BARRY: *(Screaming)* This is why you're so lonely. You're such a coward, you can't hear hard truths!

Blamed but devaluing masochistic insufficients can be neuroticized by the blaming and restrictions of their blaming but devalued sadistic insufficients. However, sometimes they can produce psychotic paranoid jealousy in their partners with their seductive, ambiguous behavior.

The following transaction shows how an avoidant hysteric masochistic insufficient (Scott) is blamed and restricted by an intrusive paranoid sadistic insufficient (Leslie), who, in turn, is subtly devalued and excluded, thus exploding into jealousy.

LESLIE: Are you free this afternoon?

SCOTT: *(Doubtfully)* Well, I don't know. It all depends.

LESLIE: *(Harshly)* It all depends on what?

SCOTT: *(Still doubtfully)* Well, you know. Why are you asking me that?

LESLIE: *(Angry)* Always trying to get rid of me. Of course, I'm asking you because I want you to go with me to the movies.

SCOTT: *(Softly)* Well, I don't know. What kind of movie?

LESLIE: Damn! It's not enough for you to be with me. I want to see *The Lonely Ranger*, about a law maker.

SCOTT *(Disappointed)* Oh, again? But I would like to see something romantic like *Torn between Two Lovers*. I already saw it, but it is so moving.

LESLIE: *(Extremely jealous)* You what? When? With whom? My God! I got you again. Who is the other lover that has you torn?

SCOTT: *(Looking mysterious, as if hiding something)* Well, you know. With one of my friends.

LESLIE: *(Suspicious)* That is what you say, but I know you well enough. *(Changing tone)* What about *Serpico?*

SCOTT: *(More receptive)* That's better. Where is the cinema you're taking me to?

LESLIE: *(Surprised)* Taking you! We are two adults, and we each pay our own way.

SCOTT: How romantic of you. I'm not going this time.

LESLIE: *(Reproaching)* Sure! You're waiting for someone who is willing to pay for your "favors." That's why you don't want to go out with honest, decent friends like me.
SCOTT: *(Ironically)* Maybe what you call honesty is plain avariciousness.
LESLIE: *(Very angry)* On top of rejecting and excluding me, you have the gall to offend me!

———————— The Sadistic Insufficient ————————

The three basic clinical traits of sadistic insufficients are (1) limited socioeconomic power, (2) dominance in the exercise of interpersonal authority, and (3) compulsive invasion of the partner's privacy. Such invasiveness does not lead to overprotection or control, however, because sadistic insufficients fear the dependence of others. Also, others tend to run away when the intrusiveness becomes intolerable.

Sadistic insufficients are often aggressive, unpleasant busybodies with a highly inflated sense of their own moral worth. They deem themselves more reliable, more sensible, and, above all, more honest than their partners. Their so-called honesty— "frank" and "forthright" utterances of the "truth" about others' conduct, clothing, life-style, etc.—coupled with their jealous though somewhat ineffectual attempts at control often causes others to abandon them. And, of course, their main anxiety stems from fear of abandonment. Abandonment by masochistic insufficients is rarely permanent, however; the latter usually return to hear the "truth" about themselves and perpetuate the pathological interaction.

The Clinical Interview

Sadistic insufficients perceive the therapist as an expert in interpersonal relations, someone who will teach them how to "make friends and influence people." The therapist will "coach" them in learning to control their strong feelings of moral outrage.

Such people usually have little or no insight into the projective nature of their reproaches.

Sadistic insufficients often live alone but try to make a virtue out of their loneliness by viewing it as a form of ascetic discipline, frugality, and austerity (Freud, 1908). Frequently they have alienated their families—another virtue in their eyes, since the family members' avoidance is merely proof of their own honesty. Something similar may happen in the initial clinical interview: our client will make some harsh, tactless remark about psychotherapy that will be exquisitely designed to upset us (Frued, 1916).

Such clients will often be "unable" to arrange a mutually agreeable therapy schedule because of other trivial activities. Or, because of their limited funds, they may not be able to attend sessions often enough. They will not perceive their own inadequacy but will carry on, instead, about the worthlessness or expense of the sessions, the inadequacy of the therapist, etc. In any case, the therapeutic relationship will appear as a solid but uncomfortable one, which may continue for years, but with little or no benefit to the client because of the client's inability to take back his or her projections.

Because of the irritating, oppressive, quarrelsome, and dishonest attitude of these clients, we therapists may become evasive, overly nice, and extremely tactful—all to avoid unpleasant confrontations and attacks. But the more we try to please such clients, the more invasive, irritating, and aggressive they become. When we try to escape these invasions, our clients become angry and desperate, imploring us not to abandon them (Henderson, 1977).

Family of Origin

The sadistic insufficient comes from the same type of family as the masochistic insufficient—a conservative, cautious family of modest but inadequate means. The parents conform to the ideal Middle American: they work hard, accept the stated values of their country and community without question, but are careful not to "get involved" (Komarita & Chertkoff, 1963).

The sadistic insufficient's opposite-sex parent is either a sadistic agent or another sadistic insufficient who is probably self-employed on a small scale. The same-sex parent is either a masochistic patient or a masochistic insufficient who, if employed, works in some low-level bureaucratic capacity. Thus, the same-sex parent may be somewhat dependent on his or her spouse.

Often, the same-sex parent deceives his or her spouse in some way—through adultery or sneaking out to bars or whatever. The sadistic insufficient may, as a young adult, appear morally justified in confronting the cheating parent, albeit in a highly judgmental and meddlesome fashion. Thus we can see the origin of our client's hypocritical views of "honesty."

Adult Social and Family Roles

Sadistic insufficients regard frugality as a virtue, regardless of external reality, such as galloping inflation. They, like their masochistic partners, are often penny-wise and pound-foolish. If married, they have small families or no children at all. They are not upwardly mobile or optimistic about the future. Hence, in their eyes, not only is it costly to have children; it is a disservice to them in view of the plight of the world today.

Sadistic insufficients are usually unsuccessful in the corporate world, since they are ungenerous, uncommitted, and suspicious of others. Therefore they usually work alone. They assiduously avoid relationships that force them into the role of agent or patient.

Object Relations and Clinical Traits

In accordance with their family experience, sadistic insufficients act as if they were always facing a masochistic insufficient—which most of their close companions are. They are tactless, irritating, rigid, quarrelsome, and overly sincere. While capable of taking care of themselves, they cannot tolerate the dependence of others in any extended way.

In work situations they usually manage to make themselves so indispensable—as a good emergency surgeon, for example—that others put up with their behavior. They become extremely anxious if for any reason they cease to be indispensable because at some level they know that others cannot stand their compulsive, aggressive interference and that they are in danger of being fired.

Sooner or later, they are usually let go and compelled to work on their own.

They become enraged by the petty rules of bureaucracies and are constantly getting involved in fights with low-level employees (many of whom are masochistic insufficients). Sadistic insufficients constantly harangue public servants for neglecting their duty. "I am a taxpayer like anyone else and deserve better treatment from these irresponsible, lazy cheaters." They themselves never think big or do any more than the job requires.

They can, however, help out in an emergency. They are efficient trouble shooters. One man, for example, lavished expensive presents on his children when they visited him once a year and provided his ex-wife with money for their daughter's emergency operation, but failed utterly to provide regular monthly child support. When berated for this, he would point out his ex-wife's "ingratitude" for his past "generosities," saying, "I'm not as rich as you think, you know".

As previously stated, such people are fanatic savers, but they never get involved in investment or trading. They are frequently able to save significant amounts of money, nest eggs for use in emergencies, such as sudden job loss or abandonment. Such people tend to be avaricious and overly cautious, withdrawing money only rarely—perhaps to buy a small piece of property, which they then will not sell under any circumstances. Consequently, close companions realize that sadistic insufficients can only be counted on for small, practical matters, never for major economic issues (Robinson & Bell, 1978).

Sadistic insufficients, like their masochistic counterparts, value their independence. They are ardent do-it-yourselfers, resourceful and practical in small matters, and view themselves as "rugged individualists" (Lasch, 1979). They put others down ceaselessly, never hesitating to point out the ways in which those close to them have "failed." In fact, they have a subtle ability to select irritating topics for discussion, topics that are designed to depress or anger others. They compulsively project their own feelings of failure, badness, stupidity, or craziness and make others extremely uncomfortable in their presence (Cook, 1975).

This process of devaluation differs somewhat from that of others sadistic types: they lack the sadistic agent's power to enslave others economically and the sadistic patient's ability to seduce people with their charisma (Nye & Keohane, 1977). Consequently, their relationships with those close to them follow a repetitive sequence. Such clients will start by devaluing their partners, but because they lack the ability (or, indeed, the desire) to enslave, they soon become aware that their partners are trying to slip away. This makes sadistic insufficients extremely anxious, so they try to hold on to their partners by tactlessly revealing the "truth" to them. This sometimes causes the partner to return (if the partner is a masochistic), but sometimes the sadistic insufficient is abandoned. Though deeply hurt and embittered, they usually gain little understanding of their own rejecting, unpleasant behavior; on the contrary, they feel like martyrs, rejected by others because of the other people's "dishonesty." In this sense they often create self-fulfilling prophecies: paranoid sadistic insufficients become jealous without realizing that they are the ones who provoke rejection (Freud, 1922).

For example, one woman constantly invaded her teenage daughter's privacy; she read her daughter's mail and diary; she secretly listened in on her daughter's telephone conversations; and so forth. In addition, she constantly upbraided her daughter for her poor school marks, messy room, choice of music and reading material, and "unsavory" group of friends. When the girl became more and more secretive—refusing to bring her friends home, staying away from the house, or locking herself in her room for hours—the mother became panic-stricken and accused her daughter of taking drugs and sleeping around. Instead of recognizing her daughter's right to adulthood and independence, the mother tried to hold on to her "baby," all the while denouncing her faithlessness. Predictably, of course, the daughter started smoking pot and having occasional affairs. One weekend, shortly after her 18th birthday, the daughter eloped with someone her mother had never met. Initially devastated, the mother soon wrapped herself in a hair shirt of moral outrage, denouncing her daughter as a cheater and an ingrate. "All those years I raised her to be a good girl, I made her go to church every Sunday, and taught her how to dress and act—she has no taste in clothes at all, and she's an incredible klutz—and this is how she thanks me!"

Sadistic insufficients regard tact and diplomacy as hypocrisy. They always "speak their mind" with no regard for or awareness of the effect on others. But these great lovers of truth, these moral crusaders, become enraged if anyone tells them the truth about their own selfish, hurtful, rejecting behavior (Fox, Payne, Priest & Philliber, 1977).

Like their masochistic counterparts they may have homosexual tendencies or fantasies that are projected onto others. They are unable to get really close to their partners and thus have on again-off again relationships (Haas, 1970).

Sadistic insufficients may suffer a minor affective crisis if their partners stop being masochistic. This may produce unhappiness and disorientation and possibly precipitate a search for a new partner. A more devastating affective crisis will result if the partner becomes a masochistic agent or sadistic patient. This will cause an explosion of anxiety because of the controlling nature of the agent and dependency of the patient. Worst of all, if a partner becomes a masochistic patient—totally dependent and humiliated—our client may experience a psychotic breakdown (Gear, Hill & Liendo, 1981).

Defense Mechanisms

Sadistic insufficients use very typical interpersonal and intrapsychic defense mechanisms in order to avoid moral unpleasure or feelings of abandonment.

Interpersonal defenses. Sadistic insufficients

1. Compulsively and unconsciously select masochistic insufficients—and reject nonmasochistic insufficients—as their significant others (selection of complementary partners)
2. Induce others to avoid and submit to them and then are rejected and abondoned by these others (induction of complementary behavior)

3. Systematically avoid all discussion of their rigid, narrow-minded management of socioeconomic reality by disqualifying others or talking about irrelevant issues (displacement by personalization or trivialization)
4. Insist that they—not their partners—are the masochists, the victims of the sadistic games of others (inversion of direction and sequence of sadomasochism)
5. Repeatedly insist on the mistreatment they receive from others in the same stereotyped way (narrowing)

Intrapsychic defenses.   Sadistic insufficiency is played out as follows:

1. Unconsciously, sadistic insufficients see themselves as (restricting-domineering) elderly-masters and others as (restricted-submissive) adolescent-servants, while consciously they view themselves as (restricting-submissive) elderly-servants and others as (restricted-domineering) adolescent-masters.
2. They take as natural their irrationally restricted socioeconomic reality and deny their interpersonal domination by maintaining that they are the ones who are forced to submit.
3. They perceive others as sadists and themselves as masochists, blaming others and idealizing themselves.
4. They always perceive themselves as mistreated by others in the same stereotyped way.

Misqualification and Reality Testing

Restricting sadistic insufficients can be of two types: either intrusive hypomanic ones, who idealize and morally entitle themselves while devaluing and blaming the restricted avoidant depressive masochistic insufficients to whom they are linked, or intrusive paranoid ones, who morally entitle but devalue themselves while blaming but idealizing the restricted avoidant hysteric masochistic insufficients to whom they are linked.

Blaming and devaluing sadistic insufficients are usually neuroticizing because they not only attack the interpersonal reality perception but also restrict the socioeconomic reality perception of their blamed and devalued masochistic insufficients. This is precisely what happens in the following transaction between an intrusive hypomanic sadistic insufficient (Mary) and an avoidant depressive masochistic insufficient (Lois).

MARY   (Reproaching) It seems to me that you're too diplomatic—rather insincere I would say. You make me feel that I can't count on your opinions, because you always prefer to say what you think is convenient for your interests rather than to be speaking freely a healthy truth.

LOIS: (Excusing herself) As you know, I'm not always like that.

MARY: (Sarcastically) I see. Why don't you sincerely speak your mind once in your lifetime?

LOIS: (Timidly) Well, to tell you the truth now, I don't think that it is either clever or considerate to constantly keep telling brutal, tactless, ugly truths. I don't want to be Public Enemy Number One.

MARY: (very angry) How is that? Are you telling me that I'm a brutal, tactless, dumb, inconsiderate person just because I'm honest and sincere. You hypocrite!

LOIS: (Frightened and worried) Not by any means did I want to be offensive to you. I think that you're really clever and straightforward. I was just speaking in general. (Excusing herself) You told me to speak my mind. (Looking at her watch) Oh, my gosh, it's very late. I've got to go now!

MARY: (Reproaching sarcastically) Run away from me.

Blaming but devalued sadistic insufficients can neuroticize their blamed but devaluing masochistic insufficients. However, they can go through psychotic episodes of paranoid jealousy when facing the seductive and excluding, ambiguous and oscillating behavior of their hysterical partners (Jacobson, 1966).

This is what happens in the following transaction between a jealous intrusive paranoid sadistic insufficient (Jack) and a jealousy-making avoidant hysteric masochistic insufficient (Amy).

AMY: (*Elegantly dressed, smiling very nicely*) Hi, there! How are you, darling?

JACK: (*Poorly groomed, looking very angry and out of sorts*) How I am? You must be kidding? What the hell were you doing out so late?

AMY: (*Looking through the window*) Well, you know, just chatting with my friends.

JACK: (*Insultingly*) With whom? Stop trying to make a fool out of me!

AMY: (*Frightened*) Well, with Lisa and Patty. About art—those cultural things that you hate.

JACK: (*Shouting violently*) That's not true at all. I talked to both of them on the phone and you weren't there. Didn't anybody teach you decency?

AMY: (*Ashamed*) Yes, you're right. You win. I wasn't with them. I was just walking around, trying to get some freedom. I didn't want to come back here to you with your offensive, unpleasant character.

JACK: (*Shouting*) I win? Look, I wouldn't be offended if you didn't lie.

AMY: (*Feeling misunderstood*) Look, I've had it. That's it. I can't take anymore of your intolerable insults and your dirty sick mind.

JACK: (*Coldly angry*) Sure! It was only my sick imagination when I saw you having a drink with Peter this evening.

AMY: (*Surprised and somewhat ashamed*) I was with him because he's so nice to me, so considerate. Instead of mistreating and insulting me, as you do. Nobody ever taught you to be nice with others, to respect their freedom?

JACK: (*Spiteful*) That's because I'm not a dirty, dishonest liar like you. I don't jump into bed with whoever talks nicely to me.

AMY: (*Offended*) I'm leaving. But remember that you are the one who is sending me to the street. If you don't learn to be more flexible you'll be abandoned by everybody.

Complementarity in the
Undercommitted Dyad

The Problem

The masochistic insufficient is concerned with the avoidance of displeasure. The sadistic insufficient is concerned with the achievement of pleasure. Masochistic insufficients are confronted, however, by a double problem of displeasure: when they are close to another, they lose their sense of identity and feel invaded rather than authenticated by the other; but when they are distant they feel abandoned, unloved, and unworthy. Thus, in their on again-off again relationships they are forced to choose between two disagreeable alternatives—and this is no choice at all.

Sadistic insufficients aspire to more pleasure than their worth and contribution can justify; they also aspire to financial security and stability. But they are negotiating from a position of weakness: unlike the sadistic agent, they do not offer survival and protection; and unlike the sadistic patient, they lack the power to manipulate affect. Thus, like the masochistic partners, they too lose the bargain. Sometimes they lose their partners and sometimes they lose their limited financial security.

Masochistic insufficients who wish to avoid being alone are seductive and ingratiating, subconsciously inviting the other to invade. Then they run away because of the anxiety thus created. If they were more able to tolerate solitude, they would be able to break the vicious circle.

Sadistic insufficients who wish to keep others near them and not be cheated act in a judgmental, unforgiving way, thus driving others to act in a sneaky way, to live a double life. If they could be less accusatory and moralistic, others would be more cooperative and open. Also, this would improve their economic situation, since they would be less subject to being fired.

Cognitive Structure

Masochistic insufficients tend to view the world in terms of the dangers of closeness (which may lead to loss of self). Their sadistic counterparts view the world in terms of right or wrong and the need to know what is going on in order to avoid being cheated. Leadership of the dyad is in the hands of the sadistic insufficient, since the masochistic partner does not like to assume responsibility or undertake a common goal. But sadistic insufficients are poor leaders, since they tend to see the world in black and white and not look at situations in a broad context. Hence, they are often deserted in stressful situations: they don't do what others want, as would the masochistic agent or the masochistic patient; nor can they get others to do what they want, as would the sadistic agent or sadistic patient (Inheler & Metalon, 1960).

Attitude toward risk. Masochistic and sadistic insufficients exaggerate the risk. Risk is seen in relation to the possibility of loss; the possibility of gain is not entertained. They either make very conservative decisions or, at times, jump in without correctly assessing the risk. The risk of being trapped or invaded is the risk to which the masochistic insufficient is most sensitive. The risk of dishonesty or of losing everything are the risks to which the sadistic insufficient is most sensitive. Both see the risk in daring action but fail to see the risk in caution (Wason & Laird, 1968).

Loss-gain strategy. Insufficients are unrealistic in their evaluation of potential loss or gain. They minimize the possibility and importance of gain and exaggerate the possibility of loss. Optimism is out of the question. Paradoxically, potentially negative effects of change may be so exaggerated that they may stay in dangerous situations where loss is almost certain. Consider, for example, those who refuse to move out of dangerously deteriorated neighborhoods, or leave their house even though toxic chemicals are seeping into the basement, or risk fighting to keep democracy alive (Young, 1969).

Error sensitivity. Although more aware of their own responsibility for failure than their partners, masochistic insufficients are too phobic to try another approach. The more they see their own failure, the more their fear paralyzes them. Sadistic insufficients blame others for their own errors, thus precluding possible change (Watzlawick, Weakland & Fish, 1974).

Breaking the Dyad

Masochistic insufficients are more open to suggestion because they are more introjective than sadistic insufficients. The problem, however, is that they have very little commitment to the treatment. They "solve" their problems by distancing from the therapist and from their partners. They neither leave nor come close enough to be really helped (Rosecrance & Stein, 1973).

Sadistic insufficients are very strongly projective and they do not easily accept responsibility in what is happening to them. But even if they have a limited commitment to the treatment, they tend to adhere to it. Because of their projectiveness, they are less curable than their masochistic counterpart (Rokeach, 1960).

The undercommitted dyad tends to be stably unstable, so to speak. Masochistic insufficients are the ones who break the relationship by distance. Sadistic insufficients usually are rather persistent, but they induce very strongly the abandonment of their partner. The bond is, consequently, fragile but tenacious.

This type of undercommitted bond tends to produce neuroses more often than psychoses or borderline syndromes. It also produces perversions; exhibitionism, voyeurism, sexual sadism and masochism, and homosexuality are much more common in insufficients than in patients or agents.

However, the undercommitted dyad is the one which asks more often for conjoint couple therapy. The authoritarian and the demagogic ones prefer to be treated either individually or through family therapy.

An Undercommitted Dyad Asks
for Consultation

The Partners

Mary, a 34-year-old white store clerk called for an appointment, stating that she was rather fed up with her husband Joe, a 36-year-old white biochemist. She informed the therapist that they had been in therapy before and that it had "helped the communication for a while but that Joe had gone back to the same stubborn closed-off person."

They arrived late for the first appointment. Mary explained that she had many complications—the phone, the baby sitter, etc.—that had held her up. Joe quietly reminded her that for different reasons she was never able to be on time.

They have been married six years and have a 2-year-old daughter. Mary had been married before and has a 14-year-old son. Mary feels that Joe is totally unfair to the boy, that he is indifferent, doesn't discipline him or take any economic responsibility for him. She adds that Joe is only interested in her money and that this has been the case from the beginning. Joe remains calm thoughout these accusations and simply listens politely until asked by the therapist to give his position.

Joe is a professor of biochemistry at the university. He is rather obese, modestly dressed, and unassuming. He reminds Mary that he maintains his family on his salary, that there is little extra money, and that he does, in effect, consider her son an expense that he cannot and will not undertake. He reminds her that this was clearly stated before their marriage. In regard to discipline, he considers it her responsibility and doesn't want to interfere.

He reminds her of their long-standing plan to establish a small private laboratory which will increase their income. After four years of saving, this is now possible—primarily because he did not support her son.

She recognizes this but reminds him that he did not do this alone, since the apartment in which they live was a gift from her father and that she also contributes to the rent from another apartment still belonging to her father but which she administers and from which she receives a small income in addition to her own salary as a clerk.

Her family is unrealistically frugal. Her own father many years before had bought a small piece of land in the outskirts of a fast-growing city. He did not do this as a result of a conscious strategy. Rather, the land was cheap and at that time isolated and he didn't like to put up with close neighbours. The land increased in value and he became rich. He neither enjoyed nor invested the money but rather suspected anyone with a business proposition as either reckless or dishonest. The other members of his own family kept their distance from him, feeling sorry for the fact that he was right and always spoke the truth but was so badly treated by everyone. Mary tried to visit him, overcoming her own resistences to do so—as if she was fulfilling a moral duty. He always reminded her of the need for caution with her money and recommended that she never forget that others were to be suspected of dishonestly.

Joe came from a family of modest means. His family had on occasion insinuated that she could help more. They had limited ambitions for him and thought that he had done well in life. In his work he was considered to be conscientious. His work was rather routine, and he had been advanced at the expected rate.

Joe read a lot, was not very talkative, let his wife decide most things, and would not fight with anyone. He had a good friend who also wanted to start a lab and had entered into partnership with him. He found his friend valuable, since "he is able to speak his mind" and in that way Joe doesn't have to.

With the boy and with his own daughter Joe admits that he doesn't assert himself much. He doesn't really like the boy, who is critical of him. The boy, like the mother, has accused him of being rather selfish and uninvolved.

MARY: I know that you're only interested in my money. You don't care about me or the children. I'm about to give up on you. I suppose that you'd like that. Then you wouldn't have any responsibility.

JOE: I'm not interested in your money. You have so little anyway. It's just that if you don't help me we can't ever get ahead. You see helping me as being taken advantage of.

MARY: Doctor, he's still the same. He came home and sat down to read. Not a word! He had arrived late and not a word! I told him about what my father said about the lab, and he didn't even reply. You know the idea could backfire. We could lose what we have.

JOE: Your father always says "be careful" and I am careful. I have selected my partner rather well. What more is there to say? I'm already afraid that I'll fail without his scaring me more.

MARY: Doctor, how much are the sessions? I have an insurance policy which will cover once a week for a year. I have to pay anything above that and there is no money to waste.

Working Diagnosis

Mary and Joe form an undercommitted dyad: Joe is a devalued and blamed, avoidant and restricted phobic depressive neuroticized masochistic insufficient; Mary is a devaluing and blaming, intrusive and restricting counterphobic hypomanic neuroticizing sadistic insufficient.

In the socioeconomic sphere Joe is restricted (inhibited) and Mary is restricting (inhibiting).

1. Responsibility is carefully and resentfully divided.
   - Joe assumes partial responsibility for the family but definitely rejects any responsibility for Mary's son by a previous marriage. He has no desire to control anybody.
   - Mary contributes but keeps careful track of what she gives and resents that Joe does not give more. She considers the apartment given by her father to be hers rather than of the couples'. Indeed, it is in her name.
2. Their attitude towards the future is cautious. He is more afraid of failure. She is more afraid of being taken advantage of.
   - He has planned his laboratory for years. He does not plan to undertake it alone but will share the risk.
   - She, like her father, suspects him and others of wanting to take unfair advantage of her, her son, etc.
   - She can, should, and does contribute to the family, but she sees it as being taken advantage of.
3. Economic decisions have been made cautiously. Saving, careful administration, and decisions to increase security have been the family strategy.
   - He has carefully saved over the years to open his laboratory rather than seeking a loan and seizing the opportunity for greater earning power.
   - He has preferred employment with security (university) over employment with greater risk and gain (self-employment or working in private enterprise).
   - She restricts Joe's initiative with her doubts about investing in the lab.

4. Problems are divided up but not treated as family matters.
   - Her son is her problem.
   - The lab is his problem.
   - The apartment is her apartment.

In the interpersonal sphere, Mary is the sadist and Joe the masochist.

1. In interpersonal authority Mary intrudes and commands and Joe avoids and submits or cautiously doubts.
   - Mary made the first therapeutic contact and decides that treatment is necessary.
   - Mary is always giving strong opinions about Joe's behavior.
   - Joe is always justifying himself to her.
   - Mary is the one who always makes the couple late.
2. In interpersonal qualifications, Joe is blamed (and eventually devalued) and gives Mary moral entitlement, justifying himself. Mary is principally blaming, feeling a strong sense of moral entitlement, which makes her speak out aggressively in relation to others.
   - Mary blames Joe for the poor communication. She considers him to be a stubborn, closed-off person.
   - Mary qualifies Joe as unfair, indifferent, and uninvolved in relation to the boy.
   - Mary considers Joe to be insincere in that he is really just interested in her money.
   - Joe's replies are self-justifications rather than counteraccusations or devaluations.
   - However, on one occasion he comments about the constant unfounded suspicions of her father and makes one comment that she is always late.
3. In interpersonal satisfaction and frustration, Mary sees herself as the frustrated victim of Joe, while in fact she frustrates him.
   - Mary complains that he does not talk.
   - Mary complains that he is stubborn.
   - Mary complains that he is potentially exploiting to her.

- Mary complains that he does not help her with her son.
- Mary frustrates Joe, attacking his honesty.
- Mary frustrates him in his cautious efforts to improve the family economically.

With respect to reality testing, Mary distorts the sadomasochistic aspects of the relationship, as well as the socioeconomic ones, in a restricting overly cautious way. She is neuroticizing. He escapes from her into silence, the newspaper, etc. when she escalates her intrusive attacks. He is neuroticized.

5

Refining the
—————Dyadic Typology—————

In the previous chapters we have broadly outlined the six basic client types and the three pathological dyads. In this chapter we will discuss subtypes and show the reader how to apply our methodology to arrive at an accurate and therapeutically useful diagnosis. Then we will link our dyadic typology to the more traditional DSM-III (American Psychiatric Association, 1980) phenomenologic classification system. Finally, we will illustrate this phenomenologic level with case material.

—————The Eight Diagnostic Axes—————

We have chosen eight variables for their strategic prognostic and therapeutic significance. In making the diagnosis there are few decisions involved; the decisions are relatively clear and the system is readily mastered. This, combined with its relevance, makes for the return of a large amount of therapeutic information (Bruner, 1973) from a minimal diagnostic effort.

Our typology is based on observations of our clients' interactions with the therapist and their relations with the micro- and macroenvironment. Using these observations we have found it of great importance to use two critical independent variables related to power: socioeconomic control and interpersonal authority. The typology is further refined by developing five axes which are dependent variables of the power relations: defensive qualifications; affect state; reality testing; centeredness; and attitude toward organizations. Finally we add a new diagnostic axis, clinical phenomenology.

The inclusion of socioeconomic power as fundamental should not be taken to represent a simplistic economism. Socioeconomic power is a variable which deeply affects mental health. Actually psychotic breakdowns, suicide attempts, delinquency, and psychosomatic catastrophes increase in periods of economic crisis. This is why the socioeconomic and interpersonal power structure of the small organizations to which the subject belongs is so relevant in the planning and outcome of psychotherapy. Power is not an end but rather a tool for access to pleasure.

Diagnosing Control and Authority

With respect to socioeconomic power, clients can adopt one of three pathological positions:

1. *Agents,* who control the socioeconomic resources of others
2. *Patients,* who are dependent on another's largesse
3. *Insufficients,* who are able to earn a subsistence livelihood but are not able to support another to any degree

All clients have a preferred socioeconomic position, which they assume when possible, and an alternate position, which they usually accept when the preferred position is not available (McNeil, et al., 1972). For example, when an agent faces a more powerful agent, he or she automatically switches into a patient position.

With respect to interpersonal power (Green & Taylor, 1969), clients can adopt one of two pathological positions:

1. *Sadists,* who are domineering and pleasure seeking
2. *Masochists,* who are submissive and pleasure denying

Here again, all clients have a preferred position and an alternate one. For example, when sadists face a stronger sadist, they automatically switch to a masochistic position (Courtright, Millar & Rogers-Millar, 1979).

The combination of the control and authority diagnoses (Della Fave, 1980) gives us the six basic client types, which are paired in complementary pathological dyads:

1. *Authoritarian dyad:* sadistic agent-masochistic patient
2. *Demagogic dyad:* masochistic agent-sadistic patient
3. *Undercommitted dyad:* sadistic insufficient-masochistic insufficient

Decisions regarding client and dyad type are relatively easy to make, but the resulting classification is quite sophisticated and powerful in terms of the therapeutic information it makes available to the clinician (Kessler, 1979).

Diagnosing Qualifications

We quickly observe that at the interpersonal level our clients measure their self-worth along superior-inferior, good-bad lines. (Sluzki, Beavin, Tarnopolsky & Veron, 1967). In relation to those close to them they adopt one of these defensive postures:

1. *Devaluers,* who have an inflated sense of their own worth
2. *Devalued,* who have an unrealistically low sense of self-worth
3. *Blamers,* who feel morally superior to the rest of the world and are highly judgmental, often even paranoid
4. *Blamed,* who feel that they are not entitled to make moral judgements because they are not really "good people"
5. *Blamed devaluers,* who have a high opinion of themselves, though others put them down morally
6. *Devalued blamers,* who perceive themselves to be morally superior, but are not perceived as valuable by others

People tend to link up in complementary pairs—as blamers and blamed or devaluers and devalued (Rogers-Millars, 1979). Different cognitive structures are implied by these defensive qualifications.

Cognitive structure of the blamer-blamed dyad.   Blamers have a very legalistic view of the world; they make the law, interpret it, and defend it. Having established what "is" and what "should be," they tend to become inflexible and closed to all new information. While on the surface they appear to have an analytic approach to life's problems, in fact their rigidity and narrowness usually make them unable to see events in their broad social context. Blamers are good at spotting recurring patterns and at classifying phenomena, but they are poor at deriving broad general principles from their observations. They are concerned, instead, with establishing right and wrong, punishment and reward (Webster & Sovieszek, 1974).

This creates a need in their complementary blamed partner to avoid being pinned down, to weasel out of taking a firm position on any issue, for fear of being challenged and found wanting. Blamed partners tend to be more dramatic, holistic thinkers than are blamers; generally, they are only slightly capable of introspective, analytic thought and remain imprecise in their speech as well.

Cognitive structure of the devaluer-devalued dyad.   The devaluer sees the broad general picture immediately but is very poor at focusing on the finer points. Devaluers tend to put down their slower, more analytical devalued counterparts for being "boring," "unimaginative," and "stupid." Their partners, in turn, are usually the ones who take charge of organizational details (Rogers, 1973). They tend to be obsessive and depressed, and their contributions often go unrecognized. They are more concrete and relatively unimaginative thinkers.

Diagnosing Affect States

Our clients' primary affect state results from a combination of their control over interpersonal and socioeconomic reality and their defensive posture. A therapeutic change in these areas may dramatically change a person's primary affect. Sometimes, however, medication may be required to modify a chronic affect state and help a client view the world in a healthier, more positive way.

The primary affect states are elation, depression, suspiciousness, guilt, anxiety, and anger. If we link these to our clients' defensive postures, we find the following:

1. *Anger* is usually experienced by blamers. They feel morally entitled to condemn others' evil and malicious actions.
2. *Guilt* is usually experienced by the blamed because of their self-reproaches and the reproaches of others.
3. *Elation* is usually experienced by devaluers. This is in keeping with their holistic cognitive structure and with their excessive sense of worth.
4. *Depression* is usually experienced by the devalued—not surprising, since no one rewards them for their efforts (Seligman, 1975).
5. *Anxiety* is usually experienced by the blamed devaluers because of the anger and disdain that they provoke in others.
6. *Anger* and *distrust* are usually experienced by the righteous devalued blamers because of the sarcasm or infidelity of others and their own sense of moral entitlement.

Diagnosing Reality Testing

According to the quality of interpersonal and socioeconomic reality testing, clients can be:

1. *Neurotics,* with poor interpersonal reality testing and fairly intact socioeconomic reality testing
2. *Borderlines,* with poor interpersonal and socioeconomic reality testing
3. *Psychotics,* with severely impaired interpersonal and socioeconomic reality testing

Clients operating at a neurotic level tend to focus their energy and attention on the interpersonal and socioeconomic levels of the relationship. They distort but do not deny reality (Freud, 1923). They are aware that their actions have certain consequences. For example, there may be distortion around who started a fight or what the partner's real motives were. The events themselves are not doubted or denied. When reality itself is denied—for example, a client denies that a family fight has occurred, even though the police had to intervene—then the client is clearly psychotic (Freud, 1924a). A borderline client may engage in severe distortion without outright disavowal, for example, failing to grasp the seriousness of a situation, although not denying its occurrence.

At each of these levels clients may be either "doers" or "done to." They may be neuroticizers or neuroticized, psychoticizers or psychoticized, borderliners or borderlined. Much depends on the client's type and dyad.

Conditions for neuroticizing.   A neuroticizing relationship can exist in all three pathological dyads but is more often related to the undercommitted one. The sadist tends to be the neuroticizer, and the masochist the neuroticized; that is, the sadist tends to be the one who distorts the others' perception of interpersonal reality, and the masochist tends to be the one whose perception is distorted.

Conditions for psychoticizing.   As one might expect, doers tend to control the interpersonal and socioeconomic reality of the done to: sadists and agents tend to do to masochists and patients. If this is coupled with a total disavowal of reality (rather than a mere distortion), we can readily see that sadistic agents have the greatest psychoticizing potential and masochistic patients have the greatest psychoticized potential. Hence the authoritarian dyad has the greatest possibility of being psychotic (Searles, 1959).

In the demagogic dyad sadistic patients can psychoticize their masochistic agents, but this would be a temporary reaction rather than a true psychotic state because sadistic patients lack the real authority to make believable their disavowal of reality (Dewald, 1970). Also, masochistic agents are not dependent for their economic survival on the sadistic patient, although emotional blackmail ("You will be alone." "No one else but you.") may keep them in the relationship.

In general, masochistic agents are not psychoticizers, since they are not interpersonally dominant. However, a particular subtype of masochistic agent, one who is a hypomanic blamed devaluer, can occasionally be a psychoticizer by subtly and persistently putting down his or her partner. This is the case with the paranoid schizophrenic, for example. However, they usually submit when their partners explode and thus "permit" commentaries on their disavowal of reality. This reduces their psychoticizing potential.

In general, undercommitted dyads do not become psychotic because neither partner truly controls the other, and hence the done-to partner can escape. Certain masochistic insufficients who are blamed devaluers can act in a subtle psychotizing way. However, the sadistic partner usually explodes or abandons the masochist, thus breaking the other's hold (Courtright et al., 1979).

Conditions for borderlining. Borderlining requires that one partner protect the other from the unpleasant consequences of reality. Both partners underestimate or deny the effects of certain actions. Only a masochistic agent can be a borderliner. As an agent he or she has sufficient control over socioeconomic reality to provide protection, and as a masochist, sufficient desire to do so. The sadistic agent always forces his or her partner to "confront" the "true horror" of reality, thus using it as a threat, not a shield to borderline (Jackson, 1961).

Hence, the demagogic dyad is the one with the greatest likelihood of being borderline. The borderlined state is common in certain sadistic patients—particularly among those who have an excessive and unwarranted opinion of their worth and right to pleasure (Kernberg, 1975). Such clients tend to be histrionic and emotionally labile, with a very low tolerance for frustration: most commonly, the psychopath. They are effectively buffered from periodic intrusions of unpleasant reality by compulsive depressive masochistic agents, whose lack of self-worth and need for company keep them in the relationship.

Diagnosing Centeredness: Narcissism and Mirrorism

In their thoughts, speech, and actions some clients focus almost exclusively on themselves, and some almost exclusively on the other. Consequently, with respect to centeredness, the client can adopt one of two pathological positions:

1. *Narcissists,* who are pathologically self-centered
2. *Mirrorists,* who are pathologically other-centered

The European understanding of narcissism is that the person is trapped in his or her own reflection as was Narcissus in the water mirror (Klein, 1952; Lacan, 1960). The American understanding of narcissism is that the person is trapped in self-centeredness, in selfishness (Kohut, 1971, Lasch, 1979).

If we try to integrate both versions of narcissism, we should remember that Narcissus was not alone: he was accompanied by the nymph Echo, who was condemned not to express her own feelings but merely to repeat the other's words. Consequently, Narcissus was absorbing an audiovisual reflection of himself while thinking that he was looking at and talking with others.

Similarly, it can be thought that the intrapsychic and inter-personal phenomenon of narcissism would not be possible without a simultaneous and complementary phenomenon of "mirrorism" (or "echoism"). This means that an exclusively self-centered person who is always looking at and talking to himself through others absolutely needs an exclusively other-centered partner who is always audiovisually reflecting others. It is possible to observe clinically that a self-centered narcissist with a hyperidentity is always linked with an other-centered mirrorist with a hypoiden-tity (or hyperalterity).

The relationship between a narcissistic "subject" and a mir-roristic "object" is an interdependent one, as Freud related when he described "His Majesty, the Baby" with his "Loyal Subjects, the Parents" (Freud, 1914).

Sadists tend to be the self-centered, narcissistic, self-entit-ling, domineering subjects who define the situation, while masochists are the other-entitling, submissive objects, who have the situation defined for them. Narcissists and mirrorists tend to form stable dyads—as happens with narcissistic sadistic patients and mirroristic masochistic agents.

This state of affairs results in certain very special therapeutic problems presented by masochists and often overlooked by both therapist and masochists. The problem is one of a lack of "presence" in treatment; by this we mean a lack of interest in themselves, a lack of discussion about themselves, and a lack of training and entitlement in relation to their own feelings and needs which is very difficult to overcome. Masochistic agents may be valuable, creative people with real potential, but they do not feel alive with their own emotions. They need the strong emotions of others to reflect and give them a sense of vitality.

As has been stated, narcissists define situations in their terms in accordance with their perception and memories of what happens. They are the ones who impose the topics of discussion in accordance with their personal interests.

Mirrorists permit others to impose their perceptions on them and to define the characteristics of the "players" and the situation. As a result, mirrorists pass their time excusing and justifying themselves while struggling to interact in terms of the others' plan of action.

They are easily contaminated by the acting off of the narcissists and execute their counteracting off rather than their own acting off. Metaphorically, it can be said that the mirrorist is more in a countertransferential attitude rather than in a transferential one (see Chapter 7).

Narcissists, on the other hand, are contaminating, making their partners, the mirrorists, change their pathology while they themselves remain more constant, always executing their own acting off.

Thus, there is a loss of identity on the part of the mirrorist with this contamination. However, mirrorists are also more susceptible to therapeutic messages because they are more pregnable. Unfortunately, the changes may be the result of accepting the projective identification of the other, rather than being actually incorporated. Mirrorists run the risk of being transformed into the mirror of the therapist's theory: they absorb it all but have not really been transformed.

This is a typical statement of a mirroristic compulsive-depressive masochistic agent.

LINDA: Surprisingly enough I had a dream last night, maybe to please you. You keep telling me that I don't pay attention to myself. In the dream somebody was pushing me closer and closer to a big house. Looking at it from a distance it seemed to be strongly built and very bright, but when I got closer I was surprised to find that it was very difficult for me to look inside the house because its windows were reflecting some lights surrounding the house. There were no lights inside.

However, when I got close enough, the house was not so strongly built. It was abandoned, as if nobody took care of it. It was empty, dark, lifeless—as if inhabited by ghosts. But, getting even closer, I found some weak signs of life here and there. I even saw a small Pinocchio there. (Pause) With that I've taken care of my obligation to you. Now let's get back to my usual worries about Tony (her husband). He is in trouble again because of his gambling. He is so careless about himself; he has me so concerned that maybe my dream is linked with him.

THERAPIST: (Joking) Maybe it is linked with you. Maybe you feel that I'm pushing you closer and closer to yourself. And you are finding yourself as you found the house in the dream. You are finding that you are not so strong and that you keep reflecting Tony or myself. In the back of your mind, you find yourself empty, lifeless, with nobody taking care of you. However, there are some vestiges of life inside you. Remember that Pinocchio was a lifeless toy that finally got a soul.

LINDA: (Smiling) And you would be Gepetto. (Sad) Sometimes I feel so empty, so desperately lonely, that I look for any kind of company.

This is a typical statement of a narcissistic borderlined sadistic patient.

TONY: It makes me so angry when the supervisor dares to question me! I am the best salesperson that the store has. She was angry because I was late. Imagine! On Tuesdays I don't get up so easily because I watch the Monday late show, and besides, the woman who didn't buy the dress I picked out for her simply has no taste. I'm not putting up with much more of this nonsense. It is absolutely too annoying to me. I'll go to a better store.

Diagnosing Attitudes Toward Organizations

Human organizations—both micro, and macro—exist to achieve socioeconomic goals unobtainable by isolated individual effort. They imply the acceptance of "intelligent altruism" with the establishment of group benefits.

However, apparently inevitably, institutions develop off-task behavior. The institutional socioeconomic goal is put aside and replaced with an interpersonal power struggle. Members become more concerned with securing their power positions than with productivity. The organization has become bureaucratized (Gear, Hill & Liendo, 1981).

This bureaucratization is not usually understood by our clients. Consequently, they either tend to identify human organizations with inefficient obstructive bureaucracies and to avoid them, or they become fascinated by the organization as an instrument of power and protection and join them.

Consequently, with respect to organizations, the client can adopt one of two pathological positions:

1.   *Bureaucrats,* who are organization members who focus on the intrainstitutional power struggle rather than the socioeconomic goal of the institution. They unconsciously sabotage institutional productivity with an as-if attitude which leads them to substitute effective action with empty rituals.

2.   *Mavericks,* who are those who do not understand that certain complex socioeconomic goals can only be reached by multi-membered social organizations and not by isolated individual effort. Besides, they are not adept at political power strug-

gles and either eliminate themselves or are eliminated by the more adept institutional bureaucrats who take advantage of them.

Masochists are more prone to become absorbed by the bureaucratizing pressures, while sadists misunderstand institutional dynamics as a whole, putting their own interests and needs first. Actually, the masochistic agent, hypomanic subtype, is the prototype of a bureaucratic leader, while the masochistic insufficient, depressive subtype, is the prototype of the bureaucratic employee. On the other hand, the sadistic agent, hypomanic subtype, is the prototype of a maverick leader, while the sadistic insufficient, paranoid subtype, is the prototype of an isolated maverick. Paul Anka's song "My Way" is the theme song of the maverick.

Bureaucrats are joiners. They need organizations to give them security or to play out their power-oriented games. They actively seek out organizations to which to belong. They may be bureaucratic leaders interested in power or bureaucratic followers interested in security.

Masochistic insufficients tend to be bureaucratic followers; sadistic insufficients, middle level leaders; masochistic agents middle or high level leaders, often dominated themselves by a higher order sadistic agent. Masochistic patients usually are bureaucratic followers.

Mavericks, on the other hand, distrust organizations and reject the status and security which come from joining or belonging. They either work as loners or they form their own personal "maverick" organizations directed by them toward their own "rebel" goals. Sadistic agents are often maverick leaders; sadistic insufficients, maverick loners and sadistic (and sometimes masochistic) patients, maverick followers.

This is a typical statement of a bureaucratic avoidant hysterical masochistic insufficient with an employee mentality.

SALLY: I finally had to tell the lady that I'd like to help her, but the rules just don't go that far. I know that she couldn't wait in line for too long with her old mother, but what am I to do? All of the others wait. The doctor usually comes at about 10:30 and he doesn't like to waste time. If I start making exceptions, can you imagine what would happen? The place would become a disaster area. There's always someone with a sore back, a broken leg pleading for an exception.

This is a typical statement of a maverick intrusive paranoid sadistic insufficient.

TOM: Always with that talk about "now if everybody puts his shoulder to the wheel." What wheel, I say! They make more cars and the company gets richer! What's all that about sharing burdens of a recession! They're just out to take advantage of me. I got right up and told them at the meeting. I'll bet they didn't like that.

Diagnosing the Phenomenologic
——————————— Subtypes ———————————

By analyzing control, authority, defensive qualification, affect state, reality testing, centeredness, and attitude toward organizations it is possible to refine the diagnosis of both the individual and the dyadic subtype. This refinement is economically useful to the therapist in dealing with the transference and treatment, as we shall see in later chapters. For now, however, let us look at the phenomenologic subtypes: their main personality characteristics, physical symptoms, mental status, and way of relating to others.

Subtypes of Sadistic Agents

As we noted earlier, the clinical traits of the sadistic agent, omnipotence and distrust, coincide remarkably well with the characteristics of the narcissistic personality as described by Freud (1924a) and Kohut (1971). In effect, the sadistic agent has an excessive degree of self-reference, an excessive need to be loved and admired, an inflated concept of self, and an inordinate need for tribute and admiration from others.

Sadistic agents' feelings of omnipotence, grandiosity, and megalomania seem to be related to their own higher objective status and superior subjective status. Their mistrust is related to the lower objective status and inferior subjective status that they attribute to their significant others.

Sadistic agents can be subdivided according to whether they are hypomanic devaluers or paranoid blamers. They can also be subdivided according to how they deal with reality to confirm their sadistic hypotheses; they will be neuroticizers if they only distort others' perception of interpersonal reality, but they will be psychoticizers if they drive others to drastically disavow reality. This leads us to the basic subtypes.

Type 1: Compulsive hypomanic subtype. This type has great energy, enthusiasm, ambition, and optimism, but at the same time is suspicious, angry, stubborn, and tenacious. Such people seem warmer, more generous, and more naive than they really are. They are charismatic and possess leadership skills and the ability to fascinate and hypnotize others. They are far more in control of themselves and their social context than they let on.

The sadistic agent, compulsive hypomanic subtype, will correspond to the DSM-III compulsive personality disorder and the atypical bipolar affect disorder.

Psychoticizing compulsive hypomanics tend to produce major psychotic depressions in their significant others by using devastating and relentless attacks on their perception, their thinking, and especially their affective state (Gralnick, 1942).

The following transaction between James, a compulsive hypomanic sadistic agent, and his wife Marion, a depressive masochistic patient, is typical of such relationships:

JAMES: *(While they wind a fishing reel)* Well, let's get the show on the road. We can get this done in no time. Here, you wind, but faster, faster. *(Laughing)* You are a genius! You don't miss a single chance to go wrong.
MARION: Oh, no! I seem to have it wrong. Which way should I go? It's tangling on me. What a fool I am.
JAMES: But can't you see! Here! I'll do it for you. You really are impossible. We are wasting time.
MARION: *(Sadly)* You're right again. I'm just no good at all.

JAMES: *That* is an understatement! And you have no staying power. We'll get it done though. I'll make up for you.

Type 2: Compulsive paranoid subtype.   This type is cold, self-confident to the point of arrogance, highly energetic, and aggressively tenacious. Such people are usually high achievers, authorities in their field, with considerable power. They often seem jealous, hypersensitive, and excessively suspicious of others' motives. They have an exaggerated notion of their own importance and feel mistreated and misjudged by others (Henderson, 1978).

The sadistic agent, compulsive paranoid subtype, will correspond to the DSM-III compulsive and paranoid personality disorder.

Psychoticizing compulsive paranoid types tend to induce schizophrenic states in their significant others by relentlessly attacking the other' perception, affective state, and thinking. In this transaction, Phyllis, a compulsive paranoid sadistic agent tries to force the therapist into the complementary role of anxious masochistic patient:

PHYLLIS: Doctor, I know how to treat my husband. I've been married to him for twenty years. Are you sure that you know what you're talking about? You don't know my husband as I do.
THERAPIST: I'm talking about you now.
PHYLLIS: Oh, come on, Doctor. He is the issue now. Don't be so indirect, so diplomatic. You know very well that it is because of his perverse craziness that we are talking here today.
THERAPIST: What about you? Why are you so afraid of analyzing your behavior?
PHYLLIS: *(Angry)* Don't try to get me into the mess that he has created. Are you trying to protect him? Did he ask you for help?

Subtypes of Masochistic Patients

The two major symptoms of masochistic patients are anxiety and depression. Anxiety stems from their inability to face reality—their lack or avoidance of economic control. Depression stems from their sadistic guardians' attacks on their subjective status. In other words anxiety is related to their lower objective status and depression to their inferior subjective status (Lane, 1959). Masochistic patients can be subdivided into those who are devalued and those who are blamed. They can also be characterized according to the degree of reality distortion, whether they are neuroticized or psychoticized, their centeredness, and attitude toward organizations.

This breakdown has lead us to identify two groups of four masochistic-patient subtypes: (1) the devalued group, which consists of depressive, neurasthenic, conversive, and dissociative subtypes; and (2) the blamed group, which consists of the schizoid, anxious, phobic and obsessive subtypes. Both depressive and schizoid subtypes tend to be psychoticized.

Type 1: Depressive subtype.   The main traits of this type are deep feelings of sadness, despair, depression, loneliness, and inner death. They are apathetic and unresponsive to the outside world. They suffer from loss of sexual drive and interest in human relations; they are usually isolated from friends and relatives. While they have difficulty in thinking and concentrating, they reproach themselves constantly and are tormented by feelings of guilt, inferiority, and craziness. They set impossibly high standards for themselves but are passively dependent on others. They are given to frequent fits of copious crying and often think about, plan, or attempt suicide. In addition to fatigue and insomnia, they often complain of gastrointestinal problems, nausea, etc. The masochistic patient, depressive subtype corresponds to the DSM-III dysthymic affect disorder.

This is a typical statement of a depressive masochistic patient.

BILL: I feel rather depressed. My wife says that I am sexually weak, that I have no interest in her, and I think that she's right because I feel as if I were dead. I'd never be able to fulfill my father's hopes for his son. I feel so stupid and worthless. It's so difficult for me to get a job. Something is very wrong with me. Maybe if I killed myself everyone would be relieved.

Type 2: Neurasthenic subtype.   Similar to Type 1, the neurasthenic suffers from chronic fatigue with occasional exhaustion. Such people have little enthusiasm for life or capacity for enjoyment. Sexual desire is inhibited. They are overly sensitive to physical or emotional stress but are heavily dependent on energetic, dynamic people. The masochistic patient, neurasthenic subtype corresponds to the DSM-III dependent personality disorder.

This is a typical statement of a neurasthenic masochistic patient.

MARIA: I would like to be more active, to push harder and harder, but, I don't know, it's just so difficult for me to keep a job. Each time there's an emergency I fail to react—and then I feel that I have no right to enjoy life. I'm so lazy compared to my husband. He's so dynamic and energetic. He's always organizing new projects, having fun. I get tired just thinking about it.

Type 3: Conversive subtype.   This type corresponds to the hysteric, as diagnosed and described by Freud. Main traits of the conversive subtype include emotional lability, lack of overt sexual desire, unconscious seductiveness, and a variety of psychosomatic symptoms, such as chest pains, headaches, abdominal cramps, etc. There may also be a sudden onset of some quite dramatic physical symptoms—all involuntary and psychogenic—such as loss of vision, hearing, speech, or sensation, paralysis, involuntary tics, and epileptiform seizures. The client is often quite unconcerned about these physical disabilities, a phenomenon known as *la belle indifference.* The physical symptoms often relieve the client's anxiety, while granting him or her respite from responsibilities and increased personal attention. The masochistic patient, conversive subtype, corresponds to the DSM-III somatoform disorder, conversive subtype.

This is a typical statement of a conversive masochistic patient.

BETTY: I have such a painful headache. Always with my stupid problems. I feel really crippled because my husband complains that I am never prepared to have sexual intercourse, that I keep parading myself in the nude in front of him, but when he wants to make love I am never prepared for him. I know he's right, but I can't help it. It's a vicious circle because finally I feel compelled to please him even though I don't feel any kind of excitement. Sex is like an obligation, not a source of pleasure.

Type 4: Dissociative subtype.   Symptoms of dissociative sub-types include psychosomatic pains such as abdominal cramps, headaches, vomiting; altered states of conciousness or sense of identity; total or partial amnesia, sometimes combined with physi-cal flight from an intolerable situation; somnambulism; and even multiple personality. In the latter instance, one personality is usually quite meek, while another is devious or sexually aggres-sive.

The masochistic patient, dissociative subtype, will corre-spond to the DSM-III psychogenic amnesia type of dissociative disorder.

This is a typical statement of a dissociative masochistic patient.

GEORGE: I was talking yesterday with my father. He was telling me something about getting a job, but he was furious—insulting me, on the one hand, because I have no initiative and I'm always looking for excuses, and on the other hand pressing me to do something concrete. But all of a sudden, after drinking a small glass of wine, I fainted. They told me that they had to take care of me. I was talking like a little boy. But I don't remember anything.

Type 5: Schizoid subtype.   The main traits of this (often psychoticized) subtype are extreme shyness and seclusiveness with an inability to form close relationships. They are often depressed and apathetic and have blunted affect, inappropriate or disordered thinking, delusions, and hallucinations. Their behavior may be quite inappropriate; they may dress oddly or neglect their personal hygiene. In less severe cases they may resemble an "inadequate personality," lacking in stamina and having inadequate social emotional and intellectual responses. The masochistic patient, schizoid subtype, corresponds to the DSM-III schizoid type personality disorder.

This is a typical statement of a schizoid masochistic patient, who projected himself onto the main character of a movie.

MICHAEL: Mmm . . . it is so difficult for me to keep speaking . . . to speak about myself. I feel guilty because I'm not helping you much, but, you know, it's like appearing nude in public. I was thinking of the movie *Being There*. Did you see it? It's about a very ignorant gardener who only knew about plants and television. He grew very isolated and, under peculiar circumstances, he was precipitated all of a sudden into public life. People misunderstood his narrowness and thought that he was some kind of original philosopher speaking with metaphor. But he was constantly in danger of being discovered, so he had to speak as little as he could.

Type 6: Anxious subtype.   This subtype is consumed by free-floating anxiety. Anxious people are constantly striving to avoid even minor disapproval; hence, they are very insecure and conformist. They are always planning escape routes from socially ambiguous situations. Anxiety attacks result in a variety of physical symptoms: shortness of breath, palpitations, chest pains, dizziness. However, these attacks are usually not associated with true life-threatening situations. Such people want to be loved by everyone; although they are dependent types, they are reliable and responsible in small matters. They usually inhibit their own sexual or hostile impulses.

The masochistic patient, anxious subtype, corresponds to the DSM-III general anxiety type of disorder.

This is a typical statement of an anxious masochistic patient.

ANNE: I'm terrified. I can hardly breathe. My husband wants to move again. I'm shaking. I don't know how to tell him. He is always making sudden and radical decisions. I'm so frightened that I can't stand even minor changes. He became very angry with me—and I think he is right. I'm not a good partner—even sexually. *(Pause)* Yesterday, after discussing the move, he wanted to have sex. I said yes even though I didn't feel like it—as usual.

And, as usual, I didn't tell him. I didn't want him to be even more furious.

Type 7: Phobic subtype.   This subtype is characterized by anxiety, tension, nervousness, depression, and, most of all, phobias. The person experiences intense fear of an external object or situation that he or she consciously recognizes as harmless; the feared object or situation is avoided, and the person develops a great dependence on people that do not have such fear. There appears to be strong use of displacement as a defense mechanism; inner danger seems to become an outer one. The masochistic patient, phobic subtype, corresponds to the DSM-III phobic type of anxiety disorder.

This is a typical statement of a phobic masochistic patient.

PETER: I don't know what to do about this family meeting in Canada. We don't have much time to go there, and I hate to fly. But going on the bus will take us too much time. My mother, who is so courageous, doesn't understand my attitude. She says that this happens because I'm rottenly spoiled and selfish. It seems quite true, but I am absolutely unable to take a plane there. I can't allow other people to take command on the plane. It's the lack of control over the situation that's so frightening.

Type 8: Obsessive subtype.   This subtype is characterized by doubt, formality, cleanliness, and a tendency to be extremely ceremonial. Their thoughts are excessively detailed, repetitive, stereotyped, and irrelevant. There is an exaggerated preoccupation with magic ideas about destruction and guilt, which results in ineffective and endless equally magic rituals aimed at undoing aggressive thoughts, expiating guilt, etc. The masochistic patient, obsessive subtype, corresponds to the DSM-III obsessive type personality disorder.

This is a typical statement of an obsessive masochistic patient.

BOB: On the one hand I believe that the philosophic significance of hate is that it probably represents an ambivalent attitude such as one has to one's father. At the same time, I doubt that hate can exist without love, although when one loves, there tends to be an integration of the two sentiments which make a clear distinction of the two emotions absolutely essential. Therefore, most people would be unable to observe the despicable aspect of themselves.

Subtypes of Masochistic Agents

The two major symptoms of masochistic agents are anxiety and depression. Anxiety stems from their overconcern about those who are dependent on them, while the depression seems to be related to their inferior subjective status. Masochistic agents are constantly underrating their own self-worth and being attacked by their dependents (Trivers, 1971).

We previously compared sadistic agents with the self-centered narcissistic personality, whose affect states are "sacred" and should be constantly taken into account by others. Complementarily, it can be said that masochistic agents are like mirrors who go into treatment with the intention of treating the sadistic patients whom they "reflect." They have an other-centered mirroristic personality and are hypersensitive to minor changes in others' affect states.

Masochistic agents can be subdivided into two basic subtypes: those who are devalued and those who are blamed. The primary affect of the devalued masochistic agent is depression; that of the blamed masochistic agent, anxiety. The latter can sometimes experience bipolar manic-depression.

Type 1: Compulsive depressive subtype. This subtype deals with sadism by being excessively kind and polite. Such people tend to be perfectionists. They are dogged by feelings of worthlessness, inadequacy, and inferiority. Although they experienced a great deal of anxiety and insecurity in their childhood, as adults they function quite well on the surface, although their emotions tend to be quite inhibited. Although they may be aware of their hostility, it is expressed indirectly through obstructionism, procrastination, and other passive modes. They may experience some well-controlled suicidal or homosexual fantasies, physical symptoms such as tension headaches or digestive upsets, etc. Family life tends to be tense, joyless, rigid, and disciplined. They themselves often feel lonely, hopeless, and helpless in the face of the demands and manipulations of others who are close to them. The masochistic agent, compulsive depressive subtype, corresponds to the DSM-III passive aggressive personality disorder and dysthymic affect disorder.

Compulsive depressives are usually "done to," that is, neuroticized or psychoticized by their sadistic-patient partners. However, they can sometimes be "doers"—specifically, borderliners. They accomplish this by simultaneously stimulating in their partners unrealistic feelings of interpersonal omnipotence and devastating degrees of pragmatic impotence. That is, they give their partners very high expectations about themselves but at the same time cripple their ability to develop the skills necessary for independence (Manderscheid, Rae, McCarrick & Silbergeld, 1982).

This is a typical transaction between Katherine, a borderlining compulsive depressive masochistic agent and her son Jim, a borderlined psychopathic sadistic patient.

KATHERINE: Son, when will you show some responsibility at school and bring home a passing grade? Then we will talk about the use of the car. Also I've been hearing rumors about a drinking party on Saturday. You aren't thinking of going there are you?

JIM: (Angry) Mother, you are always suspecting me! How do you expect me to be motivated for anything if I'm stuck at home without any fun! You want to take away my initiative!

KATHERINE: (Worried) What I want is that you develop your excellent potential. You could be a great writer. Your imagination and your use of words are exceptional. But you must learn to apply yourself.

JIM: (Fed up) But, mother, I am applying myself! I have to be in touch with the world and with others. Be a good girl and give me the car. I know that I can always count on you. You're not as selfish as Dad.

KATHERINE: (Doubting) Well, yes, I don't want to let you down.

I'll let you have mine. Your father would object if I give you his. He always says that I spoil you. He is no longer a young man. Maybe that's why he can't understand your needs.

JIM: *(Warm and grateful)* Don't worry, Mother. I'll keep your little secret. Oh, by the way, I took some money from your purse. We need booze for the party.

KATHERINE: *(Smiling tenderly)* Oh, you know that you shouldn't do that anymore.

Type 2: Compulsive hypomanic subtype. These clients are similar to the compulsive depressives in that they are overly kind, polite, calm, perfectionistic, passively hostile, and inhibited in their emotions. They tend to use subtle humor or irony to express hostility. They often have difficulty listening to others and concentrating. They are also often indecisive and compulsively energetic. These types may devalue and manipulate their sadistic-patient partners to some degree, but then their dependents will turn on them and attack viciously, blaming them for all that goes wrong until they finally accept their "guilt" (Ellis, 1979). The masochistic agent, compulsive hypomanic subtype, corresponds to the DSM-III compulsive personality disorder and atypical bipolar affect dissorder.

This is a typical transaction between Sam, a compulsive hypomanic masochistic agent, and his wife Diane, a sadistic patient.

SAM: My dear, your dress is simply gorgeous! All ready to go?

DIANE: *(Angry)* Are you playing with me again? I'm not dressed up. These are my ordinary clothes. When is it that we have to go?

SAM: When is it? Why, tonight, of course.

DIANE: No, no, I know that, but what time tonight?

SAM: You know that! Well just imagine. You're more organized than I thought! Congratulations. It's in half an hour. Put on your cocktail dress. But hurry up! We're going to be late.

DIANE: Don't you be that way with me! *(Crying)* I can't stand it any longer.

Subtypes of Sadistic Patients

The major symptoms of sadistic patients are omnipotence and destructiveness. The destructiveness seems an attempt to deny their social impotence and lower objective status; it gives them a false feeling of freedom and power, but it is also an excellent means of achieving interpersonal domination—through blackmail and threats—of those who actually have some social control (Lefcourt, 1976). On the other hand, omnipotence seems to be related to superior subjective status. Sadistic patients idealize themselves and are idealized by their others, who constantly remark on their charm, wit, or intelligence (Cook, 1975). Their destructiveness feeds their omnipotence; although they cannot build anything constructive, they think they can destroy whatever they want.

Sadistic patients can be divided into two groups, each with three subtypes: (1) the devaluing group, which consists of the histrionic, hypochondriac, and psychopathic subtypes; and (2) the blaming group, which consists of the paranoid depressive, dissociative explosive, and paranoid schizophrenic subtypes.

Type 1: Histrionic subtype. These clients are usually emotionally labile, overly dramatic attention seekers. They tend to dress in a flashy, exhibitionistic, and sexually provocative manner. They are shallow, fickle, egocentric, and flighty. Their vanity makes them easy prey for those who use flattery and compliments. When frustrated or disappointed they become reproachful, tearful, abusive, and vindictive. In love affairs they are possessive, demanding, and unrealistically romantic.

Both men and women of this subtype act like caricatures of femininity, in that they make exaggerated use of the seductive tactics that society allows women once it has made them powerless. Certain types of male homosexuals can be found in this group.

Borderline clients also overreact to social approval or dissapproval. They need constant reassurance of their physical or sexual attractiveness and are overwhelmed with a sense of total failure at the slightest hint that they have failed. They often threaten suicide when deprived, but in fact rarely carry through on the threat (Grinker, Werble & Drye, 1968). The sadistic patient, histrionic subtype, corresponds to the DSM-III borderline personality disorder.

This is a typical interaction between Ann, a borderline sadistic patient, and her husband Tommy, a compulsive depressive masochistic agent.

ANN: Tommy, be a dear and bring me breakfast in bed. You know how I love you when you do that.

TOMMY: I'll fix it so you really like it.

ANN: Oh, you sweet boy. You know how I like it. And with you to serve me I really do like it. Naughty! Naughty! Always thinking about sex with me. You have work to do.

TOMMY: Oh, my God! It's late. I don't have time. Gee, I'm sorry, honey.

ANN: Oh! you always work me up and leave! I could kill myself. I'm always frustrated. How can you do that to me.

TOMMY: I'm awfully sorry, darling. *(Doubting)* OK! To hell with the office. I'll stay home with you. I don't want to disappoint you.

ANN: *(Angry)* Oh, no! This is not fair on your part. Now you want to stay here just because I demanded it from you. Because I know that I don't count! *(Starts crying)*

TOMMY: *(Desperate)* Oh dear! What did I do wrong now!

Type 2: Hypochondriac subtype.   These clients are completely preoccupied with their bodies and fear disease even where none exists. They have a heightened awareness of bodily sensations or minor somatic abnormalities and present their complaints at length, in detail, and with urgent, insistent, and often pressured speech. They are worried, anxious, and concerned about very minor symptoms, going from doctor to doctor and clinic to clinic for endless examinations and evaluations. However, they rarely receive compassionate objectivity because of their obsessive-compulsive obstinacy, defiance, and narcissism. They are so focused on their own bodily functions that they exclude almost completely the people in the world around them.

The hypochondriac subtype is notoriously refractory to treatment; it is almost impossible to penetrate the wall of somatic complaints and to bring out their underlying anger and depression. On the contrary, they usually develop a mistrustful attitude toward the people who do not believe in the reality of their symptoms. Moreover, they believe themselves to be altruistic people who are mistreated and misunderstood by their significant others. The sadistic patient, hypochondriac subtype, corresponds to the DSM-III hypochondriacal type of somatoform disorder. As an associated condition anorexia nervosa may develop.

This is a typical statement of a hypochondriac sadistic patient.

HELEN: I'm in such pain. It's terrible. I can barely move my left shoulder. My God! I don't deserve this punishment. And my stupid husband is doing nothing to relieve me. He didn't call my doctor again, maybe because it is too much for him. It seems that he enjoys mistreating me! (*Actually the husband is a very submissive, caring person whose main concern is how to relieve his wife.*)

My daughter is also selfish. She never asks my grandson to visit me. He only comes to see me when I'm desperately sick, because of my fragile health. She tells me that my grandson can't stand my constant "complaining"—as if I were a maniac and not a very sick person, crippled by my own body. They keep telling me that I should go and see a psychiatrist. They are the ones who should do that! It's my shoulder that's in pain, not my head! My head is just fine.

They know that I've made all kinds of sacrifices for them, but they keep insinuating that I'm a very selfish person. My God! They say that I'm always sick from something that doesn't allow me to take care of my responsibilities. Can you imagine that? They can't even imagine how I'm suffering. Now I'm *really* crippled. I don't know why God is doing this to me.

Type 3: Psychopathic subtype.   These clients are completely uninhibited in acting out their selfish impulses. They have had repeated clashes with society and the law. From early childhood they have been consistently and unconsciously encouraged to act out. Their caretakers were totally unable to set limits and, more-over, even sabotaged the limits that other people set (Katz & Lazarsfeld, 1955).

Psychopaths usually have a very low level of achievement in school and employment because of their chronic acting out—lying, stealing, and vandalism. They were often promiscuous and sexually aggressive at an early age. They rarely stay married for long and experience a wide variety of deviant sexual behavior. They abuse alcohol or other drugs, have repeated automobile accidents and traffic violations, and are frequently arrested for various criminal offenses. The sadistic patient, psychopathic sub-type, corresponds to the DSM-III antisocial type of personality disorder.

This is a typical statement of a psychopathic sadistic patient.

TOM: Damn! My wife is so stupid. She doesn't understand that I went to Las Vegas because this gives meaning to my life. In the same way that she likes to eat or make love, I like to gamble. Nobody is perfect! She says that she feels so abandoned, that she misses me so much, but actually I give her what she wants in bed. After all, it's been a long time since I went to Vegas. (*Actually he was there the previous week.*) She says that I'm irresponsible, that I'm throwing away all the money that we earn and save. This just isn't true. I'm using only my own money. (*Actually he borrows money from his friends, and his wife has to repay it to them.*) Don't you think that every individual has the right to enjoy life from time to time? My wife wants to make a little pet out of me, a prisoner, but I'll fight for my freedom, for my rights!

Type 4: Paranoid depressive subtype. These clients are anxious, agitated, and guilt ridden. They suffer from somatic or paranoid preoccupation, frequently of delusional proportions. They are very rigid, tense, hostile, and suspicious. They often break down totally when they realize that their social and economic goals of earlier years will never be accomplished. They feel betrayed, cheated, and manipulated by those close to them. Despite their low self-esteem, they often feel morally superior. In brief, they are fragile, irritable, devalued blamers. The sadistic patient, paranoid depressive subtype, corresponds to the DSM-III paranoid personality disorder and major depressive affect disorder.

This is a typical statement of a paranoid depressive sadistic patient.

VANESSA: My husband started again with his ironies and ambiguities. He told me that God blessed him by allowing him to marry me. In this way he can purge his guilt every day. I became very angry, and I told him he was a cynic. He begged me not to scream at him, and I asked him not to provoke me. He denied doing that. He said he could have married another woman not so harsh—kinder than me, but that I had other assets. I ended up confused and depressed.

Type 5: Dissociative explosive subtype.   This client is characterized by great outbursts of rage or physical aggressiveness. They can be quite normal between episodes and after such an outburst may feel extremely repentant; but they appear out of control during these rages, which may be related to epilepsy or excessive alcohol intake, and which culminate a period of irritability and hostile behavior.

They also resemble the dissociative masochistic patient in that they can experience altered states of consciousness, total or partial amnesia, and hysterical fugues. They may use drugs, alcohol, or gambling to avoid experiencing depressive episodes and get back at their masochistic-agent partners, who have an unconscious ability to drive them out of control. The sadistic patient, dissociative explosive subtype, corresponds to the DSM-III intermittent explosive type of disorder of impulse control.

This is a typical statement of a dissociative explosive sadistic patient.

VERA: It was terrible. Yesterday I was talking to my husband, and he was teasing me, making fun of me in that vicious way he uses with me. Then he asked me to have a drink with him—and from then on I completely forget what happened to us. He says that

I lost control and I started attacking him savagely—that I beat him so hard that I broke his glasses. It must have been awful! After smashing his glasses it seems that I began crying and accusing him. Finally we had sex in a very obscene way—I behaved like a prostitute. I think he is perverse, that he really enjoys it, because it's not the first time it has happened. And knowing how things are, he is the one who insists that I drink, that nothing will happen, that I should enjoy life. And I don't know how I allow him to convince me. This morning he admitted his guilt. He admits that he enjoys seeing me act like a furious lioness and then behave like a whore. I was very angry at him this morning for doing this to me. He was very repentant, but I don't know for how long. How long it will take for him to start making fun of me again, with his vicious ironies, his oblique comments. You know how vicious he can be behind his angel face and his saintlike attitudes.

Type 6: Paranoid schizophrenic subtype.   Such clients have totally inappropriate and ineffectual responses to the demands placed on them. They lack judgment and are often disorganized. They may suffer from delusions of persecution and control. They may believe that others are spying on them, spreading false rumors about them, planning to harm them, control their actions, or read their mind. They may also have auditory hallucinations; voices seem to come from within the patient's body or from outside sources, such as radios or walls. These voices may criticize, ridicule, or threaten. Often they urge the clients to do something they believe is wrong. Visual hallucinations of violence are also frequent. The sadistic patient, paranoid schizophrenic subtype, corresponds to the DSM-III paranoid type of schizophrenic disorder.

It is possible that these voices, criticisms, threats, and compulsive mandates represent the subtle, subliminal, and unconscious messages that are sent to paranoid schiozphrenics by the psychoticizing masochistic agents in their lives. One of the more striking chracteristics of paranoid schizophrenics is their paradoxical aggressive reaction toward a kind, warm, therapeutic approach: they think that they are being manipulated. This is a typical statement of a paranoid schizophrenic.

LENORE: (*After a long pause*) I don't know if I should start talking. (*Looking around*) Maybe you are in the plot with my mother. *Suspiciously*) She is so dangerous, you know, so tricky. She appears very kind to me, but I know she wants to kill me, to poison me. (*Hallucinating*) Can you hear those noises? They're coming for me. She's in league with the communists (*Whispering*) They're disguised as devils who are making fun of me. Listen! They're calling me a stupid, homosexual. They sent me here (*to the hospital*) because I tried to strangle her when she was sleeping. It's the only way you can get her. She is so dangerously astute. She hates me because I tried to be independent of her. (*Actually, the client's mother appears to be a very pleasant, warm old woman who was physically attacked by her daughter, apparently with no motive.*)

Subtypes of Sadistic Insufficients

The relationships of insufficients are unstable in nature, owing in part to the sadistic partner's compulsive, intrusive aggression toward his or her significant others. The latter react by running away, at least for a while and sometimes for good. Sadistic insufficients are of two basic types: hypomanic blaming devaluers and paranoid devalued balmers.

Type 1: Intrusive hypomanic subtype.   These clients are full of boastfulness and braggadocio. They have very poor impulse control, especially with regard to their hostile, aggressive, or sexual feelings. They are given to outbursts of rage, promiscuity, and dramatic showing off. They are intrusively jealous of their companions, with the result that they often experience rejection, ostracism, and hostility from others. This simply feeds their sensitivity and basic mistrust of others. The sadistic insufficient, intrusive hypomanic subtype, corresponds to the DSM-III narcissistic personality disorder and atypical bipolar affect dissorder.

This is a typical transaction between Charles, an instrusive hypomanic sadistic insufficient, and Monica, an avoidant depressive masochistic insufficient.

MONICA: (*Trying to be pleasant*) Hey! Did you see these flowers?

Aren't they beautiful?

CHARLES: *(Sarcastically)* Of course. I have my own eyes, and I can see by myself, you know. What's the big deal about them, anyway?

MONICA: *(Surprised)* I hadn't seen such beautiful flowers for a long time—with such magnificent colors.

CHARLES: *(Sarcastically)* Haven't you? That must be because you were raised on the frozen prairies where everything is dull and gray.

MONICA: *(Depressed)* At least people at work told me how lovely they were, so bright and delicate.

CHARLES: *(Laughing)* Your good old friends. Listen, those people must be morons. Or maybe not. Maybe they were just trying to be nice to you, to overlook your poor taste. *(Pause)* If you were born in California like myself, you would know what really beautiful flowers are.

MONICA: *(Anxious and depressed)* I'm sorry, I have to go upstairs now.

CHARLES: *(Blaming)* Oh yes! Running away from facing the truth, just like you always do.

Type 2: Intrusive paranoid subtype. These people are similar to the hypomanic subtype in that they are given to explosive outbursts and lack of sexual inhibition. They are vengeful, provocative bullies who have a deep inner core of depression and self-hatred. Their basic mistrust and suspiciousness of others runs deeper than the hypomanic's as does the degree of ostracism and rejection they experience as a result of their behavior. In general, they lack insight and tend to make heavy use of projection as a defense. The long-term prognosis is not good. The sadistic insufficient, intrusive paranoid subtype, corresponds to the DSM-III paranoid personality disorder.

The following is a typical transaction between Joan, an intrusive paranoid sadistic insufficient, and her husband Paul, an avoidant hysteric masochistic insufficient.

JOAN: The trouble with you is that you are a lazy bastard. I knew from the first that you weren't going to do your part.

PAUL: I do intend to do it, but I had other things.

JOAN: I'm always being taken advantage of. You and your other things. Confess! You had no intention of doing it.

PAUL: Well, really, I have but *your* part isn't done, and I think that it has to be done first.

JOAN: Excuses! I'm not doing mine first! Then for sure you'd leave me in the lurch. There's no way to win with you.

Subtypes of Masochistic Insufficients

The two major symptoms of the masochistic insufficient are claustrophobic anxiety and cyclical interruption of affective relationships. The anxiety stems from their inferior subjective status, and the frequent interruptions in their relationships stem from their fear of closeness—a fear made worse by the intrusive, aggressive partners they select (Cook, 1978).

Masochistic insufficients are of two types: (1) the blamed avoidant depressive subtype, who is either neuroticized or psychoticized, depending on the degree of reality distortion; and (2) the blamed but devaluing avoidant hysteric subtype. The latter may not only be neuroticized, but because they are also devaluers, they can be neuroticizers and at times even psychoticizers.

Type 1: Avoidant depressive subtype.   These clients are similar to anxious masochistic patients: they suffer from free-floating anxiety, fear of even minor disapproval, inhibition of hostile impulses or sexual desire, and deep-seated feelings of worthlessness and insecurity. They make strong use of displacement and denial, running away from threatening situations. They can become very depressed and isolated from friends and the world around them. The masochistic insufficient, avoidant depressive subtype, corresponds to the DSM-III avoidant personality disorder.

This is a typical statement of an avoidant depressive masochistic insufficient.

SHARON: Last night I dreamt something that made me very

anxious. I got into a swimming pool very carefully, trying not to hurt anyone, but as soon as I got into the pool the other people came closer to me and started pushing me down under the water. I was getting drowned. I could breath, but it seems clear in the dream that I could save my life only if I started screaming at the others. But this was impossible, first, because each time I tried to open my mouth the water came into it, and second, because the others got very angry at me for trying to scream and started accusing me of molesting them and pushed me down into the water again. It was terrible! Finally I woke up and stopped dreaming. At least I could escape in this way. By the way, I was sleeping with John *(her boyfriend)* last night, and he was taking up the whole bed, leaving no room for me. He was moving around and kicking me all night. Actually, my dream was interrupted when I finally fell off the bed. John pushed me out!

Type 2: Avoidant hysteric subtype. These clients are very similar to avoidant depressives—overly anxious and apprehensive, conformist and perfectionistic, with a desire to be loved by everyone, passive and inhibited. They may also be genuinely phobic about social situations, first running away from closeness and then experiencing a temporary feeling of liberation. This is because their passivity and fear of their own aggression makes them unable to stand up to the hostile attacks of others who are close to them. The masochistic insufficient, avoidant hysteric subtype, corresponds to the DSM-III histrionic personality disorder.

This is a typical transaction between Johnny, an avoidant hysteric masochistic insufficient, and his mother Elizabeth, who is an intrusive paranoid sadistic insufficient.

ELIZABETH: You've been playing in the mud! How could you come into my clean house like that?
JOHNNY: I fell and hurt my knee.
ELIZABETH: Always a clumsy boy. Let's see the knee, then you can clean the floor.

JOHNNY: Ouch! *(Wincing)* It hurts, Mom!

ELIZABETH: Now, don't complain. I'm helping you.

JOHNNY: But it does hurt.

ELIZABETH: *(Sarcastically)* I know you very well. You're more skillful than a professional actor when you need to justify yourself.

JOHNNY: *(Trying to escape)* Well, I have to finish my homework. Can I go now?

Subtype Dyads

In Chapters 2, 3, and 4 we discussed the major pathological dyads: the authoritarian, demagogic, and undercommitted. Subtypes within each of these dyads also tend to link up, in a further refinement of the *folie à deux,* a fact that the therapist should be aware of in making a diagnosis. Tables 1, 2, and 3 show how the subtypes link up within each dyad and the defensive posture and primary affect of each dyadic subtype.

Relationship between Dyadic
——————— Typology and DSM-III ———————

Many therapists maintain that classification systems are ultimately detrimental to treatment because they stereotype individuals and force them to conform to the confines of a diagnostic label. Indeed, we have all experienced the unthinking use of such vague terms as "narcissistic personality," "separation anxiety," "unresolved oedipal conflict," and so forth. In these circumstances the label becomes a substitute for thought, not a useful treatment tool.

However, a good classification system—one that is both precise and comprehensive, without being inflexible or overly general—can be invaluable to the clinician. For one, it can simplify communication among professionals. Common definitions of specific syndromes are essential in gathering scientifically valid statistical and epidemiological data. The third edition of the Diagnostic and Statistical Manual, DSM-III, is such a system.

DSM-III uses a multiaxial, phenomenological, descriptive approach in defining mental disorder. That is, certain traits are

Table 1
Authoritarian Dyadic Subtype

Sadistic Agent	Masochistic Patient
Type 1: Compulsive hypomanic	Type 1: Depressive
	Type 2: Neurasthenic
	Type 3: Conversive
	Type 4: Dissociative
Defense: Devaluer	Defense: Devalued
Affect: Elation	Affect: Depression
Type 2: Compulsive paranoid	Type 5: Schizoid
	Type 6: Anxious
	Type 7: Phobic
	Type 8: Obsessive
Defense: Blamer	Defense: Blamed
Affect: Anger	Affect: Guilt and anxiety

Table 2
Demagogic Dyadic Subtype

Masochistic Agent	Sadistic Patient
Type 1: Compulsive depressive	Type 1: Histrionic
	Type 2: Hypochondriac
	Type 3: Psychopath
Defense: Devalued	Defense: Devaluer
Affect: Depression	Affect: Elation
Type 2: Compulsive hypomanic	Type 4: Paranoid depressive
	Type 5: Dissociative explosive
	Type 6: Paranoid schizophrenic
Defense: Blamed devaluer	Defense: Devalued blamer
Affect: Anxiety, bipolar manic depression	Affect: Anger and distrust

Table 3
Undercommitted Dyadic Subtype

Sadistic Insufficient	Masochistic Insufficient
Type 1: Intrusive hypomanic	Type 1: Avoidant depressive
Defense: Devaluer	Defense: Devalued
Affect: Elation	Affect: Depression
Type 2: Intrusive paranoid	Type 2: Avoidant hysteric
Defense: Devalued blamer	Defense: Blamed devaluer
Affect: Anger and distrust	Affect: Anxiety

described and observed to gather in clusters or clinical syndromes (axis 1); certain clusters of traits also indicate a particular personality disorder (axis 2). Related physical disorders (axis 3), situational stress factors (axis 4), and optimum level of functioning in the previous six months (axis 5) are also part of a DSM-III diagnosis.

In order to make our dyadic typology readily accessible to professionals throughout the mental health field, we have shown the correspondence between our system and DSM-III. We have arranged them in tabular form according to dyadic subtype for ease of reading (see Table 4).

In Chapter 6 we will apply the information discussed in this and preceding chapters to actual cases, so that the student of dyadic typology can see how we arrive at a diagnosis and what that diagnosis tells us about the dynamics of a particular case.

Table 4

Dyadic Subtypes and DSM-III Category

Dyad	Type	Subtype	Clinical Syndrome (Affect Disorder)	Personality Disorder	DSM-III Associated Disorders
Authoritarian: Subtype A	Sadistic agent	Type 1: Compulsive hypomanic	Atypical bipolar	Compulsive	Insomnia; somatization; abuse of alcohol and hypnotics
	Masochistic patient	Type 1: Depressive	Dysthymic	Dependent	Insomnia; somatization; dependence on tranquilizers, stimulants, and alcohol; psychosexual disorders
		Type 2: Neurasthenic	Dysthymic	Dependent; avoidant	Somatization; dependence on tranquilizers, and stimulants; inhibited sexual desire
	Masochistic agent	Type 3: Conversive	Somatoform: conversive subtype	Dependent	Abuse of psychoactive drugs; inhibited sexual desire
		Type 4: Dissociative	Dissociative: psychogenic amnesia; fugue		Somnambulism; abuse of psychoactive drugs
Authoritarian: Subtype B	Sadistic agent	Type 2: Compulsive paranoid		Paranoid	Insomnia
	Masochistic patient	Type 5: Schizoid	Depersonalization; schizoaffective	Borderline: schizoid	Somatization; drug abuse; inhibited sexual desire
		Type 6: Anxious	Anxiety disorders	Dependent; avoidant	Somatization; abuse of alcohol and barbiturates; premature ejaculation
		Type 7: Phobic	Phobic anxiety disorder	Avoidant	Inhibited sexual desire
		Type 8: Obsessive	Obsessive-compulsive disorder		Anxiety; depression; phobia

Table 4 (Continued)
Dyadic Subtypes and DSM-III Category

Dyad	*Type*	*Subtype*	DSM-III		
			Clinical Syndrome (Affect Disorder)	Personality Disorder	Associated Disorders
Demagogic: Subtype A	Masochistic agent	Type 1: Compulsive depressive	Dysthymic; anxiety	Obsessive-compulsive; passive-aggressive	Insomnia; somatization; alcohol and amphetamine abuse; masochistic sexual disorders
	Sadistic patient	Type 1: Histrionic	Impulse disorder (kleptomania, gambling addiction)	Borderline; narcissistic; dependent; histrionic	Somnambulism; night terrors; bulimia; alcohol and drug abuse
		Type 2: Hypochondriac	Anxiety disorders: depressive, dysthymic Somaloform disorder Hypochondriesis.	Borderline; dependent; paranoid	Somatization; anorexia nervosa; tobacco abuse
		Type 3: Psychopath	Impulse disorder (kleptomania, vandalism, etc.)	Antisocial; borderline; narcissistic	Drug dependence and abuse
Demagogic: Subtype B	Masochistic agent	Type 2: Compulsive hypomanic	Atypical bipolar	Compulsive	Insomnia; bulimia; somatization

Table 4 (Continued)
Dyadic Subtypes and DSM-III Category

Dyad	Type	Subtype	Clinical Syndrome (Affect Disorder)	DSM-III Personality Disorder	Associated Disorders
	Sadistic patient	Type 4: Paranoid depressive	Depressive; melancholia; paranoia; anxiety	Dependent; paranoid	Insomnia or hypersomnia; somatization; alcohol and amphetamine abuse
		Type 5: Dissociative explosive	Impulse disorder; dissociative disorder with amnesia and fugue	Dependent; histrionic; narcissistic	Somnambulism; night terrors; bulimia; alcohol and tranquilizer abuse
		Type 6: Paranoid schizophrenic	Paranoid schizophrenia; impulse disorder	Schizotypal	Insomnia; anorexia; drug abuse
Undercommitted Subtype A	Sadistic insufficient	Type 1: Intrusive hypomanic	Phobic anxiety; impulse disorder; atypical bipolar	Narcissistic	Insomnia; bulimia; tobacco abuse; inhibited sexual desire; attention deficit
	Masochistic insufficient	Type 1: Avoidant depressive	Phobic anxiety; dysthmic	Avoidant	Insomnia; somatization; alcohol and tobacco abuse; inhibited sexual desire
Undercommitted Subtype B	Sadistic insufficient	Type 2: Intrusive paranoid	Phobic anxiety; explosive impulse disorder; paranoia; depression	Undersocialized aggressive; paranoid	Anorexia; alcohol and tobacco abuse; inhibited sexual desire
	Masochistic insuffient	Type 2: Avoidant hysteric	Phobic and general anxiety; conversion	Histrionic; avoidant; depersonalization	Insomnia; tobacco abuse; exhibitionism; inhibited masochistic sexual desire; premature ejaculation

6

Making the
───────────Diagnosis───────────

A clinical case can never be completely understood if it is viewed only in the abstract, devoid of the rich and individual detail that the client conveys to the therapist. The therapist, however, is helpless without some sort of theoretical framework on which to array these elements. The classification system and diagnosis, then, become tools for understanding the individual case.

In the last chapter we defined the diagnostic framework with its two organizing axes derived from the independent variables of interpersonal and socioeconomic power. We refined the diagnostic typology with the inclusion of five dependent variables: the defensive qualification, reality testing, affect organization, centeredness, and attitude toward organizations. We then included the phenomenologic axis and made clear the correspondences between the subtypes and DSM-III.

In this chapter we will get down to specifics on the individual case level. For example, although we know that the strategic therapeutic goal for all masochistic agents is to help them to give up control and submission, it is by listening to the discourse and observing the action of an individuals that we know how to achieve this goal with particular clients. Generalizations are important and concretely useful when linked to these specifics. Freud (1912) called the manifest content "a sacred text"; he meant that the client's material should be carefully considered and analysed in all its detail to achieve a specific understanding.

The pragmatic base of clinical observations is found in the client's speech and actions as well as in the speech, actions, and affects of the therapist. For this reason, we include a final structural diagnosis of speech and action obtained by analyzing this material on an individual case level to give the unique defensive and therapeutic action plan for each client; that is, each client's fundamental acting off and acting on.

A Multiaxial Diagnostic Decision Sheet (MADDS) is then presented as an instrument to quickly systematize the clinical material. The MADDS replaces the cross-sectional psychotomogram and sequential psychoflowchart used by us in earlier efforts to systematize clinical information (Gear, Hill & Liendo, 1981).

The chapter terminates with a series of cases in which we use the theoretical model and the MADDS to illustrate the diagnostic procedure.

Diagnosing Speech and Action

The Monotheme

Subjects tend to repeat in their speech the same personal stereotyped plot with the same roles, sequence of actions, and outcome in what they perceive as an interpersonal drama of suffering and victimization (Lévi-Strauss, 1963).

Fundamental acting off.   This monothematic story is accompanied by the compulsive stereotyped repetitive sadomasochistic action plan, which is acted inversely in direction and sequence to what the subject narrated and consciously perceived. This is the *fundamental acting off;* fundamental because it is the compulsive repetition of the historic interpersonal action relations; and acting off because it is action which is "off the task" of solving current socioeconomic and interpersonal problems. Subjects replace these problems with a focus on their historic sadomasochistic problem.

Fundamental counteracting off.   To enact this drama requires the complicity of another who will complement in speech and action this stereotyped, narrow, and inverted sadomasochistic story. To do so is to take the fundamental counteracting off position. The subject either selects another with an already closely complementary structure or induces the complementary role in another by speech and action.

Fundamental acting on. Psychotherapy specifically aims at the correction of the fundamental acting off behavior by amplifying perception and speech to include relevant socioeconomic problems and in a nonstereotyped way (moving beyond agent-patient-insufficientism). Relevant interpersonal problems are also considered, but in a way which amplifies the possibility beyond the historically narrow sadomasochistic paradigm (moving beyond sadomasochism).

The defensive speech is also reverted so that what is being done is what is perceived and described. And the behavior is rectified so that sadomasochism and excessive controlling-dependent or restrictive plans are overcome. This specific therapeutic correction is called *acting on* because it is "on the task" of solving the clients' current problems as opposed to confirming pet theories about personal relations.

Fundamental counteracting on.   When the significant others stop automatically reacting to the client's defensive action plan and induce the acting-on behavior in the client, then these others are executing the counteracting on. The other's behavior is therapeutic and corrective rather than a force that perpetuates pathology.

Structural Analysis of Speech and Action

The therapist selects understandable verbal material, with a clear plot, character, action sequence, and outcome. The narrative flow is segmented into a series of distinct anecdotes (Eco, 1966).

These are then compared with one another to determine the structure of the repetitive pattern of relationships unique to that individual.

An analysis of the clinical material in the case of Dora (Freud, 1905) is an excellent example. Reading Freud's paper, it can be observed that Dora says no less than forty-one times that she has been seduced by ill-intentioned others (her father, Mr. K, Mrs. K, the governess, Freud). The protagonists change but the roles, characters, and plot give a constant, repetitive, unchanging relationship.

Once this conscious narrative structure is determined, the therapist inverts the direction and sequence of the actions to obtain the unconscious structure which should correspond to the observed action of the client (Greimas, 1966). A further confirmation is made by observing the actions of the client in respect to the therapist. Here the therapist also uses his or her countertransferential affect reaction to further the diagnostic effort.

For example, again in the case of Dora, by inverting the direction and sequence of the narrative structure we will find that Dora initiates the ill-intentioned sexual seduction toward the other. If we take the recording of her actions with Freud, we will find that this is what actually happened in treatment.

If we wish to diagnose the narrative structure of the other, the most reliable material is direct quotes given by the client (Todorov, 1965) or direct observations in couple and family therapy. In this way we can determine if the client is responding with fundamental counteracting off, therapeutic counteracting on, or with fundamental acting off.

Degree of Complementarity

On the more general level of power and pleasure, dyads tend to be totally complementary. For example, a controlling, domineering, blaming, angry psychoticizing self-centered maverick compulsive paranoid sadistic agent will tend to form a dyad completely complementary on these levels with a dependent, submissive, blamed, guilty, psychoticized other-centered bureaucratic obsessive masochistic patient. However, fundamental counteracting off has an individual content, and dyads cannot be so totally complementary, since even in the same family each individual's relationships are unique. Also, the client's speech and action structure is molded within the psychosocial matrix of the family of origin, this matrix varies from family to family and from culture to culture.

Consequently, with the possible exception of father-son or mother-daughter, there are always at least slight differences between what is projected and what is introjected and, therefore, on the personal level of acting off, the attributed role is not identical to the role taken. These differences may become crucial when the partners were raised in totally different cultures. A Mexican hypomanic sadistic agent projects a different style and content to what a Canadian depressive masochistic patient will introject and enact (Festinger, 1957).

Contamination

Another important thing happens on the level of speech and action structure. In the last chapter we stated that sadists are self-centered; they are the narcissistic reflected ones who define the situation in terms of themselves. Complementarily, masochists are the mirroristic reflecting ones, whose situation is defined in terms of others; therefore, they become contaminated with the sadist's personal definition of the world. They begin to put aside their own style and content and become swallowed by the others' style and content.

The therapist will find that sadists tend to determine the thematic content of speech and the particular stereotyped action plan. It is the sadist's acting off rather than the masochist's. The masochistic partner disappears as an individual subject and becomes the other's reflecting counterpart.

The Dynamic Explanation of Acting Off

From a psychoanalytic perspective, the speech and action structure of fundamental acting off results from the simultaneous functioning of seven intrapsychic unconscious defense mechanisms.

1. *Naturalization* of the subject's representation of so-cioeconomic dependence, control, or restriction
2. *Substitution* of it by the representation of the interpersonal paradigm
3. *Narrowing* of the interpersonal paradigm to the stereotyped representation of sadomasochism
4. *Repression* of the representation of the subject's own sadism or masochism
5. *Projection* (projective identification) of this sadistic or masochistic position
6. *Denial* of the representation of the other's complementary sadism or masochism
7. *Introjection* (introjective identification) of the other's complementary sadism or masochism into the subject's representation

Our concept of defensive naturalization of the subject's intrapsychic representation of the socioeconomic structure is convergent with Daniel Glauser's enlightening sociosemiotic notion of "symbolic naturalization" of the subject's social identity (Glauser, 1978).

After naturalizing their socioeconomic position in the power structure, sadists repress and project their sadism, while denying and introjecting the others' masochism. The opposite is true of masochists: they repress and project their maschism while denying and introjecting the others' sadism.

Dora is an example of a borderlined sadistic patient. We find that she naturalizes her socioeconomic dependence, substitutes it with her narrowed representation of interpersonal reality as sadomasochistic, represses and projects her sadistic seduction, denies and introjects the others' acceptance of her seduction.

In keeping with our previous distinction of psychic space into conscious, preconscious, unconscious, and transconscious (Gear et al., 1981), we can say that the stereotyped pattern of perception and action is in the subject's preconscious because it can be made present in consciousness without resistance, being "unthought" because of a lack of attention to it (see Figure 2).

What is inverted is in the unconscious and even if it is unpleasant to think, it is thinkable by the subject. What is naturalized are the restrictions of the problem space, which limit what can be thought. What is outside of previously conceived experiences is in the transconscious because is unthinkable for the subject. When what has been naturalized is challenged and new information and experience are actually introduced from the transconscious, the problem-solving space is enlarged to entertain totally new possibilities.

The client's stereotyped (unthought) preconscious interpretation of the world is usually introduced into consciousness by using therapeutic descriptions: this is pattern recognition.

The client's inverting (painful to think) unconscious interpretation of the world is usually introduced into consciousness by using therapeutic interpretations: this is inversion recognition.

The client's mutilated sadomasochistic and socioeconomic intrapsychic code (unconscious interpretative paradigm) is usually introduced into consciousness by using code constructions: this is paradigm definition.

The unthinkable transconscious interpretations of the world that have never been previously included in the client's consciousness are usually introduced into it by using therapeutic openings: this is paradigm denaturalization and amplification.

Looking to other authors for similar concepts, we find that Freud (1924a) described mental illness as the substitution of one reality for another, just as we say that the fundamental acting off is

	Symbolic Content
Preconscious	Stereotyped representation of sadomasochistic speech and action structure, usually unthought
Unconscious	Correct (noninverted) representation of sadomasochistic speech and action structure, painful to be thought
Transconscious	Representations of alternative interpersonal and socioeconomic positions, previously unthought

Figure 2.   The Dynamics of Acting Off

the particular way that each client substitutes socioeconomic reality with a sadomasochistic interpersonal reality.

Melanie Klein (1952) made clear that sadism is projected in the schizoparanoid position. The sadism is projectively identified by using acting outs. She failed to see that masochism can be equally projectively identified, and she did not consider the socioeconomic reality defensively displaced onto the interpersonal. She occupied herself exclusively with the interpersonal.

Wilfred Bion (1965) interprets mental illness as an attack on the symbolic links of the client with his external world. The client's perception, memory, and thinking are attacked, and he is contained within a hostile inner object which isolates him from the real world.

Jacques Lacan (1966) insists that the symbolic representation of socioeconomic reality is substituted by the imaginary representation of interpersonal reality. When the subject cannot make contact with the father's phallus (as his socioeconomic "big other"), he is imprisoned in his narcissistic dyadic relationship, with himself "within his mother's womb" (as his interpersonal "small others") which operates as a mirror rather than another subject.

From Acting Off to Acting On

Certain corrections are necessary to go from acting off to acting on.

1. Reversion of the inversion in direction and sequence of the story of mistreatment
2. Control of the compulsive tendency to mistreat or be mistreated by others and the inclusion of newly constructed nonsadomasochistic interpersonal action plans (Millar, Gallanter & Pibram, 1960)
3. Attention to and discussion of the previously naturalized excessive socioeconomic monopoly, dependence, or restriction
4. Overcoming this excessive monopoly, dependence, or restriction with the inclusion of new, more adequate socioeconomic action plans (Newell & Simon, 1972).

In Dora's case, for example, the fundamental acting on consists of:

1. Rectification to recognize that she is the ill-intentioned one who actually tries to sexually seduce others
2. Control of her compulsive ill-intentioned sexual seduction and blaming behavior toward others and including new, realistically trusting and respectful interpersonal relationships
3. Discussion of her naturalized excessive spoiled dependence on her family and others
4. Overcoming this excessive socioeconomic dependence on others

The therapeutic rectification of the client's defensive action plan and the learning of a healthy one implies, of course, a transformation of the client's intrapsychic perceptive, cognitive, and affective organization: that is, of the client's interpretive paradigm of the world (Mischel, 1973).

From Counteracting Off to Counteracting On

When the partner or therapist helps the client to correct the fundamental acting off, they execute the fundamental counteracting on by doing the following:

1. Reversion of the inverted description of the sadomasochistic transaction
2. Control of the automatic reaction to mistreat or be mistreated while talking about it in reverse and the insistence upon the inclusion of a new nonsadomasochistic interpersonal relation
3. Analysis and discussion with the client of his or her naturalized excessive socioeconomic dependence, control, or restriction
4. Changing the action plan with the client to overcome his or her excessive dependence, monopoly, or restriction

In the case of Dora, for example, the fundamental counteracting on to be executed by the therapist or significant other (Mr. K, Mrs. K, etc.) would be:

1. To rectify, recognizing that they themselves have been sexually seduced by ill-intentioned Dora and then blamed by her

2. To control the automatic reaction of accepting her ill-intentioned seduction and blaming and to enter into a sincere relation with her

3. To discuss openly and objectively with her the naturalized excessive socioeconomic relationship of control and dependence

4. To overcome with her, her excessive dependency by refusing to accept the controlling role

The therapeutic correction of the client's environmental significant others' counterdefensive action plan also implies a transformation of their intrapsychic organization.

The Multiaxial Diagnostic ——————— Decisions Sheet (MADDS) ———————

The therapist will be making diagnostic decisions in nine successive areas defined in this and the previous chapter. In order to have this therapeutically important information at hand, we suggest that the therapist review each case with the MADDS in hand. The decisions are organized from the most general to the specific and individual content.

1. Decision: Socioeconomic control
   - Does the client control the socioeconomic relations of others? If yes, the client is an *agent*.
   - Do others control the client's socioeconomic relations? If yes, the client is a *patient*.
   - Does the client control only his own socioeconomic relations? If yes, the client is an *insufficient*.

2. Decision: Interpersonal authority
   - Does the client say that he is a submissive victim, while he acts like a dominating victimizer? If yes, the client is a *sadist*.
   - Does the client say that he is a dominating victimizer while he acts like a submissive victim? If yes, the client is a *masochist*.
3. Decision: Defensive qualification
   - Does the client chiefly blame others? If yes, the client is a *blamer*.
   - Is the client chiefly blamed by himself and others? If yes, the client is *blamed*.
   - Does the client chiefly devalue others? If yes, the client is a *devaluer*.
   - Is the client chiefly devalued by others? If yes, the client is *devalued*.
   - Is the client blaming toward others but devalued by them? If yes, the client is a *devalued blamer*.
   - Does the client devalue others while being blamed by them? If yes, the client is a *blamed devaluer*.
4. Decision: Affect state
   - Does the client feel of superior competence? If yes, the client is chiefly *elated*.
   - Does the client feel of inferior competence? If yes, the client is chiefly *depressed and anxious*.
   - Does the client feel morally superior and entitled? If yes, the client is chiefly *angry*.
   - Does the client feel morally inferior and give moral entitlement to others? If yes, the client is *depressed and guilty*.
   - Does the client feel morally superior but of inferior competence? If yes, the client is *distrustful*.
   - Does the client feel superior but receive moral attacks and give moral entitlement? If yes, the client is *anxious*.
5. Decision: Reality testing
   - Has the client poor interpersonal reality testing (IPRT)

but intact socioeconomic reality testing (SERT)? If yes, the client is *neuroticized*.

- Does the client mildly attack others' IPRT but respect their SERT? If yes, the client is a *neuroticizer*.
- Does the client have poor IPRT and poor SERT especially in regard to consequences? If yes, the client is *borderlined*.
- Does the client strongly attack others' IPRT and SERT, especially by protecting from consequences? If yes, the client is a *borderline*.
- Does the client have severely impaired IPRT and SERT? If yes, the client is *psychotized*.
- Does the client severely attack others, IPRT and SERT, doing so from a position of power? If yes, the client is a *psychotizer*.

6. Decision: Centeredness
   - Is the client excessively centered on himself? If yes, the client is *narcissistic*.
   - Is the client excessively centered on others? If yes, the client is *mirroristic*.

7. Decision: Attitude toward organizations
   - Does the client focus on intrainstitutional power struggles rather than organizational goals? If yes, the client is *bureaucratic*.
   - Is the client unable to understand and participate in group goals of social organizations? If yes, the client is a *maverick*.

8. Decision: Clinical phenomenology
   - Does the client belong to the type characterized chiefly by anxious, depressed dependent, and submissive behavior? If yes, the client is a *masochistic patient*.
     Within this group is the client chiefly sad and apathetic? If so, the subtype is *depressive*.
     Chronically fatigued and without desire? If so, the subtype is *neurasthenic*.
     With somatic complaints, emotionally labile, seductive? If so, the subtype is *conversive*.

With psychogenic amnesia? If so, the subtype is *dissociative*.

Seclusive with inappropiate or disordered thinking and inadequate social response? If so, the subtype is *schizoid*.

Insecure, conformist, high anxiety? If so, the subtype is *anxious*.

Phobias, anxiety-avoidance behavior? If so, the subtype is *phoboic*.

Ceremonial, stereotyped, repetitive thought? If so, the subtype is *obsessive*.

- Does the client belong to the type characterized chiefly by omnipotent, destructive, controlling, and dominating behavior? If yes, the client type is a *sadistic agent*.

  Within this group is the client chiefly energetic, ambitious, tenacious, and charismatic? If so, the subtype is *compulsive hypomanic*.

  Cold, self-centered, suspicious, feeling mistreated? If so, the subtype is *compulsive paranoid*.

- Does the client belong to the type characterized chiefly by mirroristic, unconditionally protective, controlling, submissive behavior? If yes, the client type is a *masochistic agent*.

  Within this group is the client chiefly empty, lonely, emotionally inhibited? If so, the subtype is *compulsive depressive*.

  Ironic, devaluing, with a bipolar affect disorder? If so, the subtype is *compulsive hypomanic*.

- Does the client belong to the type characterized chiefly by omnipotent, destructive, dependent dominant behavior? If yes, the client type is a *sadistic patient*.

  Within this group is the client chiefly exhibitionist and provocative, vascillating between seduction and threat? If so, the subtype is *histrionic*.

  Overly centered on body function and conditions? If so, the subtype is *hypochondriacal*.

  Exhibiting delinquent behavior, lying, stealing, promis-

cuous, and aggressive? If so, the subtype is *psychopathic*.
Irritable, blaming, somatic, and displaying paranoid preoccupations? If so, the subtype is *paranoid depressive*.
Irritable, intermittently explosive, aggressive, and displaying dissociative episodes? If so, the subtype is *dissociative explosive*.
Having delusions of persecution and control of a paranoid
type, with hallucinations? If so, the subtype is *paranoid
schizophrenic*.

- Does the client belong to the type characterized chiefly
by disagreeable, intrusive, dominant behavior, with control only over himself? If so, the type is *sadistic insufficient*.
Within this group is the client chiefly characterized by
jealous, show-off, narcissistic behavior? If so, the subtype
is *intrusive hypomanic*.
Projective, vengeful, and mistrustful behavior, and often
rejected by others? If so, the subtype is *intrusive paranoid*.

- Does the client belong to the type characterized chiefly
by anxious, avoidant, submissive behavior in control of
his own socioeconomic reality? If yes, the type is *masochistic insufficient*.
Within this group is the client depressed, placating, and
insecure? If so, the subtype is *avoidant depressive*.
Conforming, superficially pleasing, ironic? If so, the
subtype is *avoidant hysteric*.

9. Decision: Speech and action structure
- If the client has been diagnosed as a sadist, in what
stereotyped way does he say that he is mistreated, while
he acts to mistreat others and thus avoid confrontation of
current problems? This is termed *sadistic acting off*.
- If the client has been diagnosed as a masochist, in what
stereotyped way does he say that he is mistreating others
while he is mistreated by others in their action and thus
avoids confrontation of current problems? This may be
termed *masochistic acting off*.

Clinical Application of the
─────────────── Decision Sheet ───────────────

In the case material presented below we will analyze and diagnose individual cases along the different axes that have been discussed in this and previous chapters (see Figure 3). The first two cases represent authoritarian dyads; the next three, demagogic dyads, and the last two, undercommitted dyads

DYADIC TYPE: Authoritarian
INDIVIDUAL TYPE: Sadistic Agent-Masochistic Patient
SUBTYPE: Compulsive Hypomanic-Depressive

Mary is an attractive, single 28-year-old who has been having frequent severe depressions. She has had a number of lovers, but none of these relations have lasted long. She felt empty, unimportant, and unloved in the relationships. Her lovers tended to degrade and abuse her, both sexually and psychologically. She began to take drugs (chiefly cocaine and sleeping pills) in the company of these lovers.

She is in conjoint couple therapy with her current lover, David, who is thinking of marrying her but is not sure if he wants to because she is "so stupid" and because he fears that she was "monstrously bad" in the past and is "likely to be unfaithful" if he marries her. David's very traditional family has rejected or ignored Mary and failed to invite her to family affairs. They have made it clear that they think she is beneath David and that she is just looking for a meal ticket.

Mary's own mother had been disapproving of her all during her childhood. She felt loved only by her father, who was disfigured by a birth defect and tended to hide himself from the public. He had a low-paying job and was verbally abused by Mary's aggressive mother. Mary recounts a childhood history of recurring abuses and devaluation. "I remember the other children laughing at me and calling me names. I was never sure what I did to deserve it."

David was divorced; his wife had been unfaithful to him. He is an industrialist who has a reputation for abusive behavior

Diagnostics Axes	Authoritarian		Demagogic		Undercommitted	
	Sadistic Agent	Masochistic	Masochistic agent	Sadistic patient	Masochistic insufficient	Sadistic insufficient
Socioeconomic control	Controlling	Dependent	Controlling	Dependent	Restricted	Restricting
Interpersonal authority	Domineering	Submissive	Submissive	Domineering	Avoidant	Intrusive
Disqualification	Blamer and devaluing	Blamed and devalued	Blamed and devalued/ing	Blamer and devaluing/ed	Blamed and devalued/ing	Blamer and devaluing devalued
Affect state	Anger	Depression	Guilt	Elation	Anxiety	Distrust
Reality testing	Psychoticizing	Psychoticized	Borderlining and psychoticized	Borderlined and psychoticizing	Neuroticized and psychoticized	Neuroticized and psychoticized
Phenomenology	Hypomanic Paranoid	Depressive; dissociative; neurasthenic; conversive phobic; anxious; schizoid; obsessive	Hypomanic Depressive	Depressive paranoid; dissociative explosive; schizophrenic paranoid Histrionic; hypochondriac; psychopath	Depressive Hysterical	Hypomanic Paranoid
Centeredness	Self-centered	Other-centered	Other-centered	Self-centered	Other-centered	Self-centered
Attitude toward organizations	Maverick	Bureaucrat	Bureaucrat	Maverick	Bureaucrat	Maverick
Speech and aim structure	Says he is victimized while he is victimizer	Says he is victimizer while he is victimized	Says he is victimizer while he is victimized	Says he is victimized while he is victimizer	Says he is victimizer while he is victimized	Says he is victimized while he is victimizer

Figure 3. Nine Diagnostic and Therapeutic Axes.

155

toward his employees. According to Mary, his secretary was "constantly depressed." According to David, one of his upper-level employees had been treated by a psychiatrist for severe depressions; during the course of treatment he talked about David's arbitrary demands and bad treatment. This had made David so indignant that he ordered his employee to stop seeing the psychiatrist or stop coming to work.

This is an excerpt from an interview with the couple. Mary enters crying.

MARY: I really don't know what to do. I never do anything right. Take this morning. We are buying the bedroom set, and I went all over town looking for information, but I didn't ask how it was to be paid.

DAVID: I can't believe it. I don't know whether she is really that dumb or if she does it on purpose, but she manages to upset my plans. Why couldn't you do such a simple thing as to ask how we were to pay?

MARY: I just never know how to talk about money. Imagine if I ruin the deal.

DAVID: You know you're right. (Ironically) I'm asking too much, really. I have overestimated your ability. How terribly stupid of me!

MARY: (Timidly) If you could explain to me what you want, what it is I have to do . . .

DAVID: If I could explain simply enough for you to understand, I'd be a genius, and you still wouldn't be able to do it. And, anyway, I told you. I just have to start expecting failure!

Diagnostic Discussion

Socioeconomic relations.   Mary does not question David's socioeconomic monopoly. In fact, she assumes it as natural and not worthy of questioning, and she doesn't ask about payment for that reason. She sees dealing with money as difficult: "They'd know I can't make a good deal, and they'd ask for more."

Mary does not work and depends totally on David, who

makes all the important decisions, economic and otherwise. He makes the decision to marry or not, to buy the furniture, the terms, etc. In the past he always quickly broke off relationships with more independent women. The women he considered as marriage partners, like Mary, were always of a lower socioeconomic level and very dependent.

Therefore David is an agent and Mary is a patient.

Interpersonal relations.   David dominates, devalues, and defines situations. For example, he dominates his employee, trying to force him to leave his treatment and submit to further abuse. He dominates Mary, making her fulfill his orders. David perceives himself as frustrated by Mary. She fails to complete the task to his satisfaction. Mary also defines herself as the frustrator, while she is totally frustrated even in her desire to be pleasing to him. In the action sequence David also claims that she is the initiator of the action: failure resulted because she behaved stupidly, not because he failed to clearly specify the information that he wanted. His only assumption of responsibility is ironic: "I'm asking too much really." "How terribly stupid of me to overestimate your ability."

Therefore David is the dominating sadist who claims to be victimized by Mary, the submissive masochist who claims to be the victimizer.

Defensive qualifications.   David devalues Mary in terms of intelligence and moral worth. For example, he continually calls her "stupid" in the interview; he is not sure about marriage to her because she is "monstrously bad." "I wonder how I put up with her."

Mary devalues herself and overvalues David. For example, "I just never know how to talk about money." "I don't know how he puts up with me." "You're so good at all that." David is an overvaluing devaluer and Mary is a devalued person who overvalues the other.

Centeredness.   David centers on his own feelings, his own entitlement, and he defines how Mary is, how he is, and what is happening in the situation. He does not even consider Mary's feelings or other possible explanations. Mary, on the hand, accepts his feelings as important. She is concerned about his "anger" and "frustration" and accepts his entitlement to be pleased as well as accepting his definition of her as stupid. She tries, rather, to excuse herself within this definition.

He is therefore narcissistic and she is mirroristic.

Primary affect.   Since David consideres himself superior in the socioeconomic sphere and morally right interpersonally, he tends to have a sense of elation typical of the devaluing self-overvaluing hypomanic. This is accompanied by anger related to his sense of indignation because of a perceived moral superiority. The elation and anger are the result of his definition of himself as interpersonally superior and his actual socioeconomic superiority.

Since Mary is and considers herself inferior socioeconomically, she has a high level of anxiety and a constant need to try to please her benefactor. The moral, intellectual, and socioeconomic put-downs produce a hopeless sense of little self-worth with a sense of depression. Her chief emotions, then, are depression when she accepts her hopelessness and helplessness and anxiety when she perceives the displeasure of her benefactor, who could abandon her.

David's principal affects, then, are elation and anger and Mary suffers chiefly from anxiety and depression. A reorganization of perception and action in the interpersonal and socioeconomic spheres is necessary to modify the affect organization.

Reality relations.   David attacks very severely Mary's interpersonal reality testing, and he does it from a position of authority and socioeconomic power. He also attacks her socioeconomic reality testing, condemning her to failure in her tasks, while, for example, he does not clarify with her exactly what he wants her to do when he assigns the task.

He uses a style which mixes direct attacks with more subtle and confusing irony and ridicule. For example, "I'm stupid to expect you to understand."

Mary could suffer a psychotic depression because of the nature of the attack, the authority of the attacker, and her own inability to abandon the field because of her socioeconomic-dependence on him.

He, on the other hand, is stabilized in his neurotic posture by her tendency to accept and confirm his distorted perception of interpersonal reality. At the same time she has little effect on his perception of socioeconomic reality, since any opinion is totally without authority.

He is psychoticizing and she is psychoticized, while she, in turn, is neuroticizing and he is neuroticized.

Attitude toward organizations. David is not a joiner. He does not enter organizations where he does not have control. Organizations are seen as extensions of his personal power and are used to his ends. There is no acceptance of the group as having, or being entitled to, a shared goal. The goals and the organization are simply his. Others join him. He is therefore a maverick leader.

Mary's organizational links have always been tenuous. She is not astute in the struggle for power. She tries to be a conforming obedient joiner who looks only for security, not productivity, and will accept ritualistic appearances. If she was in an organization she would be a bureaucratic employee who says, "Give me the rules clearly and I'll abide by them".

Phenomenologic diagnosis. David has been seen to be dominating and controlling. He tends to omnipotence and is destructive in his devaluing attacks. He is therefore a sadistic agent. Within this group he is chiefly devaluing, energetic, and ambitious. This would make him of the compulsive hypomanic subtype.

Mary is anxious, depressed, dependent, and submissive, which confirms the diagnosis of masochistic patient. Within this group she is sad and empty and is a member of the depressive subtype. Her drug dependence is a frequently associated secondary characteristic of this group.

The corresponding DSM-III diagnosis would be:

David

- Affect disorder: bipolar (hypomanic)
- Personality disorder: narcissistic

Mary

- Affect disorder: depressive
- Personality disorder: dependent
- Associated disorders: drug dependence; sexual masochism

Speech and action structure.   The acting-off behavior will be taken from the position of David, the sadist, who tends to impose his definitions on Mary, the masochist. David talks mono-thematically in a way which devalues Mary intellectually and morally (stories of Mary's stupidity and enormous badness). He claims to be frustrated by her, while he acts to frustrate her in any attempt to obtain moral or intellectual pleasure.

He therefore acts rather than confronting his interpersonal problem of excessive self-valuation and other-devaluation with its excessive sense of entitlement to moral and cognitive pleasure. He has naturalized his socioeconomic problem of a need for excessive control which is replaced in perception and thought by this historic sadomasochistic personalization.

David should recognize and control his tendency to frustrate the other and to justify his sense of overentitlement with repetitive devaluations of this other and overvaluations of himself. He must include the possibility of a realistic evaluation of the other and must accept the entitlement of the other to pleasure. He must identify his tendency to monopolize socioeconomic control and conceive of and execute behavior which allows the other to share this control.

DYADIC TYPE: Authoritarian
INDIVIDUAL TYPE: Sadistic Agent-Masochistic Patient
SUBTYPE: Compulsive Paranoid-Anxious (Phobic)

Jean, a 50-year-old married woman, was referred by a cardiologist after she had been hospitalized for tachycardia. She had been thoroughly studied, and no underlying cardiac pathology was found. She dated the onset of her tachycardia to ten months before when she suffered a "delayed anaphylactic shock" to an injection and "almost died." Since that time she has feared death and has had panic attacks about every two weeks. The episodes begin with dizziness, blurred vision, then tachycardia and panic. Her fear of dying is so great that she goes to the nearest emergency room and asks for treatment.

She is afraid to be alone, and for that reason she calls her husband many times each day. When asked if she had other fears she presented a list filling two pages. These phobias date back many years. She is a housewife with few outside interests or friends. She can no longer read because of "eye trouble."

Two daughters are married. One is in the process of divorce and tends to be quite irresponsible. The other daughter is understanding and helpful. The client is worried about the divorce and about her daughter's irresponsible attitude. She expressed the fear that she was somehow to blame for raising a daughter so bad as to be indifferent to her own children.

Her husband Gerald is an army colonel and is due to retire in six months from a lifelong career. He is cooperative, though somewhat cold and aloof. He accompanies his wife to the session and generally responds to her pleas for help by taking charge of her. His work is his hobby, and his wife's illness is interfering with this. He is doubtful about the value of psychotherapy and comes because the cardiologist insisted.

She tends to blame herself for being a burden and fears that he will finally leave her. He agrees that she is to blame and could do something if she would just discipline herself, since there is "nothing wrong." He can't understand all the fuss she makes and feels that she really is to blame for this irresponsible disruption in his life.

The following is an excerpt from an interview with Jean.

JEAN: I am terrified to be alone, Doctor. I need to know that someone is there to help me. When an attack comes I feel like I'm going to die. My eyes blur, I feel weak, and then it starts and I lose control. It all started with an anaphylactic shock last December.

I'm sure you know what that is, Doctor. It is apparently something dangerous, but I don't understand it at all.

THERAPIST: *(Smiling)* You see me as the wise adult who knows all and yourself as the little child who knows nothing.

JEAN: Well, yes. Like my husband. He is always so sure. And, thank goodness, he is there when I call. He is home by 5 P.M., but he has to leave by 7 A.M. I just don't know what he'll do with me when he retires. I'm such a bother and a bore. I know that he is going to leave me when he has had too much. It is bad of me to call, but I can't help it. You know I'm calm until the tachycardia comes. Then I'm terrified. Once I had to go to the neighbor's. Usually I make it to the emergency room. They always know what to do.

THERAPIST: Again you attribute great powers to the others and a great lack of personal capacity to yourself. Let me see if you can help me to link these attacks to something. Are there any particular circumstances or people that stand out?

JEAN: You know, it happened twice at funerals. They were people I knew I could count on to help. They were always there and knew for sure. Even though I bothered them, they always helped.

THERAPIST: It would appear that you have a strong need for protection and an equally strong fear that you will be left.

JEAN: Oh, yes, and sometimes an attack happens when my husband leaves for work in the morning. I feel so guilty, but sometimes I feel that he almost looks satisfied by it all, even though he tells me that I should feel guilty for what I'm doing to him. Doctor, I really think that I'm going crazy. I came on my own. I want help. Do you think that I'll be all right?

THERAPIST: There are many things that will be done with your help, just as you have helped us to focus on the problem and clarify it today.

Diagnostic Discussion

Socioeconomic relations. Gerald is a military man in a position of command. He makes the decision about therapy. He also has economic control, producing and distributing the economic resources and rewarding and punishing. Jean does not work. She has little control over information, ignoring the medical details of her illness. She isolates herself from social contacts except for those of a dependent sort (emergency rooms; strong, reliable, protective friends). She has less education than her husband.

Gerald is the agent and Jean is the patient.

Interpersonal relations.   Gerald dominates at work and at home. He is clearly the authority figure. He tends to perceive himself as frustrated by and a victim of Jean and bored by her fears. At the same time she submits to and induces his overprotective control and sees herself as his victimizer, who bores him and makes demands on him.

Therefore Gerald is the dominant sadist who claims to be the victim of Jean. She is the submissive masochist who claims to be the victimizer.

Defensive qualifications.   Gerald blames Jean, considering that she lacks discipline. He considers her to blame for this "irresponsible disruption" of his life. She blames herself as well as being blamed by him. For example, she blames herself for her daughter's behavior. She blames herself for boring and bothering others. She is also self-devaluing and overvaluing of the other in the socioeconomic sphere, considering that she knows nothing and that the other is omniscient.

Gerald then is blaming and self-exonerating. Jean is blamed and self-blaming as well as self-devaluing.

Centeredness.   Gerald centers on his own reactions, not understanding and also blaming the other for his reactions, for instance, for the "unnecessary" fuss.

Although very concerned about herself and talking about her body, Jean is very much dependent and concerned that the other define her as "sick" or "well" and very aware of her possible effect on the other. She is therefore basically other-centered, needing the definition, reaction, protection, etc., of the other in order to survive.

Gerald is a narcissist. Jean is a mirrorist in fear of losing the other that she needs to reflect in order to survive.

Primary affect. Gerald's principal bothersome emotion is anger, which is related to his sense of moral entitlement. He blames because he feels more dutiful, more disciplined, etc. and is angry because his wife does not meet his standards. This is typical of the compulsive paranoid agent.

Jean has two principal affects, anxiety and depression. Her anxiety is related to her excessive socioeconomic dependence and devaluation and her fear of abandonment, with the real knowledge that she can't make it alone.

Her depression is related to self-blame. She feels inferior and then guilty about this inferiority and the trouble that it causes others.

Gerald is angry. Jean is anxious and guilty.

Reality relations. Gerald is not strongly psychoticizing in his actual verbal communication with Jean, in that he attacks her interpersonal reality testing only to the degree that he judges and blames her for what he sees as a "voluntary" "undisciplined" lack of control. He does not say that he, not she, is out of control, etc. Therefore interpersonally he is only mildly distorting.

However, socioeconomically he keeps her very dependent. She is at home; he answers her calls. He does not encourage friendship. He manages everything. In this way he creates or contributes to a perception of socioeconomic reality as hopelessly and frighteningly difficult. At the same time he threatens in some way not to continue to contain her in this area. He is a distant, aloof, untrusting person. He talks of retirement and boredom with her and she fears abandonment (death of friends, mother, husband).

The threat of psychosis to this woman comes with the taking away of the support structures, especially in the socioeconomic sphere.

Jean then is severely neuroticized with slight distortion in interpersonal reality and a severe distortion in socioeconomic reality. She is threated with decompensation on loss of the agent. She could be psychoticized on abandonment.

Gerald's interpersonal qualification of Jean as guilty and inferior is accepted and made true. No one touches his socioeconomic sphere. There he has the power and authority, which is also accepted, and thus his position is confirmed.

He is neuroticized by the confirmation of his structure. Therefore Gerald is neuroticized, but is a neuroticizer and is himself potentially psychoticizing if he withdraws his "protective" socioeconomic shield.

Jean is neuroticized with a potential for psychosis if her compensatory system does not work, at the same time as she is a neuroticizer of Gerald and others who complement her. She has no power to impose a distortion but the acceptance of Gerald's distortion keeps him balanced and stabilizes his neurotic pathology.

Attitude toward organizations. Gerald is in a position of command in the army. He is accustomed to knowing his place and to giving and receiving commands. He is aware of the power structure and has risen in it. Therefore he has bureaucratic leadership characteristics, but in a bureaucracy in which "obedience" and acceptance of dependence is what is ritualistic.

Jean would like to be a good foot soldier protected by the rigid observance of the rules in an unthinking and ritualistic obedience pattern. Her isolation, her fear, and her lack of development of any area of competence make her a soldier only in the family army. She is a "bureaucratic employee" type who has not joined others except through the family.

Gerald is a bureaucratic leader. Jean is a bureaucratic employee.

Phenomenologic diagnosis. Gerald has been seen to be totally dominating and controlling. He tends to omnipotence in that he knows more than Jean and probably the therapist, the cardiologist, etc. His work reenforces this appreciation. He is destructive in the degree of control that he maintains. He is therefore a sadistic agent. Within this group he is chiefly self-centered, aloof, blaming and feels resentful, as if the illness of Jean were a mistreatment of him. He is therefore of the compulsive paranoid subtype.

Jean is anxious, depressed, very dependent, and submissive, which confirms the diagnosis of masochistic patient. Within this group she is phobic, with avoidant anxious behavior—and is therefore a member of the phobic subtype.

The corresponding DSM-III diagnosis would be:

Gerald

- Personality disorder: compulsive; paranoid

Jean

- Affect disorder: depression
- Personality disorder: dependent, avoidant
- Associated disorders: panic disorder; agrophobia

Speech and Action Structure. The acting-off behavior will be taken from the position of the masochist, since she is brought as the "patient" in need of an urgent resolution to her problem.

Jean talks monothematically about her fear and insecurity and the possibility of abandonment while blaming herself and being blamed by Gerald for her fear. She feels that she has frustrated and victimized Gerald with her illness and emotion, while Gerald and others act to frustrate her morally and cognitively, leaving her with guilt, lack of knowledge, fear, and constantly vulnerable to the threat of abandonment.

She therefore acts off rather than dealing with an historic problem of excessive interpersonal submission to a powerful protective and self-exonerating other whom she idealizes and to whom she gives moral and cognitive pleasure in exchange for her survival.

At the same time, she naturalizes her socioeconomic problem of excessive dependence, which is not dealt with but is replaced in thought and attention with the personal historic sadomasochistic problem of submission, frustration, guilt, and fear of abandonment.

Jean should recognize and control her tendency to frustrate herself and to give cognitive and moral pleasure to the other, accepting guilt and submissive dependence in exchange for survival. She should include the possibility of a realistic evaluation of the power of herself and of the other, accepting that a claim to entitlement to a fair share of moral and cognitive pleasure does not terminate in abandonment by all.

She must identify her tendency to depend excessively socioeconomically on a monopolizing controlling other. She must instrument herself, conceive of behavior, and gradually execute behavior which gives her a share in a cooperative socioeconomic control.

DYADIC TYPE: DEMAGOGIC
INDIVIDUAL TYPE: MASOCHISTIC AGENT-SADISTIC PATIENT
SUBTYPE: COMPULSIVE DEPRESSIVE-HISTRIONIC

Yvonne sought help in managing an "impossible child." Her son Edward is 9 years old and is verbally and physically abusive to his mother and sisters. She also complained that her husband was very self-centered and not at all helpful to her. Yvonne brought Edward and criticized him without controlling him. She complained and accused him of cruelty. He finally exploded and screamed that "she won't let me do anything I want."

The woman is a former beauty queen. She soon confides that she thinks she is getting old and that she no longer seems to attract men so easily. Her husband George is a professional who works in his own business. He is unable to develop a consistent authority relation with the children. When he moves in to discipline them, she screams at him and rescues them. When he returns to the peace of his newspaper, she complains that he is indifferent and abandoning. The following is an excerpt from an interview with the couple.

YVONNE: Doctor, my son Edward is an absolute monster. Do you know that he tells me that he doesn't love me and then he runs away from me. He does it because he wants his own way. He is so egocentric. He never thinks of anybody else. I have to take him here or there. I never have a minute to myself. Oh yes, and my husband is the same. He took me out to dinner because we don't have a maid. We went with friends and, you know, instead of asking me where I wanted to eat, he asked them!

GEORGE: But I thought that it would be better to ask them. When we go alone, we can go where you want.

YVONNE: That's the second time this week that you have done that to me. And the other thing, Doctor, is his violence with Edward. He beat the child the other day.

GEORGE: That's not exactly true. As I recall, you screamed at me that the boy was hitting you, so I went to grab him. I hit the door and it accidentally hit him—but you wanted me to stop him.

YVONNE: Yes, but not to beat him to death! You're always exploding. And you still read the paper more than anything else. I feel so alone. I need company.

GEORGE: Well, when I talk to you, you're not interested.

YVONNE: I wonder why! You only know about cars, airplanes, and what your business friends say. How could I be entertained by you?

Diagnostic Discussion

Socioeconomic relations. George is in control. He earns the money, makes and maintains the friendships, and generally takes responsibility for the family. In his profession he is successful, although very compulsive and detail oriented. This is, in fact, one important reason for his success. Twice friends have prevailed on him to make unwise investments. He has taken their advice out of "friendship" and lost his investment. He was the one, however, who controlled the resources and made the decisions.

George is an agent. Yvonne is a patient.

Interpersonal relations. George is generally dominated and manipulated by others and is not an effective leader. In relation to his friends' investment advice, he allowed them to dominate the situation and use him. He did not perceive them as dishonest, although they were of questionable reputation in the community. His wife claims to be dominated and frustrated by him, while in fact the reverse is true. She calls him an egoist while demanding her own way: "You considered our friends instead of me."

Because she does not drive, she demands that he pick her up after work wherever she may be.

The son is a small version of the mother. His behavior is sadistic. He sees himself as put-upon and accuses others of egoism just as his mother does. She has no leadership qualities, but unfortunately neither does George. He vascillates between accommodating other people's wishes and imposing his own will in a sudden explosion of aggression.

George is a masochist and Yvonne is a sadist.

Defensive qualifications. Yvonne blames George chiefly because he does not put her first and value her enough; also, he doesn't provide enough "leadership." When she puts him down enough, he explodes, thus justifying her blaming. Then he submits to her demands until he cannot contain his anger.

Yvonne is essentially a self-overvaluing blamer, George accepts the blame most—but not all—of the time. He is a "blamed" who at times subtly devalues his wife.

Centeredness. Yvonne is excessively self-centered, defining situations and defending her own needs and emotions. For example, she expects to choose the restaurant when they invite guests. She defines "his violence with Edward," etc. Her own emotions are what are important. She is narcissistic. George tries to take the feelings and needs of the other into account. For example, he is concerned that his guests be pleased. He tries to fulfill his wife's desires and is very mirroristic.

Yvonne is narcissistic. George is mirroristic.

Primary affect. Yvonne is emotionally unstable and dysphoric. She responds violently to any changes in the socioeconomic and interpersonal reality. She can be elated at one moment and angry and depressed at the next moment.

There is no solid sense of future plans or projected possibilities. This makes her overreact to the here and now as is characteristic of the borderlined personalities.

George tends to be depressed as a result of the constant blaming. He feels guilt, and occasionally becomes angry when excessively frustrated. This manifests itself in periodic explosive loss of control.

Reality relations.   Yvonne severely attacks interpersonal and socioeconomic reality. For example, she claims that her husband is selfish. She also claims that he tried to beat the child to death. The attack on the perceptions is strong and constant. However, since she has no socioeconomic control, he is able to put distance between them when the blaming becomes too bizarre and depressing. For example, he flies his plane, reads his paper, etc. She is then neuroticizing to George.

George is a spoiler and borderliner of his borderlined wife and child. He has the socioeconomic power to permit them a denial of the real consequences of their behavior, and he does not have the interpersonal power to prevent just this.

Edward, the son, is in even more danger of being borderlined or even psychoticized because his mother further protects him from the father's weak attempts to impose socioeconomic reality, and she severely distorts his reality relations. With her son she has a greater position of power (authority), which makes her more psychoticizing to him.

Yvonne is neuroticizing to George and psychoticizing to her son. George is neuroticized by her and is borderlining to her.

Attitude toward organizations.   Yvonne does not conceive of goals and needs beyond her own. She therefore tends to be a maverick loner unable to join an organization.

George works for himself. He exercises authority poorly and does not understand manipulation. He would lead "where others want to follow" because of his demagogic characteristics. He could be a bureaucratic leader where leadership consists of following the rules.

Phenomenologic diagnosis.   George has been seen to be mirroristic, unconditionally protective, controlling and submissive, subjected to severe attacks of blame. He is therefore a masochistic agent. Within this group he is chiefly lonely and emotionally inhibited. This would make him of the compulsive depressive subtype.

Yvonne is dependent, dominant, destructive, and demanding, which confirms the diagnosis of sadistic patient. Within this group she is exhibitionistic, provocative, seducing, and threatening and corresponds, therefore, to the histrionic subtype.

The corresponding DSM-III diagnosis is:

George

- Affect disorder: dysthymic
- Personality disorder: compulsive; passive-aggressive

Yvonne

- Affect disorder: dysphoric
- Personality disorder: dependent; borderline; histrionic
- Associated disorder: frigidity

Speech and action structure. The acting-off behavior will be described from the position of Yvonne, the sadist, who tends to impose her pathology on the other.

Yvonne talks monothematically about how selfish and cruel the other is and how she is his victim. She blames the other and takes the pleasurable position of moral superiority. She expects all hedonic pleasure as well and is selfish and cruel in her treatment of the other.

She therefore acts rather than confronting her interpersonal problem of an excessive sense of entitlement to moral and hedonic pleasure. She has naturalized her socioeconomic problem of excessive dependence, which is replaced in perception and thought by this historic sadomasochistic personalization.

Yvonne must recognize and control her tendency to selfish, cruel, and frustrating behavior toward the other and her tendency to blame the other. She must include the possibility of an equitable distribution of pleasure in a kind, unselfish, nonfrustrating relationship. She must identify her tendency to depend excessively socioeconomically and must conceive of and instrument herself to execute plans which allow her to participate in and share control.

DYADIC TYPE: Demagogic
INDIVIDUAL TYPE: Masochistic Agent-Sadistic Patient
SUBTYPE: Compulsive Hypomanic-Dissociative Explosive

Irene, a 40-year-old woman, consulted us after she became alarmed at her own anger. She had cut her husband's wardrobe to pieces in a fit of rage when he had failed to come home, spend time with the family, and give her the agreed-upon housekeeping money. She was considering separation and justified her attack as "the only way to get a message across to him."

She keeps complaining about how impregnable her husband is unless she loses her temper, but the therapist found it extremely difficult to get a necessary message across to her unless he lost his temper.

The following is an excerpt from an interview.

IRENE: I did go crazy, but I will not be manipulated. If I'm not angry and if I give an inch, he just does it all again. He thinks that if he's sweet now and goes to bed with me and pays the bills, that means that nothing happened. And that's the way it will be. When I stop being angry and demanding, he will stop taking care of the family.

He spent all last month helping his secretary's family. The money went to providing for his proteges. He always has to be the big man. I admit that he earns a lot, but most of it goes to impress someone or so that he can get his name in the newspaper as a big charitable donor. And meanwhile he forgets to give me the money to buy the newspaper!

It has always been this way. I have to scream and dramatize as if I were in the opera, and then he submits like a little mouse. I want to get a job and become independent so that I don't have to put up with this any more. I think that I really have stopped loving him.

After the fight he came home with flowers. It would have been more appropriate to bring the tailor. I don't know why I went after his clothes. Maybe because he always dresses so well—and if I fail to sew on a loose button, he carries on and says that I obviously don't love him. What does he expect? That I have nothing more to do than check his buttons every day, just in case? Why doesn't he ask? I told him; "You're dishonest, you're a baby, a cynic, totally undisciplined." I really let him have it, and he just kept agreeing and saying, "Yes, dear. No, dear."

Ed is a pleasant, active fellow who manages two businesses in a very productive way. He gets along well with others and is able to obtain contracts for his company. He is a compulsively "good" man, always looking out for someone. He is dramatic and generous in his promises but underestimates the amount of his financial and time commitment. He is always too optimistic and sees things as too easy. This is taken from an interview with Ed.

ED: You know, my wife is just a child. She gets totally unrealistic and can't take any responsibility. This incident pretty well proves that.

THERAPIST: Could her behavior have anything to do with how you are?

ED: Oh, no! She has always been like that. She has a jealous nature, but she'll be all right now because I'm paying lots of attention to her.

THERAPIST: Could it be that your behavior makes her feel excluded and that this makes her angry?

ED: But, Doctor, I have a living to make. I can't spend my time as a nursemaid. You know that. Why, just on doctors alone I spend hundreds of dollars a month.

THERAPIST: Maybe you only return to the people you love when they behave like desperately spoiled children. Wouldn't you say so? Actually on three occasions I have had to push you to keep your appointments, and you only come to placate me, not for yourself.

ED: Yes, Doctor, it keeps happening to me. But you know that I don't want the people I love to become anxious. Doctor, what do you want me to do—be selfish? Those people need me. Since when is it a sin to look after the poor or weak?

Diagnostic Discussion

Socioeconomic relations.   Ed is in control of the earning and the distribution of money. He takes care of all big expenditures and further controls Irene by failing to give her the housekeeping money on time. Irene is economically dependent, with much less formal education or job experience than Ed.

Ed is an agent and Irene is a patient.

Interpersonal relations.   Irene dominates and defines the relationship in a cruel, explosive fashion. Her sadistic behavior is episodic. She considers herself to be a victim of his behavior, which she finds overdemanding (sew on my buttons, love me).

Ed is dominated and submits "like a little mouse" to direct aggressive attacks, which he interprets as expressions of childlike dependence. He also submits to the seduction of being needed by his secretary, etc. He does somehow consider himself a victimizer in that he adopts an appeasing attitude after the explosion. However, he does not see his provocation in being overcommitted to others and not attending his wife until she resorts to explosions. His pleasure comes from being needed to "calm the troubled beast" and therefore feeling so powerful as to never be abandoned.

Irene's behavior is basically sadistic, with periodic outbursts of an excess of sadism. Ed's behavior is a sacrificing, submissive, other-entitling masochism.

Defensive qualifications.   Ed is a subtle, seductive devaluer. He sees himself as having to placate explosive, angry, childish dependents. For example, he refers to Irene as "a little child." "I can't spend my time as a nursemaid."

Irene on the other hand is a "blamer." She blames him constantly for forcing her into exploding, and she makes blaming derogatory remarks about him.

Ed is a blamed devaluer and Irene is a devalued blamer.

Centeredness.   Irene centers on herself. Her needs and feelings and entitlement are paramount to her. She is therefore narcissistic. "When I stop being angry and demanding," "I have to scream and he submits." Ed comes home with flowers after the fight. He is concerned about her feelings. He centers on his wife, secretary, etc. and responds to their needs, demands, and feelings. He talks about his wife in therapy. He is mirroristic, and this is what makes him overcommit himself in terms of other's needs.

Irene is narcissistic. Ed is mirroristic.

Primary affect.   Irene is chiefly angry, related to her sense of moral entitlement. She is also depressed intermittently when she captures the subtle devaluations and the abandonment of Ed.

Ed is elated, related to his superior socioeconomic control and his feeling of being essential to so many people. Underlying the elation is a sense of a self who is not essentially lovable so much as needed by others.

Reality relations.   Ed mildly attacks Irene's interpersonal reality testing in that he sees her as "naturally" explosive and infantile without recognizing the effect of his abandoning behavior. Ed does consciously and voluntarily lie, thus witholding information from Irene and increasing her confusion and anxiety. These, however, are not "reality disavowals" so much as deliberate lies. Lying is conscious manipulative behavior which certainly affects the perception of the other.

Irene, the secretary, and the spoiled others are in danger of being borderlined by Ed's overprotective attitude toward their irresponsible behavior. He has a borderlining effect. That is, Irene gets flowers after cutting up the clothes. She is neither confronted with the seriousness of what she has done nor confirmed in that it was an inadequate response to a provocation.

Irene is neuroticizing in that she permits Ed's mild distortions of interpersonal and socioeconomic reality. He is thus confirmed in his neuroticism by her and she is borderlined by him.

Attitude toward organizations.   Irene is a maverick. She tends to selfishly look out for her own interests and to not be concerned for the group. She is not a joiner.

Ed on the other hand is a joiner, and in these groups he takes a demagogic position. Since being admired and liked are his goals, he will sabotage productivity for the promise of admiration by his colleagues. Therefore, he could be considered a bureaucratic leader, and Irene a maverick loner.

Phenomenologic diagnosis.   Irene is dependent, dominant, destructive, and demanding. She is therefore a sadistic patient. Within this group she is chiefly irritable, with intermittent explosive and aggressive episodes. She therefore most closely fits the dissociative explosive subtype.

Ed is unconditionally protective, controlling, submissive, and mirroristic. He is therefore a masochistic agent. Within this group he is charismatic, devaluing, and somewhat subtle and ironic in his devaluation. He is therefore most like the compulsive hypomanic subtype.

The corresponding DSM-III diagnosis is:

Ed
- Affect disorder: atypical bypolar (hypomanic)

Irene
- Impulse disorder: explosive
- Personality disorder: histrionic

Speech and action structure.   The acting-off behavior will be taken from the position of Irene, the sadistic member who tends to define relationships.

Irene talks monothematically about Ed's manipulative indifferent and thoughtless behavior, blaming him for frustrating her. In her actions she is thoughtless and manipulative in her relationship to him. She frustrates him in his need to receive attention (sew on buttons, etc). She is therefore acting rather than confronting her interpersonal problem of excessive infantile demands and excessive sense of entitlement to moral and hedonic pleasure.

She has naturalized her socioeconomic problem of excessive, demanding, spoiled dependence, which is replaced in perception and attention by the historic sadomasochistic personalization.

Irene must recognize and control her tendency to selfish, thoughtless, and manipulative behavior in which she frustrates and blames the other and retains a sense of overentitlement, both moral and hedonic.

She must include the possibility of a true equitable sharing of pleasure with the other, accepting and responding to his love needs in a thoughtful and sincere way.

She must identify her tendency to exploiting dependency and conceive of and instrument herself to execute a plan of shared socioeconomic control, where she contributes as well as demanding to receive.

DYADIC TYPE: DEMAGOGIC
INDIVIDUAL TYPE: MASOCHISTIC AGENT-SADISTIC PATIENT
SUBTYPE: COMPULSIVE HYPOMANIC-PARANOID DEPRESSIVE

Mary, a 45-year-old housewife, came to consultation with her husband at his insistence. His complaint is that the family life is without enjoyment.

She is depressed and almost never leaves the house; even simple tasks seem unachievable. This state is chronic but was greatly exacerbated one year before, when she discovered that her husband was involved with his secretary. Her mother had died two years previously, and Mary frequently lamented the loss of her mother, wishing that she herself had died. Her two adolescent daughters take care of her.

Mary's depression dates back to her childhood. Her father died when she was 12 years old, and she was raised by her mother in a small rural town in a very primitive country. Her brothers were sent out of the country, where they received an excellent education. Her role as a woman was to accompany her mother, who "could not be left alone." She recalls feeling isolated and afraid because the townspeople were "cynical and crude" in their treatment. These ignorant townspeople managed to cheat her family and to end up as owners of much of the family fortune. She concluded that the world was a frightening place where success was given to the cruel, uneducated, and dishonest. Her only companions were books. She read voraciously.

At the age of 20 she came with her mother to the city where she obtained a job as her husband-to-be's secretary. She was a good secretary, educated and responsible. The job required taking orders, and she was both responsible and submissive. She married her husband after three years on the job.

Her husband and the mother got on well together. The mother lived with the family. She was a woman who enjoyed herself. "Plans for pleasure were made by the mother, supported by the husband, and accepted by me." They were the enthusiasts, she the passively compliant.

Her husband Bob achieved economic success by hard work and calculated risks. She reacted to his economic success as evidence that "he was like the townspeople," somehow exploiting others in a dirty way. She couldn't conceive of success as being the result of hard work rather than cheating. In fact, Bob was more cheated than cheater: his business partner took an equal share of the profit but not of the work or responsibility. He used to enjoy his success, sharing it with the mother-in-law. The death of the mother-in-law had made him feel very frustrated with his marriage. His affair with his secretary was a result of "loneliness and no one to have fun with." "Really, Doctor, I was desperate. My wife never liked sex."

His wife gives him periodic "barbs of blaming" related to the affair, which she never quite lets pass. She gives his affair as the reason that she cannot accept generous gifts from him or share pleasures with him. In fact, Mary will not even accompany her husband on his weekly visit to his parents, because she does not like them and the effort is too great.

This is an excerpt from the first visit.

Bob: Doctor, I need your help, I really don't know what is going on between us. I finally have money, and it would be wise to enjoy it. It seems that this is impossible for her to understand. She won't let me spend anything on her. You can't believe how hard it is to live with an ascetic saint.
Mary: He's right, Doctor. The family would be better off if I were dead—but I can't bring myself to do that. I can't stand to be alive. How I wish I were dead! The suffering is just too much. He can't possibly know. I have thought about killing myself, and at the same time he wants to go out to dinner with me! I have no appetite, and I have no money. I can't take his money. He earned it. It's not mine. I don't want to be more of a burden.

BOB: Doctor, its not just that she won't go out to dinner. She won't go to bed either. Going to be with her is as much fun as going to a funeral. It's as if I force her into something disgusting and unpleasant.

MARY: Since he had the affair with his secretary I can't have sex with him, that's true. I have no desire. I should be looking after the family, but I don't do that either. I'm a burden. I don't sleep at night, so I'm tired all day. My friends have been calling. They want me to go back to the book club. We were reading Sartre. They are all so intelligent. Bob, of course, doesn't take us seriously. He isn't interested in intellectual things—just money, eating, sex, tennis, and running. He is so physical.

BOB: (*Justifying himself*) Well, this is partly true. I don't behave properly with her lady friends. Please, Doctor, make her forgive me once and for all.

Diagnostic Discussion

Socioeconomic relations.   In the parameter of socioeconomic reality relations, Bob is an agent and Mary is a patient. He pays all the bills, takes care of practical matters, and is successful in the business world. He has more education than Mary. Mary actually considers socioeconomic success to be evidence of unscrupulousness, and it is as forbidden to her as something dirty and inferior. She refuses to have any responsibility in relation to money (not even to spend it). She does not assume social responsibilities such as visiting her husband's relatives, nor does she guide her daughters or assume a maternal role.

Interpersonal relations.   Interpersonally, although Mary is completely dependent and outwardly submissive, in fact she does not "allow" her husband to spend money, enjoy sex, visit his family, etc. She makes her suffering and disapproval known. Although she apparently suffers unbearably to the point of contemplating suicide, he is so insensitive that he thinks only of such things as eating in restaurants. In fact, however, he is dominated by her accusatory and suffering attitude and actions and by her emotional blackmail, such as when she threatens suicide.

He, on the other hand, feels very guilty about her suffering and can find no way to get her to pardon him. He is generally solicitous, polite, and considerate toward his wife. They both consider him the victimizer and her the victim.

Therefore Mary is the sadist and Bob is the masochist.

Defensive qualifications.   There are some indications of irony in Bob's attitude, for example, the statement that "going to bed with her is as much fun as going to a funeral" and the referral to the ascetic saint, but generally Bob blames himself. "I don't behave properly with her lady friends. Please, Doctor, make her forgive me."

Mary blames, reminding him of the affair, calling his attempt to distract her as "insensitive." She also devalues, considering him somehow intellectually inferior. In addition she devalues and blames him for his economic success. Bob is blamed but devalues slightly. Mary is a blamer.

Centeredness.   Mary is the one who defines who is cruel, intelligent, cynical, or crude. She centers on her own feelings and needs, her depression her suffering, and ignores the sexual and social needs of her husband.

Bob centers on Mary. He wants to know how to be forgiven by her. He tends to accept her definition of what is happening, and he asks the therapist to define for him what is happening. His pleasure is in pleasing the other.

Mary is narcissistic. Bob is mirroristic.

Primary affect.   Mary has a strong sense of moral entitlement which accounts for her underlying anger. She is depressed, feeling interpersonally devalued as a result of the affair and being aware that she is unable to undertake the socioeconomic tasks which her role as mother and wife would imply.

Bob is defending himself against underlying guilt and depression related to the moral attacks. Outside the home, where he has a sense of usefulness and self-worth, his hypomanic defense of elation is more characteristic.

Reality relations.   Interpersonal relations are inverted. Mary perceives herself as an innocent victim, and she blames others for being self-interested, while she shows little interest in giving pleasure to others. The distortion is mild in the interpersonal and socioeconomic spheres, and Mary's power as an authority is weak.

Bob accepts the interpersonal inversion but is not greatly affected in his socioeconomic functioning by her devaluations and blaming. Therefore, she has a neuroticizing effect on Bob.

Bob also neuroticizes her by his acceptance of her interpersonal and socioeconomic distortions.

Attitude toward organizations. Bob is able to enter into cooperative relations with others in the seeking of goals beyond his own capacity to achieve. For instance, he forms a therapeutic alliance readily. He is not very power oriented and tends to be taken advantage of, since he assumes the same cooperative honesty in other people. He is in no way a maverick. His leadership tends to be sacrificed for the good of the other or the organization. He is a joiner.

Although she considers herself to be a victim of the self-interested townspeople and suspects her husband of maverick behavior (i.e., pursuing his own goals over the common goals of the community), in fact, Mary is the maverick. She distrusts all organizations and is totally apart from them. She talks like an idealist, but she lives like a maverick nonjoiner.

Bob is a bureaucratic sacrificed joining leader. Mary is a maverick loner.

Phenomenologic diagnosis. Bob is mirroristic, rather unconditionally accepting, and protectively controlling and submissive. He is, therefore, a masochistic agent. Within this group he is slightly ironic and slightly devaluing and has bipolar affect consisting of elation and an underlying depression related to guilt from the blaming. He is therefore of the compulsive hypomanic subtype.

Mary is dependent, dominant, critical, and demanding, which confirms the diagnosis of sadistic patient. Within this group she is irritable and blaming and is a member of the paranoid depressive subtype.

The corresponding DSM-III diagnosis is:

Bob
- Affect disorder: bipolar hypomanic
- Personality disorder: compulsive

Mary
- Affect disorder: dysthymic; depressive
- Personality disorder: dependent; paranoid; avoidant
- Associated disorders: persistent insomnia; inhibited desire

Speech and action structure.   The acting-off behavior will be taken from the position of the sadist, Mary. Mary talks monothematically and blames others for selfishness and dishonesty, considering herself to be the victim while she acts to frustrate and victimize others, thinking exclusively and selfishly of her own needs and retaining moral pleasure at the expense of creating moral displeasure in the other. She therefore acts rather than confronting her interpersonal problem of excessive moral entitlement and selfish, blaming behavior. She has naturalized her socioeconomic dependence as well as rationalizing it by qualifying it as "goodness." Socioeconomic dependence is replaced in perception and thought by the historic sadomasochistic personalization.

Mary must recognize and control her tendency to frustrate the other and to repetitively blame the other for selfishness and dishonesty. She must include the possibility of a nonblaming, mutual, morally gratifying relationship. She must identify her tendency to depend excessively in the socioeconomic sphere and must conceive of and instrument herself to execute behavior which allows her to share control.

DYADIC TYPE: Undercommitted

INDIVIDUAL TYPE: Sadistic Insufficient-Masochistic Insufficient

SUBTYPE: Intrusive Paranoid-Avoidant Hysteric

This young couple consulted us when the wife, Laura, became desperate; in the past two years her husband Jim had separated from her on four occasions. He refused to accept the commitment of marriage, but he also refused to continue to the point of divorce.

He claimed to be able to "stand her from a distance." "Every time I get close she starts pushing me around and screaming at me. When I live like this, she treats me nicely."

She claimed that he would not take her into account and would put her down until she could stand it no longer. Then she would explode and he would run. Their two children were explosive, socially insecure, and constantly "defending their own rights while fighting with others." The family lacked leadership, a sense of cohesion, and cooperation.

They were both professionals. She was employed by a large company; he was in partnership in his own company. Neither one was extremely successful. She had left three jobs because of differences with the boss. "They weren't fair to me. They ended up cheating me, and I wasn't going to take that. I'm suing my last employer for my severance pay. He tried to cheat me."

Jim would always find her another job, since his public relations were good. But in his own business, he would not even supervise his secretary enough to be in charge of the office. He never quite contributed enough for the month to be able to have the money go around. She considered hers to be hers and resented paying part of the expenses from what she earned.

The following is an excerpt from an interview after a punitive explosion on her part:

LAURA: He intervened again. He never takes charge, but he absolutely destroys my authority! You don't run the house. You're not able to give us that much time. You are a specialist in destroying authority. I looked ridiculous. Isn't it enough that the neighbors laugh at me for letting you move in and out every few weeks. I know that you're there for sex. Certainly not to do your part.

JIM: Look, Doctor, I realize that I have to start participating in my house, but I didn't count on my wife. I know that she is unable to do better, but just listen to this. Anybody else would know better. Our son was invited to a party. We bought him a suit and everything. I know he wanted to go. We had promised him. Then Laura decided that he was lazy and that she would only let him go if he cut the lawn first. He started and worked hard and had it half done by dark, but she took that as more evidence of laziness and told him that he definitely couldn't go. His friends were coming around to pick him up. He had even invited a girl—you know, he's not very sociable, but I had been trying to encourage him to go out and have friends to the house. Now this! I congratulate you, Laura. You really did a job.

LAURA: We had agreed that you would stop encouraging the children to rebel against me. And you do it again! There is no way to live with you! Another thing, Doctor. He put me down again. Some friends came over, and they talked about a trip to the lake next week. He said, "Oh, we would love to go." The children are on holidays. He didn't ask me. He didn't look at me. He just included us all. He made the decision by himself.

JIM: But you could get off work. It's only for three days. I thought that you'd like a holiday.

LAURA: I'm not going to go. You didn't want me along, or you would have asked me. I've made up my mind. Not only won't I go, I won't lend you my stationwagon either.

JIM: Well, I understand. I thought that it would be good to get away with the children, but I guess I did it again. I'll go with them. I know we bother you.

LAURA: Let him go—but really go, with divorce papers and everything.

Diagnostic Discussion

Socioeconomic relations.   The four attempts at separation and the use of distance as a defense ("The only thing she understands is distance") are characteristic of insufficient couples. In the two years of off-again, on-again marriage neither one formed any other couple relationship. There was no sense of a parent team and no agreement on discipline.

Also, it was clear that Jim was in control of his financial reality, and Laura of hers. Both work. Both contribute economically. Cooperative effort is minimal, however. He doesn't provide enough money. Each contributes grudgingly. Both have approximately equal status. Both are professionals. She has difficulties working in organizations.

Interpersonal relations.   Laura dominates, blames, and defines situations. For example, she dominates her husband and son in regard to going to the party. She dominates her husband in regard to the vacation. Laura perceives herself as the victim. For example, she was her husband's victim in regard to his not taking charge, while she actively blocks any attempt to take charge.

Jim submits, is blamed, and lets Laura define situations while he justifies himself. He feels like her victimizer when he tries to take charge. Therefore Laura is the sadist and Jim is the masochist.

Defensive qualifications.   Laura is blaming in her attacks: "He doesn't take charge." "He doesn't give us time." "He is a specialist in destroying order." "Gets the neighbors to laugh at me." "Comes only for sex." "My son is lazy." "My former boss was crooked." She tends to frustrate others and satisfy herself. This was clear in her treatment of the son who was promised a party; when this was conditioned to completing an impossible task, then he was frustrated and had to miss the party—while she blamed him for frustrating her.

Jim normally takes her blaming with a certain air of irony and devalues her in a provocative way: "She is unable to do better." Although he ridicules her primitive attempts at domination, he doesn't take the authority role. She explodes periodically because of his sarcasm. The more he runs away, the more he infuriates Laura, who then blames him further.

Laura is a devalued blamer. Jim is a blamed devaluer.

Centeredness.   Laura is self-centered. She defines the situation in her terms. She does not consider her son's feelings or her husband's point of view. She is narcissistic.

Jim is able to center on and empathize with his son, seeing the situation from the son's or the friend's point of view. He is mirroristic.

Primary affect.   Since he is constantly blamed but does resort to subtle ironies which expose him to explosive attacks, Jim's major affect is anxiety. He is avoidant, as is seen in his tendency to criticize and then leave and his failure to form another couple relationship. He has some hypomanic traits, as evidenced by his superior devaluing attitude. His behavior can be quite charming, and with others he may be quite pleasantly seductive, ingratiating, and placating.

She is counterphobic. She has been held up on three occasions. Her jewelry is very ostentatious, and she is very careless about her personal safety. On each occasion she has screamed and fought the attackers, not measuring the danger of threats, guns, etc. Her major affect is anger arising from her moral indignation—others are "bad"—and the provocative devaluation of her husband.

Reality relations. Laura distorts interpersonal reality rather severely, but is not effective in nor concerned by socioeconomic reality. Here the distortion is mild. Therefore she is neuroticizing.

Jim accepts her distortion of interpersonal reality and does not distort socioeconomic reality to a severe degree. He is also a neuroticizer.

Attitude toward organizations. Laura is unsuccessful in her dealings with organizations. She clumsily denounces the other and does not understand or use well the power relations of organizations. In fact, she gets into bureaucratic organizations as a bureaucratic employee but is soon removed because of her aggressive behavior.

Jim is self-employed and power shy. He does not like to take command and is unable to stand the restrictions of an imposing authority. He is not a joiner. He is a loner and could be considered to be a lonely maverick.

Phenomenologic diagnosis. Laura has been found to be disagreeable, intrusive, and dominant with control only over herself. She is therefore a sadistic insufficient. Within this group she is chiefly projective, vengeful, mistrustful, and rejected by others. She is of the instrusive paranoid subtype.

Jim is anxious, avoidant, submissive, and in control only of his own socioeconomic reality which confirms the diagnosis of masochistic insufficient. Within this group he is conforming, superficially pleasing, and ironic. This would make him of the avoidant hysteric subtype.

The corresponding DSM-III diagnosis is:

Laura
- Affect disorder: (counter) phobic; social phobia
- Personality disorder: paranoid
- Associated disorders: impulse disorder, inhibited sexual desire

Jim
- Affect disorder: phobic
- Personality disorder: avoidant; histrionic
- Associated disorders: inhibited sexual desire

Speech and Action Structure. The acting off will be taken from the point of view of Laura, the sadist who tends to impose her definition of the situation. Laura repeats monothematically how she is the victim of defiant, inconsiderate, and rejecting behavior for which she blames the other, saying that she is his frustrated victim, while she is inconsiderate, rejecting, and arbitrary in her relations with others, who are truly victims of this behavior.

She stays with the moral pleasure. She therefore acts rather than confronting her interpersonal problem of excessive moral entitlement and rejecting, arbitrary, inconsiderate behavior.

She has naturalized her socioeconomic condition of restrictions such as those that result from her poor work relations, for example. The restriction is replaced in perception and thought by this historic sadomasochistic personalization.

Laura must recognize and control her tendency to victimize the other with blaming, inconsiderate, rejecting behavior and to remain with the moral pleasure. She must include the possibility of considerate, accepting behavior and must permit others their share of moral pleasure. She must identify her tendency to restrict socioeconomically and must conceive of and execute behavior which offers opportunities for sharing of control in a nonrestrictive way.

DYADIC TYPE: UNDERCOMMITTED
INDIVIDUAL TYPE: SADISTIC INSUFFICIENT-MASOCHISTIC INSUFFI-
CIENT
SUBTYPE: INTRUSIVE HYPOMANIC-AVOIDANT DEPRESSIVE

George, a doctor specializing in traumatology, has been married to Betty for six years. She was his nurse but stopped working to raise their two children. Betty is always "complaining and disagreeable and uncooperative." George is insistent that she return to work with him.

George's family is middle class. His father was a company employee who achieved a low executive level. He contributed to the cost of his own education by student loans, his family helped to the degree that they could, and Betty carried some of the load, since they were married in his student years when she graduated as a nurse.

Of nursing Betty says "It's a job like any other, but I'd rather not work for him. With him I can never do anything right, and I feel like a failure."

They state that they fight about almost everything—money, work, what to buy, etc.—and then they end up separating for a while and get back together. As he puts it, "It's about as bad alone as it is together and it costs more."

She states, "I think that I really love him, but sometimes I get so down and feel so worthless that I just feel like running away. At the same time, he is so wonderfully faithful. When I need to be near him, he is always there. He is a really special person and so competent."

The following is an excerpt from an interview with the couple.

GEORGE: You asked what we fight about, Doctor. Well, take last night as an example. You know I work hard putting food on the table. I come home and Betty is in one of her saving moods. You know she administers the household money and what she saves is hers. I do keep her pretty tight, but it is necessary. I don't want to be wasteful. But what happened was the ultimate stupidity. I found her baking bread! The kids were fighting, the house was a mess, and anyway, it's no saving because you pay for the oven being on and all that. But what got me was she wanted me to look after the kids! I want a rest. I work all day! Where is the consideration! I really had to tell her off! She isn't even capable of organizing the house.

BETTY: Of course, you're right. I should have done the bread in the morning, but I went to the hospital to ask about a job. You know how you're always telling me to go back to work. And, by the way, you're in trouble. They told me that you had insulted the chief surgeon by telling him how you would have fixed the Smith boy's leg better and that you blame him for the need for the pin. They said that he's so mad that he wants you out of the hospital. I'm worried you might lose your operating privileges.

GEORGE: A lot of good it will do him to attack me. He *can't* get me out. I am the best trauma specialist they have, and besides I'm always there and available day or night. They can't do without me. It's not my fault that he's such an incompetent surgeon. But what's the idea of going back without asking me. I want you with me.

BETTY: I know, but I can charge more to someone else. Oh well, if you insist. I guess you find it hard with someone else. I'm also worried about leaving the children. It has to be mornings when they're in school.

GEORGE: You always complain or worry, so what difference does it make if you do it there or here? Besides, with you working we can buy the new rug.

BETTY: But I had thought about a sofa.

GEORGE: I said a rug. I like to lie down in front of the fire and that wooden floor is so uninviting. Stop being selfish. We'll get the rug.

Diagnostic Discussion

Socioeconomic relations.   In the socioeconomic sphere Betty tends to make her own minor economic decisions and to administer the little resources that she has. She decides, however, in favor of her husband. For example, she looks for work without first consulting George, but then she accepts working for him. She keeps for herself the money left over from the household expenses. She has and will contribute economically to the family. She is restricted in her plans and is careful and saving in her administration.

George is very aware of what he contributes to the family. He wants greater help from his wife. He is not happy carrying the economic load alone and wants his wife to return to work. He does not want to do very much in relation to the children. He would like her to attend to them alone. There is no spirit of shared responsibility. He carefully defines what he is willing to give. He wants her to return as soon as possible to increase her economic commitment at the expense of her duties to the family.

Interpersonal relations.   George is dominant and intrusive. He commands Betty to work for him. He tries to dominate his chief surgeon in an intrusive, tactless way. He devalues the chief surgeon and blames Betty as well as devaluing her. He considers himself to be a victim—of his wife, the chief surgeon, etc.

Betty is submissive and avoidant. She apologizes for not following his commands. She apologizes for "doing wrong"— making bread, going to the hospital, wanting to work for someone else. She sees herself as frustrating to George.

George is the sadist. Betty is the masochist.

Defensive qualifications.   George devalues Betty and the chief surgeon. She is considered stupid and incapable, as is the chief surgeon. For example, he sees her as "the ultimate in stupidity." "She isn't even capable of organizing the house."

At the same time he overvalues himself. "I am the best trauma specialist." "They can't do without me."

Betty is devalued and tends to accept the devaluation, getting so down that she feels like running away. She tends to overvalue him: "He is so wonderfully faithful." "He is a special person and so competent."

George is a devaluer who overvalues himself. Betty is a devalued and an overvaluer of others.

Centeredness.   George centers on his needs, feelings, and entitledness. For example, he wants Betty with him—not where she would like to be. The chief surgeon's opinion of him is not even taken into account. He doesn't justify himself but rather attacks, redefining the situation in his terms. Betty centers on his desires.

She allows him to define her in terms of what he says she is and what she will do.

George is narcissistic. Betty is mirroristic.

Primary affect.   Because of his self-overvaluation and other-devaluation with its accompanying sense of socioeconomic superiority, George has a sense of elation. At the same time he also feels moral entitlement and feels frustrated or the victim of the other's incompetence. This also produces a sense of anger.

Betty is so often devalued and devalues herself that she has a resultant sense of depression. The lack of confirmation of socioeconomic worth and the submission to aggressive attacks also make her an anxious person.

Reality relations.   George chiefly distorts interpersonal reality but in a rather mild way. Betty accepts and reenforces the distortion. The socioeconomic reality is mildly distorted by George.

They are both therefore neuroticized and neuroticizing in their relationships.

Attitude toward organizations.   George is able to stay in an organization because of his personal skill. However, he does not identify with the group goals. He responds to his own goals. We can say that he is a maverick loner in an organization but not really part of it.

Betty on the other hand is a bureaucratic employee, in that she has little real initiative but knows how to take orders and follow rules and can join organizations but not exercise authority.

Phenomenologic diagnosis.   George has been found to be disagreeable, intrusive, and dominant with a desire for control only over himself. He is therefore a sadistic insufficient. Within this group he is chiefly a show-off and narcissistic. This would make him of the intrusive hypomanic subtype.

Betty is depressed, anxious, avoidant, submissive, and in control only of her own socioeconomic reality, which confirms the diagnosis of masochistic insufficient. Within this, she is depressed, placating, and insecure. This would make her a member of the avoidant depressive subtype.

The corresponding DSM-III diagnosis is:

George
- Affect disorder (Counter) phobic; bipolar (hypomanic)

Betty
- Affect disorder: depressive
- Personality Disorder: avoidant

Speech and action structure. The acting-off behavior will be described from the position of George, the sadist who tends to define what will be done and talked about. George repeats monothematically how he is frustrated by interior, uncooperative people who commit serious errors. He devalues these others. In his actions he frustrates others and tends to be uncooperative and to commit serious social errors, such as attacking his employer, who—like his wife—is frustrated by him, losing both moral and cognitive pleasure.

Therefore, he acts rather than confronting his interpersonal problem of excessive self-overvaluation and devaluation and blaming of others.

He has naturalized his socioeconomic condition of restriction resulting from his poor work and social relations. The restriction is replaced in perception and thought by the historic sadomasochistic personalization.

George should recognize and control his tendency to frustrate others with his devaluing, uncooperative, foolish behavior, which deprives others of moral and cognitive pleasure. He must include the possibility of cooperative, socially intelligent, realistically valuing interpersonal relations. He must identify his tendency to restrict socioeconomically and must conceive and execute plans which offer opportunities for the cooperative development of shared nonrestrictive control.

Treatment

7

Transference and
——Countertransference——

——————————Defensive Action Plan and——————
Transference

Transference and Countertransference

According to traditional psychoanalytic theory, the client sees in the therapist "the return, the reincarnation, of some important figure out of his childhood or past, and consequently transfers onto him feelings and reactions which undoubtedly applied to this prototype" (Freud, 1938, p. 21). In other words, the client acts out his or her clinical neurosis in the therapeutic relationship. The client's stereotyped feelings and actions, both positive and negative, constitute the *transference*. Therapy then consists of elucidating and analyzing the transference relationship in order to uncover—and work through—the original clinical neurosis.

In terms of cognitive theory the historic paradigm of understanding has been indiscriminately applied to a distinct social situation. This results in a narrow and stereotyped perception and action plan and an emotional reaction commensurate with this historic understanding.

Transference is not only an intrapsychic phenomenon; it is also a behavioral and interpersonal phenomenon. The client's transferred feelings and reactions elicit a *countertransference* in the therapist (Racker, 1968). The therapist's responses to the client cease to be totally objective; instead the therapist becomes "hooked" by the client's transference, acting (and being perceived) as a mirror image of the client's neurosis. In other words, the client assumes his or her typical position in the pathological dyad—authoritarian, demagogic, or undercommitted—and elicits in the therapist the complementary role (Grinberg, 1979).

We restrict the definition of "countertransference" to the unconscious reaction induced in the therapist by the verbal and nonverbal aspects of the client's acting-off—i.e., the client contaminating the therapist. We define "therapist transference", as the unconscious execution by the therapist of his own "acting-off behavior," i.e., the therapist contaminates the client.

Transference of the Neurosis and the Transference Neurosis

It is strategically important to distinguish between what is called the "transference of the neurosis" and the transference neurosis (Bird, 1972). We define the "transference of the neurosis" as that process in which the client succeeds in transferring his or her historic pathological transactional patterns to actual new situations with new people. This implies that he or she either selects others who naturally prefer and take the complementary socioeconomic and interpersonal position or that the subject forcefully induces this position in them (Searles, 1973). For example, an intrusive hypomanic sadistic insufficient in the transference of the neurosis successfully induces the role of an avoidant depressive masochistic insufficient in the partner, thus successfully confirming the historic paradigm of understanding.

When the therapist disconfirms the historic paradigm by explaining, pointing out errors, rectifying perceptions, and expanding possibilities, all by engaging in new noncomplementary action patterns, the transference of the neurosis is specifically blocked and the transference neurosis appears (Daniels, 1969). In the transference neurosis subjects respond to the therapist with an escalation of inductive acting-off behavior, persisting in their attempts to elicit from the other the usual complementary response, which would confirm the historic paradigm with its acting-off behavior. They therefore enter into a crisis of personalization and competence, where any effort to face and work through interpersonal and socioeconomic problems is ignored, being rather responded to by an increase in the interpersonal defensive postures of blaming and devaluing.

For example, if the therapist does not accept the complementary role of an avoidant depressive masochistic insufficient when treating an intrusive hypomanic sadistic insufficient clients will increase the pathological inductive pressure by escalating their devaluing defensive posture. They will personalize excessively as they struggle to induce the confirmation of their historic understanding. The energy is so redirected to the interpersonal, thus creating an even greater failure in the socioeconomic sphere.

Transference as "Reality Twice Removed"

Psychoanalytic therapy aspires to make the unconscious conscious, that is to replace the pleasure principle with the reality principle. In transference the socioeconomic and interpersonal realities have been replaced by a narrowed and inverted representation of the historic interpersonal problem of sadomasochism. Reality has been twice removed, or substituted twice. The socioeconomic has been substituted by the interpersonal, and the interpersonal has been narrowed to the sadomasochistic. Therapy, then, must correct this double removal from reality. It must help the client to perceive and attend socioeconomic reality problems and perceive correctly and rectify interpersonal reality problems.

What relation would this double-substitution concept of transference bear to the concept of perversion? Perversion is defined as the substitution of the natural goal of the sexual instinct for a deviant one: fetishists substitute the sexual partner with a piece of cloth, shoe, etc. Transference, as has been stated, makes a double substitution of reality. Metaphorically speaking, it is, then, a double perversion. In this sense Freud's statement that "neuroses are the negative of perversions" becomes surprisingly true (Freud, 1905, p. 165). Since the client's perception of interpersonal sadomasochism is the "negative" of what is actually being done, this negative further substitutes a clear and realistic perception of interpersonal and socioeconomic reality.

If we think of perversion as the deriving of pleasure from the substitution of a deviated goal for the natural one, we could consider sadomasochism as a double perversion in both the interpersonal and socioeconomic spheres. Pleasure is interpersonally linked to abusive domination or sacrificed submission. Socioeconomic pleasure is linked to infantile dependence, infantilizing control, or restrictive undercommitment.

Furthermore, defensive sadomasochistic personalization of socioeconomic mismanagement can even be considered a "fetishism of the subject" in the sense that clients distort their affective interest in the whole relationship with the other by concentrating exclusively on their mutual stereotyped interpersonal mistreatment. This mistreatment is itself described as the inverse of what is actually happening. Life is like a soap opera, with emotional drama and trivia taking center stage while more mature relationships and socioeconomic reality are put out of sight. This may explain the nationwide popularity of soap operas in times of social and economic crisis; it is nothing less than defensive acting-off escapism on a massive scale.

Clarity in the concepts of the "transference of neurosis" and "transference neurosis," with its accompanying excessive or exclusive personalization, is of great therapeutic importance. Certain dynamically oriented psychotherapists think that an increment in defensive personalization is somehow of itself therapeutic. When clients attempt to work through their interpersonal and socioeconomic problems, the therapist responds with pressure to excessively, exclusively, and repeatedly discuss their interpersonal relationship. By artificially and counterproductively focusing the client's attention on the transference-countertransference relationship, these therapists actually contribute to, reinforce, and perpetuate the perversion of the client's contact with reality (Lacan 1960). It can be striking to see how an individual has been progressively disconnected from reality after many years of this type of "dynamic" treatment. This could be called "the psychoanalytic perversion of reality."

Transference of Authority and Transference of Control

It is also strategically important to distinguish between clients' transference to the therapist of socioeconomic dependence, control, or restriction and clients' transference of interpersonal domination or submission (Klein, 1952b).

In effect, when clients transfer interpersonal power, they perceive, and treat the therapist as either their equal, their master, or their servant. When they transfer socioeconomic power, they perceive and treat the therapist as either another adult, a dependent child, a monopolizing parent, a restricted adolescent, or a restrictive old person (Gear, Hill & Liendo, 1981).

In the transference of the neurosis both the socioeconomic and interpersonal dimension are successfully transferred. In the transference neurosis, however, the transferring of socioeconomic dependence, control, or restriction is successfully blocked by the therapist, whereas the client's attempts at interpersonal domination or submission become escalated.

Paratransference and Paracountertransference

When clients act out with others this reactional increment in their sadomasochism, this pheonomenon is called *paratransference*. Paracountertransference exists when the significant others react complementarily to this increment in our client's sadomasochism (Gear & Liendo, 1979).

The therapist should be prepared to deal with this transference neurosis and should, if possible, prepare the significant others to deal with the paratransference and paracountertransference, the "side effects" of the treatment, so to speak.

Transference and Acting Off

Both the transference and the countertransference neurosis are based on the defensive exacerbation of the client's fundamental acting off and the therapist's counteracting off, respectively, that is, on the exacerbation of the defensive naturalization and displacement of socioeconomic dependence, control, or restriction—and its substitution in consciousness and speech—by a stereotyped and inverted representation of sadomasochism, which is all unconsciously reinforced in speech and action by the therapist (Balint & Balint, 1939).

If the characteristics and development of the transference and countertransference neurosis are products of the fundamental acting off and counteracting off, the therapeutic strategy—that is, the resolution of that neurosis—requires the corrective use of the fundamental acting on and counteracting on. Consequently, once the client's specific individual fundamental acting off has been diagnosed the therapist is in a position to predict, with a high degree of accuracy, the specific plot, characters, relations, sequence, and style of each client's future transference neurosis (Turillazzi, 1979).

In brief, the transference neurosis is the specific way in which each client avoids the task of working through excessive socioeconomic dependency, monopoly, or restrictions by creating a stereotyped sadomasochistic "personal" problem with the therapist—a problem which is talked of in reverse. This transference neurosis tends to get much more intense when the therapist tries to correct the defensive, inverted, and stereotyped sadomasochistic personalization and to discuss and work through the client's socioeconomic mismanagement.

Complementarily, the countertransference neurosis (Racker, 1953) is the particular way in which the therapist gets "personally" involved in the client's stereotyped sadomasochistic game and speaks in reverse about it instead of trying to correct it in order to discuss and work through the client's excessive socioeconomic mismanagement.

Consequently, it is important to bear in mind the typical defensive maneuvers that clients use in therapy—and, indeed, in everyday life—to avoid confronting unpleasant realities. Whenever therapists try to get their clients to focus on failures in the socioeconomic sphere, clients tend to shift attention into a stereotyped sadomasochistic transaction in the interpersonal sphere. For example, if the therapist begins to discuss a client's helplessness and total financial dependence on her husband, she may "explain" this dependence by pointing to personal inadequacies—her stupidity, craziness, etc. A healthy response would involve, for example, a realistic discussion of the client's education—or lack of it—age, past experience, the employment situation, lack of day care, pressure on women to stay at home, discrimination, etc.

Having personalized the problem—that is, having shifted from the socioeconomic to the interpersonal or sadomasochistic sphere—clients will then tend to stand reality in its head, talking about their domineering abusive attitude toward their partner, or protesting their own docile submissiveness to their partner's unreasonable demands, when in fact the reverse is true.

Because clients usually are very convincing and forceful in enacting their defensive plan, therapists can be very easily "contaminated." That is, they act out their clients' specific complementary role. Thus, for example, a sadistic patient would shift the discussion away from his financial dependence on his wife and repeatedly blame his flagrant adultery on her "frigidity." This is his particular acting-off position. His wife accepts the blame and allows herself to be victimized. That is, she shares his distorted view of reality.

Stages of the Transference-Countertransference Process

Transference usually proceeds in a predictable sequence, starting with the client's selection of a particular therapist. Clients subconsciously look for any detail that will reveal the therapist's style in exercising interpersonal authority and socioeconomic control. For example, if the therapist is badly dressed, has bags under his eyes, and looks exhausted, there is a strong possibility that he could be a sacrificing masochist. Or if the therapist's office is not only poorly decorated but also within a hospital setting, there is a strong possibility that she is a dependent masochistic patient. These would be the types of therapists that a sadistic agent would most probably select. The client will try to validate his or her selection by actively testing the therapist. For example, such clients may denigrate and verbally abuse the therapist, fail to pay their bills on time, etc. (Freud, 1912a).

Once clients have tested the therapist's way of handling power, they start to push the therapist into the complementary role in the interpersonal sphere. A masochistic client will push the therapist into the position of sadist and vice versa. If therapists suddenly change their interpersonal position, their clients may escalate their own masochism or sadism. If this proves unsuccessful, such clients will either abandon the treatment or change positions after experiencing a period of crisis (Bryce Boyer, 1979).

When the therapist's interpersonal position has been established, clients start to push the therapist into the complementary role with respect to socioeconomic power—as either agent, patient, or insufficient. If the therapist suddenly changes socioeconomic positions, the client may attempt to reinforce his or her own socioeconomic position. If this is not successful, the client will probably abandon treatment or experience a major psychological crisis and then change positions.

If the therapist fails to recognize or control the transference-countertransference relationship, the client will be forced to compulsively reenact it, and the therapeutic outcome will be poor indeed. However, as we shall see, the therapist can *voluntarily* play the complementary role in a client's pathological dyad and actively conduct the transference neurosis to the benefit of the client. (Racket, 1957). In the pages that follow we will discuss the development of transference-countertransference neurosis in the six basic client types.

The Masochistic Patient

Masochistic patients, generally speaking, are naive, dependent clients who blame and denigrate themselves while idealizing the therapist. They subconsciously induce the therapist to torture and abuse them and leave all important life decisions in the therapist's hands. They create in others an overwhelming countertransferential feeling of omnipotent responsibility toward them (Reich, 1966). The therapist feels like a sadistic, powerful, master-parent, while the client appears to be a totally powerless, helpless child who will have a psychological breakdown if the treatment is interrupted or altered for any reason.

Testing the Therapist

Masochistic patients unconsciously select therapists who are sadistic-agent types, that is, therapists who may be prone to mistreat and abuse their clients and assume socioeconomic responsibility for them.

It is usually very difficult to find a sadistic agent working as a dynamically oriented psychotherapist. Sometimes it is possible to find sadistic agents among traditional biologically oriented psychiatrists or among some dogmatic therapists who believe that clients are "sinners" who must confess and accept their guilt.

Once treatment starts, masochistic patients will try to make sure that the therapist is really able to tactically function as an abusive guardian (Sandler, 1976). If the therapist accepts—or at least does not flatly reject—the client's submissiveness and socioeconomic dependence, the client will feel contained, albeit mistreated, by the therapist, and treatment can proceed.

MARY: I am so stupid and naive. Tell me, should I have supper at my boyfriend's place this evening or not?

THERAPIST: What are your feelings about that? Yesterday you told me that the last time you went out with him, he behaved very rudely and inconsiderately toward you, that he abandoned you in the middle of the night.

MARY: Well, I really don't know. I'm so attracted to him. But with your experience and knowledge maybe you should make this decision—to protect me. I know I'm a burden to you, but will you?

THERAPIST: Remember, you told me that this was exactly what your mother did with you. You are asking me to be like your mother—to protect you from something that you already know is inconvenient for you. But you behave as if you were a little girl. If I do decide for you, you will continue to be naive and infantile forever.

MARY: *(Smiling)* Thank you, doctor. I knew you wouldn't fail me. Now I know what your advice is—that it is not good for me to accept his invitation this evening.

Stepping into Submission and Sacrifice

Once masochistic patients have checked out the therapist's sadism and agentism, they start increasing the pressure to transform the therapist into a devaluing, blaming, abusive "master."

Such clients are clearly submissive to the therapist, trying to please in any way possible—even at the expense of their own pleasure and comfort. They behave like exquisite servants. They attempt to seduce the therapist into playing the sadistic role by acting like faithful, blindly obedient pets who expect to find in the therapist a harsh but protective master. They also tend to fall "hopelessly" in love with or idealize the therapist (Freud, 1915).

These clients praise and reward the therapist's sadism. They cannot tolerate any sign of masochism on the part of the therapist because they fear the loss of the therapist's protection. The therapist "must" behave as an implacable, ruthless prosecutor because the client is a ruthless, malicious, ill-intentioned criminal. Because of inversion, these clients view themselves as selfish, stupid, crazy, cruel masters—and the therapist as a generous, clever, sensible, tolerant servant—while behaving in exactly the opposite way.

If the therapist stops devaluing or blaming, such clients think either that they have manipulated the therapist with their tricks (Heimann, 1950) or that the therapist is just trying to play nice in order to give the client some compassionate support.

MARY: I want to apologize for something I did this morning. You were telling me yesterday very clearly that I should modify my submissive attitude toward my children, that it was not good to let them walk all over me. But I did it again. This morning they started screaming at me, and again I started crying and apologizing to them. Gosh! What a stupid human being I am!

THERAPIST: Correction: I didn't tell you that you "should" modify your lack of authority. From what you were telling me it was very clear that . . .

MARY: *(Interrupting)* You see how stupid I am! I misinterpreted you again! Poor Doctor, having to deal with such a moron. I'm hopeless.

THERAPIST: Look, it is this compulsion to constantly put yourself down, to call yourself stupid, that does not allow you the necessary mistakes that one has to make when one is learning something new.

MARY: I understand. You are very kind to me, Doctor. But let's be straight—I am a very difficult case because I have at least two problems: I call myself stupid and I really am stupid.

Thus, Mary unconsciously creates a negative moral and intellectual consensus against herself and a positive one for the therapist; she states openly how difficult and tricky she is as a client and how patient, bright, and down-to-earth the therapist is, that her life would be impossible without the tough but sensible direction of the therapist, that this is exactly what she needs to survive.

The masochistic patient constantly attacks his or her own memory, perception, and feelings and pushes the therapist into attacking them too. Hence the therapist's intervention should be "corrections" of the client's "wrong" perception of reality (Searles, 1958).

The client is constantly absorbing unpleasure with a chronic masochistic acting off and the therapist is constantly injecting unpleasure with a chronic sadistic counteracting off. The client can suffer an affective crisis each time the therapist stops behaving sadistically or starts being too sadistic. But as soon as the therapist comes back to the "usual" degree of devaluation, blaming, domination, and abuse, the masochistic patient will "improve" clinically.

Stepping into Socioeconomic Dependence

Once the terms of the interpersonal agreement have been agreed upon, these clients try to exclude themselves from all fundamental socioeconomic decisions and responsibilities and delegate them to the therapist.

In other words, the therapist is in charge not only of the treatment but of the client's whole life. The therapist is pushed into infantilizing such clients, acting as a socioeconomic adviser or coach (Sandler, Dare & Holder, 1973).

The masochistic patient acts as if such matters are either too difficult to understand or very disagreeable. Whenever these clients must talk about their financial dependence, they either justify and rationalize it or introduce irrelevant, trivial issues.

MARY: Yesterday I couldn't buy some vitamins necessary for the children because, even though the doctor recommended them, my husband didn't agree with him, and I didn't have the money. You know how he is about doctors.

THERAPIST: But you were supposed to have some money. As I recall, you told me last week that you were asked to give some dance lessons to a group of girls. Moreover, you told me that it could become a permanent activity for you, a sure source of money.

MARY: Oh yes, but it didn't happen. (Pause) Do you think that I must persist in asking my husband for the money for the vitamins?

THERAPIST: What I think is that I must insist on asking you why you're not giving the dance lessons.

MARY: Well. . . . Actually I failed to call the girls to make the necessary arrangements. I don't know, I'm so forgetful. In fact they were very angry and disappointed with me.

THERAPIST: We can say, then, that your forgetfulness, your resistance to becoming independent, is what makes you against the necessary "vitamins" of a psychotherapy that I—the doctor—prescribed and that you—your husband—are reluctant to buy and to actually take.

MARY: (Crying) Oh yes! You're right! I'm so weak, so cowardly, so lazy. I don't know what to do with myself! There is no cure for me.

THERAPIST: (Jokingly) I don't know what to do for you either.

MARY: (Surprised) How is that?

THERAPIST: There is no point in continuing to blame yourself here. The point is that you must overcome your resistance to independence.

As we said before, the masochistic patient punishes severely any glimpse of dependence on the part of the therapist and also thinks that the therapist will punish severely—with devastating affective and socioeconomic abandonment—any of the client's attempts to achieve some kind of autonomy. Such clients constantly waste opportunities to improve their education, occupation, or income. They represent all possibilities as dangerous or counterproductive, so that the therapist will automatically try to "protect" them. However, if the therapist persists in getting the client to work through this excessive socioeconomic dependence, the masochistic patient will unconsciously induce his or her sadistic-agent partner into interrupting the treatment or at least into aborting all movements toward autonomy.

These clients tend also to become affective and socioeconomic "hostages" of the therapist. Consequently, other people will constantly urge them to consult the therapist before taking any major decision. Such clients can suffer serious emotional crises if the therapist starts behaving in too controlling a fashion, but they will suffer a devastating breakdown—even attempting suicide—if the therapist suddenly stops behaving as an agent (Segal, 1956).

The Sadistic Agent

Sadistic agents, generally speaking, are very astute, domineering, abusive, dependency-making clients who blame and denigrate the therapist while idealizing themselves. They try to induce the therapist to accept this blame and hand all authority over to them. They may even try to make decisions about the therapist's life or attempt to destroy the therapist's reputation. They arouse in the therapist an overwhelming feeling of impotent helplessness. The therapist feels powerless, stupid, bad, crazy, and totally dependent in the presence of this type of client (Cohen, 1952).

Testing the Therapist

Sadistic agents unconsciously select masochistic-patient types as therapists, that is, somebody who may be prone to accept blame, domination, and abuse from a client. This type of therapist is relatively rare. They may have originally entered therapy because of their own anxiety and depression and, later on, become therapists themselves (Gitelson, 1952).

Once treatment starts, sadistic agents will make some initial attempts to disqualify the therapist and overqualify themselves and to control the socioeconomic arena. If the therapist appears to accept these opening moves without too much resistance, the treatment will usually go ahead.

SAM: While I was waiting for you I was looking at your furniture. Maybe I shouldn't tell you this, Doctor. But, you know, doctors don't know much about decorating their offices—elegantly, I mean. This chair, for example, is not as fine as it should be. I'm sure that you paid a fortune for it, but it's a question of taste. Listen, I'll give you my card, and you use it at Top-Quality Furniture Store. *(Ironically)* They'll help you to take care you this.
THERAPIST: I'm the one who is supposed to tell *you* what to improve.
SAM: *(Interrupting and laughing)* I understand, Doctor. No hard feelings, eh? I'm not saying this to hurt you, but it is true—it lacks taste. It's not my fault. Be a good boy and listen to my advice. I know what I'm talking about.
THERAPIST: If we were talking about furniture. But we are talking about you.
SAM: You must learn to be more open. If you are so stubborn, you'll never improve. Psychiatrists are supposed to be openminded, flexible people, aren't they?

Stepping into Domination and Abuse

Once sadistic agents have checked out the therapist's masochism and patientism, they start increasing the pressure to transform the therapist into a devalued, blamed, abused "servant."

Such clients are domineering and abusive toward the therapist. They unconsciously seduce the therapist with offers of protection if the therapist, in turn, will submit obediently to their abuse. These clients view themselves as clever, generous, and sensible—and therefore entitled to exercise authority and control over others. They view the therapist as a selfish, stupid, crazy person that they tolerate out of the goodness of their hearts; if the therapist weren't so hopelessly in love with them, they would leave.

If the therapist steps out of the masochistic role, such clients may become more paranoid, accusing the therapist of lying, trying to put them down, or plotting against them.

SAM: I would like to know why the hell you cancelled my session yesterday. It was extremely inconsiderate of you to call me at the last minute to tell me that you weren't going to see me. What do you take me for—your stupid servant, or something? Maybe you think that I'm some dumb guy who will take it just like that and that you'll get away with it.

THERAPIST: I must remind you that this is the first time in three years of treatment that a session was cancelled with such short notice. Moreover . . .

SAM: *(Screaming)* Don't try to justify yourself, Doctor. You psychiatrists are very good at twisting the thoughts of your clients, at indulging yourselves and blaming the nuts. But I'm not one of those, you know. I want to be respected as a human being!

THERAPIST: So do I. You keep blaming and insulting me even before listening to my reasons. It seems that you desperately need to put your guilty feelings off onto me.

SAM: *(Furiously)* Now—on top of being let down by an irresponsible professional—I have to recognize *my* guilt?! *(Ironically)* Maybe I'm the one who should apologize. Don't play games with me, Doctor. Maybe I'm crazy, but I'm not stupid, you know.

Sam unconsciously creates a negative moral and intellectual consensus against the therapist and a positive one for himself; he tells others how stupid, vicious, or crazy the therapist is and how patient, smart, and down-to-earth he is as a client.

Sadistic agents constantly attack the therapist's memory, perception, and feelings. For example, they will try to justify or deny that they have arrived late—not just to one session but to most. Or they will deny that the therapist's feelings of depression are provoked by their own denunications. They will suggest that the therapist is suffering from delusions or hallucinations when their own sadistic behavior is pointed out.

Such clients frequently attack all the relationships that they suppose the therapist has; they jealously criticize all the therapist's friends, family, and colleagues—or at least the therapist's opinion about them. In this way they try to separate the therapist from all other object relationships and make the therapist totally dependent on them.

The therapeutic relationship stabilizes itself with a chronic sadistic acting off on the part of the client, and a corresponding masochistic counteracting off on the part of the therapist. The client is constantly injecting unpleasure into the therapist, and the therapist is constantly absorbing unpleasure. The client can suffer an affective crisis each time the therapist stops behaving masochistically or starts being too masochistic. But as soon as the therapist comes back to the "usual" degree of self-devaluation, self-blaming, submission, and sacrifice, the sadistic agent tends to improve clinically.

Stepping into Socioeconomic Monopoly

At this point such clients will begin to behave in a clearly controlling way at the socioeconomic level. They will try to exclude the therapist from all fundamental socioeconomic decisions and responsibilities. They will try to take charge not only of the course of the treatment but of the therapist's life as well. Such clients react very badly—often with furious attacks—to any sign of autonomy on the part of the therapist. They want to transform the therapist into a totally dependent cripple (Langs, 1976b). Because they seem so alert and confident with respect to socioeconomic matters, very soon the therapist begins to relinquish control in this area. Furthermore, sadistic agents keep their therapists in the dark about such matters and usually censor all discussion of the therapist's socioeconomic infantilization—unless, of course, they want to remind the therapist of his or her "true" place.

THERAPIST: You're supposed to pay me at the end of each month. You're not supposed to hold my money and put it in your bank in Eurobonds, even if you think that this is to my "advantage." You're violating the therapeutic contract. Moreover, you're treating me as if I were a little child who doesn't know what to do with money and, thus, you must administrate and invest it for me.

SAM: That's right. *You* are the expert in psychiatry, but *I'm* the expert in finances. How can I be sure that you won't spend all this good money that I'm giving you in some stupid way. Doctors are very stupid with their money—you know that! I don't have to explain it again, do I?

THERAPIST: In the first place you are not giving me this money; you are paying me my money. Secondly, I didn't hire you as my financial analyst.

SAM: You are very ungrateful and mistrustful. How can you pretend that I accept your help if you are so grandiose and pedantic that you can't accept mine? I'm generously trying to help you. Does this mean anything to you?

THERAPIST: You invested my money in your bank.

SAM: Dammit! Are you suggesting that I do so in my own interest?

THERAPIST: You told me last week that your bank manager wasn't happy with the amount of money you had in the bank. Remember?

SAM: You are a very ungrateful person!

Sadistic agents punish severely any glimpse of automony on the part of the therapist; they blame the therapist for being ungrateful and mistrustful, for not depending on the client. These clients can be emotionally overloaded if the therapist starts being too dependent, but they will become seriously disturbed if the therapist stops behaving like a patient. Most probably they will abandon the treatment (Langs, 1976a).

The Masochistic Agent

Masochistic agents are dependency-making, spoiling caretakers who are so afraid of not being loved that they tolerate extreme abuse from their dependents. They will try to control the therapeutic situation economically, but they will not attack the therapist.

Testing the Therapist

Masochistic agents unconsciously select sadistic-patient types as therapists, that is, somebody who may be prone to devaluate, mistreat, and abuse the client but who will, at the same time, give the client socioeconomic control. This type of therapist can usually be found practicing the more esoteric and sadistic kinds of therapies, usually with disastrous results in the long run.

Once treatment starts, masochistic agents will make some attempts to overqualify the therapist and to disqualify themselves and control some basic socioeconomic decisions. Treatment will continue if the therapist does not flatly reject the client's opening moves (Little, 1951).

JOHN: What you told me at our first interview was extremely interesting. It was especially helpful to me in understanding my wife. You know how sensitive she is. Maybe with your help I can convince her not to abandon me. On the other hand, I don't have the guts to convince her—or the brains.

THERAPIST: It seems that what I told you in our first interview was more helpful in understanding your wife than yourself.

JOHN: You're right. You're very sharp, you know. But I'm not the important person in the picture. All my hope for happiness depends on her. By the way, Doctor, how would you like me to pay you? I was thinking that maybe you'd like cash, but I can also pay you in foreign currency if you want. It won't be easy, but it is possible. This is so important to me that I'd like to help you in any way possible.

THERAPIST: Thank you. But you still keep thinking mostly of your wife and of me—how to help us—or please us. What about yourself?

JOHN: Right again, Doctor. It's very difficult for me to think about myself—how to change and be less boring to others.
THERAPIST: You did it again—thinking about the others.
JOHN: (*Interrupting*) You'll have to be very patient with me, Doctor. Maybe I'm tenacious, but I'm not very clever. Or maybe it is that I don't want to help you. This is what my wife tells me.

Stepping into Submission and Sacrifice

Once masochistic agents have checked out the therapist's sadism and patientism, they increase their efforts to transform the therapist into a devaluing, blaming, abusive "master." They behave submissively to their therapists, trying to please them in any possible way even at the expense of their own pleasure and comfort—like a faithful, reliable mother or nurse. They induce sadism in the therapist by praising and rewarding the therapist's sadistic attitudes. They also punish any sign of masochism in the therapist. Paradoxically, as soon as the therapist stops being sadistic, the client becomes indifferent to treatment. In other words, masochistic agents have a very persuasive spoiling attitude, which the therapist must be aware of in order to avoid being contaminated (Gear & Liendo, 1975).

Masochistic agents also idealize the therapist as a clever, generous, and sensible person—as a unique genius or beauty who is entitled to exercise authority over them. Simultaneously they describe themselves as mean, mediocre, and crazy, constantly provoking the therapist to escape.

JOHN: I'm desperate. You must help me with my wife. She wants to divorce me. She is very angry with me because she says that I spoil her but that I do not recognize her real achievements in life. And I don't know what to do about it. Because I really can't see any actual achievement in her. I have tried to be insincere, but she didn't like that either.
THERAPIST: You keep talking about your wife, but what about you? Maybe you feel that I'm the one who doesn't recognize your achievements? Or when I do, you think that I'm just being insincere.

JOHN: I haven't done anything remarkable, actually. But I get the point. You want me to associate freely. OK, here we go. On my way here I was listening to the radio. They were talking about Margaret Thatcher rejecting the demands of the Irish hunger strikers who are seeking status as political prisoners. *(Pause)* She is a very kind, soft, smiling lady. At the same time she is stubborn. It seems to me that it would be very difficult for them to make her change her mind and recognize another status for the prisoners.
THERAPIST: It seems that you are like Mrs. Thatcher. You are also a very kind, soft, smiling person, but actually very stubborn. It is very difficult for you to recognize others' status, isn't it? At least, this is what your wife keeps telling you.
JOHN: Gosh, Doctor! You are very good at making these subtle parallels. *(Smiling)* You see how I recognize your achievements.
THERAPIST: Actually, you didn't recognize the accuracy of my interpretation. You just praised my literary skills. As you said before, it will be very difficult for us to get you to change your mind and recognize a different status for your wife and myself. That is, the status of efficient adults, not of inefficient but spoiled children.

Whenever the therapist stops criticizing or blaming him, John tends to think either that he has manipulated the therapist with his tricks or that the therapist is just trying to be nice to him.

It is striking how masochistic agents constantly attack their own memory, perception, and feelings—and push the therapist into attacking them too. Because they tend to perceive themselves as sadistic spoiled brats the therapist tries constantly to "protect" these clients from their exploitative dependents. This has counterproductive results: the client becomes the defense lawyer of the "poor" dependents (Klein, 1946).

Masochistic agents do not have as many doubts about their perception as masochistic patients. On the contrary, they are very stubborn, and it is difficult for the therapist to make such clients doubt their accuracy. For a long time treatment consists of clients asking the therapist how to better protect their sadistic dependents—without any awareness either of the spoiled sadism or spoiling masochism involved. Moreover, they are not interested in discussing or modifying their behavior in this respect. Instead they act like therapists-in-training during this stage, and the therapist functions as a supervisor.

Such clients are usually very fond of the therapist, particularly if the therapist behaves like an impulsive, opinionated tyrant. Unlike the masochistic patient, these clients don't become affectively dependent on the therapist, because they don't abandon their relationships with their other dependents. At the most, they will hide these "perverted" relationships from the therapist. In this respect they behave like alcoholics who hide information about their real alcohol intake (Glover, 1955).

The masochistic agent can suffer an affective crisis each time the therapist stops behaving sadistically or becomes too sadistic. But as soon as the therapist comes back to the "usual" degree of devaluation, blaming, domination, and abuse, the masochistic agent will "improve" clinically.

Stepping into Socioeconomic Monopoly

Masochistic agents keep the therapist at least somewhat informed about socioeconomic matters. They are, in this respect, more manipulative and demagogic and less authoritarian and exclusive than the sadistic agent. They will outwardly acquiesce to the therapist's "demands" but will consciously or unconsciously sabotage them.

In other words, the therapist is no longer truly in charge of the treatment; what is worse, the therapist is driven by the client to believe that, on the contrary, he or she is totally in charge. In this way, the client tries to make the therapist comfortable and relaxed because the client is following directions when, in fact, it is the client who is in charge of the therapist's affairs, including the goal and method of the treatment itself.

Masochistic agents are very skillful in making their therapists believe that they are lucky because they can delegate some of their socioeconomic worries to the client: that it is wiser to let other people think and care about this type of "dirty" job and to "freely" enjoy life in an omnipotent (but fragile) way. The masochistic agent usually censors any open comment by the therapist about this socioeconomic infantilization (Grinberg, 1962).

JOHN: I brought you some tickets for Pavarotti's "La Traviatta." They are for tomorrow night.
THERAPIST: Oh thank you, but . . .
JOHN: (Interrupting) Don't mention it, Doctor. I noticed that you enjoy opera, looking at your library. I knew that these tickets were very difficult to get: row 12! I won't be going. I can get another ticket for next Saturday.
THERAPIST: But you told me that you especially enjoy Pavarotti in La Traviata.
JOHN: Oh yes, but it doesn't matter because I have the record.
THERAPIST: So, you are sacrificing a special pleasure of your own just to please me. On top of that you're violating our contract.
JOHN: (Interrupting) I knew that you would tell me that. But this is a very special situation, you know.
THERAPIST: The point is that you are overprotecting me. And that is exactly what we are trying to change.
JOHN: Oh, I'm very sorry, Doctor. But don't get upset with me. I'm really pretty dense. I don't know if I'll ever be able to change.

These clients are apparently very modest about their socioeconomic skills and lead the therapist to think that the therapist can be a real wizard if he wants to. Only if the therapist is pushing very hard for—and is very close to—achieving socioeconomic autonomy and mastery will the masochistic agent speak openly about the therapist's shortcomings and potential devastation if the client stops giving behind-the-scenes support. As we said before, the only time masochistic agents lose their sweet, warm, overprotective, submissive attitude is when their socioeconomic control is endangered. They fear that they will be abandoned if they are not needed and start blaming and/or devaluing their would-be independent others (Gill, 1979).

Such clients can suffer feelings of emotional overload if the therapist starts being too dependent, but they will despair and sometimes become seriously depressed if the therapist stops behaving as a patient altogether. As soon as the therapist comes back to the "usual" degree of overdemanding, unrealistic, omnipotent dependence, the masochistic agent will "improve" drastically (Freud, 1914).

The Sadistic Patient

Sadistic patients are unable to take care of themselves, but they are very much able to make others take care of them. Sadistic patients usually appear to be devaluing, blaming, dependent, autodestructive, torturing tyrants. They constantly threaten suicide if they don't get their way.

Testing the Therapist's Masochism and Agentism

Sadistic patients unconsciously select masochistic-agent types as therapists, that is, somebody who may be prone to accept devaluation, blame, domination, and abuse and socioeconomic dependence on the part of the client. Such therapists are often of the social-worker type. They have a loving, tender, altruistic approach and view their clients as "victims" of society (Epstein, 1979b).

Once treatment starts, sadistic patients will make some initial attempts to disqualify the therapist and to overqualify themselves as well as to hand over all responsibility to the therapist. If this works, treatment will continue.

THERAPIST: Remember that we initially agreed that it was critical for the treatment that you arrive on time for your sessions. (*The client arrived late to the first four sessions.*)
RENEE: (*Angry*) I know that! I know that! But you should realize that it's not easy for me to arrive on time here because your office is in such a remote area, so difficult to reach.
THERAPIST: You could solve that problem by leaving earlier.
RENEE: (*Interrupting*) Reproaching me in this way does not make

things easier. Knowing that you'll blame me in this unjustified way
makes me leave later, not earlier.

THERAPIST: You are the one who is blaming me. Actually I was
reminding you of some of the conditions that are necessary for the
treatment to work.

RENEE: Are you trying to drive me crazy? To make me desperate?
It seems to me that you should be more considerate of your new
clients, Doctor. (Ironically) Especially if you want to seduce them
into accepting treatment.

Stepping into Domination and Abuse

Once these clients have established the therapist's masochism
and agentism, they start to transform the therapist into their
abused, devalued, submissive "servant." The therapist is seduced
by such clients, who suggest that they will love and never abandon
the therapist—provided that the therapist functions as a sure
source of pleasure for the client. In other words, unlike the sadistic
agent, sadistic patients are sophisticated and charming and offer
some affective satisfactions to the therapist from time to time
(Freud, 1912b).

Sadistic patients idealize themselves as generous, original,
smart, valuable people who are fully entitled to be obeyed and
served by others. The therapist, on the other hand, is a dumb,
worthless, selfish, manipulative, crazy person that must be tolerated. As we have already pointed out, sadistic patients tend to have
an acute and painful contradiction between their very high expectations of what they are supposed to achieve in life and what they
are really trained and capable of doing. They are supposed to be
intellectual geniuses or extremely talented artists, but even if they
have the potential for such achievements, they absolutely lack the
discipline (Klein, 1955). Instead of either lowering their expectations or disciplining themselves, they blame the therapist for
sabotaging their achievements. This could be partially true, because the more the therapist tries to "help" them achieve these
goals, the more evident are their shortcomings, and the more they
blame the therapist. This vicious circle is very difficult to open up.
Usually the therapist becomes so frightened of really helping the

sadistic patient that he or she finally accepts the role of "castrator" (Kernberg, 1965).

Sadistic patients actively attack the therapist's perception, memory, and feelings. They tend to be extremely tricky about their own violations of the therapeutic setting. The few times that they are able to recognize that they are the offender, they claim that it was the therapist who pushed them into doing so. This is very typical, for example, of alcoholics, who may attend the session partially drunk but—instead of excusing themselves—will either deny their drinking or blame it on the therapist's "cruelty" during the previous session (Freud, 1924a).

These clients are very jealous of the therapist's other clients. They act in an extremely spoiled, histrionic way if the therapist exhibits any kind of autonomy or refuses to play the masochistic role. They may threaten or attempt suicide, alcoholic binges, etc. They may try to take advantage of therapeutic confidentiality. In the following example, the psychotherapist was a new member of the faculty. He was undoubtedly concerned about improving his professional image and prestige. His office was located on the university campus. The client had been treated there before and may have had an affair with her therapist. The material belongs to the fourth month of treatment.

JUDY: Did I tell you about my crush on this young architect. I was really crazy about him, but in some way he failed me. Maybe this was the reason why I told my husband about him. My husband— you know how he is—became furious and even tried to kill him. It was horrible. (*Pause*) Maybe I'm telling you this because I'm so attracted to you. (*Passionately*) You have such a sparkling personality.

THERAPIST: (*Perplexed*) Do you mean . . .?

JUDY: (*Interrupting*) Yes, yes, darling. I mean that I love you, that I wanted you the very first moment I saw you. I would like to go to bed with you. (*Standing up*) Would you like that? Will you accept me? I suppose that you are clever enough not to be as rigid as those stupid, old-fashioned, traditional therapists.

THERAPIST: (*Surprised, trying to look professional and, at the same time, flexible)* What you are feeling is known as a typical defensive emotional reaction. It's something that happens often when the client has to face a difficult time in treatment.

JUDY: *(Disillusioned)* Oh, no! *(Trying to be sweet)* Come on, darling. Maybe you are afraid of me. But you are such a handsome man. I understand you. I'm sure you like me. But you are being cautious, right?

THERAPIST: *(Trying to remain calm)* No, I'm not being cautious. I'm trying to be helpful. I really meant what I said. Remember that you were just talking about your crush on the young architect.

JUDY: *(Interrupting)* Aha! I've got it now—you're jealous, aren't you? My poor little thing.

THERAPIST: No, that is not the case here. It isn't anything personal. What I'm trying to say to you is precisely that this crush on me that you are feeling now is an unconscious defense. It seems to me that even that crush you had on the young architect was also a defensive episode. Maybe this was one of the reasons why you told your husband about it. Maybe you were feeling that something was wrong.

JUDY: Now I understand—you're afraid of my jealous husband! Don't worry about him—he's dumb.

THERAPIST: That's not the point. Apart from my fears and desires, as your therapist, what I'm saying to you is that by trying to develop a love affair between us you're avoiding anxiety-provoking changes within yourself. It is as if you try to make love to the surgeon to avoid having him operate on you.

JUDY: *(Angry, resentful, and tearful)* You don't want me. You don't like me, you bastard. How do you expect me to be cured if you reject me in such a cold, cruel way?

THERAPIST: Listen, you're the one who is rejecting me as a therapist. How do you want me to cure you if you insist in taking my remarks in the wrong way? I'm not rejecting you. I'm rejecting some of your unconscious defenses.

JUDY: *(Still very angry and tearful, but in a threatening tone)* Listen. If you don't go to bed with me right away, I'll tear off my clothes and run out of your office, screaming that you attacked me and tried to rape me. *(Defiantly and seductively)* It's up to you, Doctor. Are you enough of a man to make love to a real woman instead of hiding behind phony technicalities?

THERAPIST: Are you enough of a woman to have therapy with a real therapist instead of hiding behind phony crushes?

JUDY: *(Still defiantly)* You know that you are risking your prestige. You're new here, and if I accuse you of trying to rape me. . . .

THERAPIST: I'm not accusing you of raping me as a therapist—you're a new patient. But you must know that you are risking your own treatment; you are making me responsible for something that *you* are doing.

JUDY: *(Surprised, thinking things over)* What do you mean?

THERAPIST: I mean that maybe you are doing something very painful to me that happened to you long ago instead of talking about yourself and working it through. For instance, maybe when you were a little girl somebody hurt you and threatened to blame you publicly if you didn't let him. You are not proposing a love affair. You are compelling me by force to obey you. If I do as you say, I'm destroying the treatment and your chances of being cured—and if I don't, you feel personally rejected.

JUDY: *(Crying and switching to a childish, helpless tone)* How did you guess that? This is something that I never told anybody because I feared that nobody would believe me. My uncle used to abuse me sexually when I was a little girl. He said if I didn't let him do it he would tell my parents how bad I was and he said that if I told on him he would tell my parents what a rotten, sexy little girl I was.

The sadistic patient tries to reach an unconscious agreement with the therapist. The therapist is supposed to absorb concern and unpleasure while injecting feelings of fragile omnipotence into the client. The client can suffer an affective crisis—possibly even a psychotic breakdown—each time the therapist stops behaving masochistically or becomes too masochistic. But as soon as the therapist comes back to the "usual" degree of self-devaluation, self-blaming and submission, the sadistic patient tends to "improve" clinically.

Stepping into Socioeconomic Dependence

Such clients try to avoid all socioeconomic decisions and responsibilities or participate only in a childish, omnipotent, emotional manner. Instead they try to make the therapist take responsibility not only for the treatment but also for the unpredictable consequences of the client's irresponsible, self-destructive behavior. For this reason therapists of sadistic patients are always asking themselves, "What's coming now?" Such clients are so self-destructive and irrational that they soon exhaust their therapists. These clients seem to live constantly on the brink, drinking and driving suicidally, etc. They constantly try to blackmail their therapists into sexual relationships, threatening suicide if rejected, and otherwise threatening to destroy the therapist's reputation (Money-Kyrle, 1956).

As in the following exchange, such clients tend to "shift gears" if the therapist confronts them with their behavior. Instead of discussing their overdependent behavior, they blame the therapist repeatedly.

JUDY: *(Very excited and anxious)* I *really* need another car—actually a sports car. You know. Many of my friends already have one, and this makes me feel very down. I was thinking that maybe I can ask my father for some money. I could also postpone your payment just for a few months. Surely you'll understand—it's so important to me!

THERAPIST: Remember that our agreement was that you would pay me regularly on a monthly basis, unless you were going through a very difficult crisis. But this does not seem to be the case.

JUDY: *(Shocked and helpless)* Oh, no! You can't do this to me. *(Angry)* Are you a doctor or a businessman? You're supposed to take care of me, to look out for your clients' well-being!

THERAPIST: That does not necessarily mean spoiling you.

JUDY: Now you are insulting me! You don't get the point. What I'm trying to get you to understand—as a psychotherapist, I suppose—is that I will feel better if there is some way to avoid feeling inferior to my friends.

THERAPIST: It is precisely as a psychotherapist that I'm telling you that there are ways of overcoming your feelings of inferiority other than buying expensive cars. You're the one who is missing the point. Your feelings of inferiority are also related to your inability to behave as an independent 28-year-old adult.

JUDY: *(In a wheedling childlike tone)* Come on, Doctor! Be good to me. You don't want to make me suffer unnecessarily, do you?

THERAPIST: It is because I'm trying to be good to you that I'm saying to you that our therapeutic contract should be respected. If we don't do that, you will become unrealistically overdependent on me just as you already are on your father. As if you were a little child. You want to buy a second luxury car—not with your money but with your father's money and with my money.

JUDY: *(Switching suddenly to a very angry tone)* So there you are. It seems to me that this is the real problem—you're concerned about your damn money. You don't really care about people but about dollars.

THERAPIST: You're trying to make a personal problem with me instead of caring about dealing with your incapacity as an adult and the inferiority feelings derived from it. You are more concerned about some dollars than about yourself as a person.

Sadistic patients think the therapist will punish any attempt to achieve socioeconomic autonomy. They feel that they have to waste opportunities for improving their education, occupation, and income. They feel unconsciously that this is the price that they have to pay to get the therapist's overprotection. Hence they manipulate in order to insure that the therapist actually attacks their movements toward autonomy. For example, they present plans that are totally unrealistic and unachievable or dangerous and counterproductive. The therapist is then constantly forced to tell the clients to lower their sights rather than pointing out that any learning process has its ups and downs or that patience and self-discipline must accompany talent in order to get the best (Tauber, 1954).

The sadistic patient tries to reach an unspoken agreement with the therapist; the therapist will function as a buffer to protect the client from his or her self-destructive actions. These clients can suffer a serious emotional crisis and commit all kinds of self-destructive acts if the therapist is too controlling, but they will have a devastating breakdown if the therapist suddenly stops behaving as an agent. As soon as the therapist comes back to the usual degree of spoiling and infantilizing "overcontainment," the sadistic patient will "improve" clinically.

The Masochistic Insufficient

Masochistic insufficients are nice, pleasant runaways who are able to take care of themselves but not of anyone else. They feel claustrophobic in any close relationship and are unable to sustain such relationships.

Testing the Therapist's Sadism and Insufficientism

Masochistic insufficients unconsciously select sadistic insufficients as therapists, that is, somebody who may be prone to mistreat and abuse the client but, at the same time, will not demand dependence or support.

It is rather easy to find this type in traditional psychoanalytic therapy not only because insufficients go into treatment but also because some of the (irrational) restrictions of the traditional analytic setting can foster insufficiency in therapists. For example, some schools of psychotherapy praise the "neutrality," uncommitment, ambiguity, and passivity of the therapist as something that enhances both the "objectivity" of the therapist and the "autonomy" of the client. Very often therapists who have been initially successful in treating psychotic and borderline clients are unable to tolerate such clients' dependence after they themselves have completed analytic training. This is so because they are taught to treat their clients as if they were able to be financially self-supporting. But this leaves no room for handling the dependency needs of patients or the controlling needs of agents.

Once treatment starts, masochistic insufficients will make

sure that the therapist is really able to function as a tactless "porcupine," that is, rather unpleasant but stable. The therapist must be somebody who will always be there—tolerating (though not without blame) the cyclical escapes of the client. If the therapist responds correctly to these overtures, the treatment will continue.

DAVID: Your interpretations were so accurate last time. I wonder how you can do that, how you can be so sharp. *(Pause)* For example, I didn't realize ever before how important my grandmother's image was for me.

THERAPIST: *(Very pleased)* Your identification with her, you mean?

DAVID: *(Enthusiastically)* Oh, yes! It's exaggerated importance, being a man who is inclined to interior decoration. *(Pause)* Right now, for example, I was thinking about the curtain of my bedroom. It occurs to me that even if it is very nice, it is a little too thick. It does not allow me to see through it. That makes me feel imprisoned. Moreover, its color is more like that of a lady's dress. Those dresses used by old ladies when they have tea and make polite small talk. I definitely don't like that curtain.

THERAPIST: I don't like it either.

DAVID: How is that? You've never seen it.

THERAPIST: *(Jokingly)* Oh yes, I have. I'm talking about the defensive "curtain" that you build when you keep trying to be nice here. Making small talk like your grandmother.

DAVID: *(Even more enthusiastically)* Isn't that something! You're amazingly witty. You're absolutely right! This is connected with my homsexual fears. *(Pause)* By the way, Doctor, I want to know if it would be okay if I go from four to two sessions per week for now. You make things so clear to me that maybe two sessions could be enough. And I have some cultural activities on Tuesdays and Thursdays. Will you agree to that?

THERAPIST: Here we have the defensive curtain again. It seems that you are feeling imprisoned here and trying to escape by being nice. As I explained to you before, if it is possible for you, four sessions weekly constitute a better and more powerful therapeutic rhythm.

Stepping into Submission and Sacrifice

Once these clients have established the therapist's sadism and insufficientism, they start to transform the therapist into an abusive "master." They try to seduce their therapists by never fighting back, despite the therapist's devaluation or blame. They escape from time to time and expect to find in the therapist a stable source of uncommitted company. They have a very persuasive and compelling attitude that drives the other into being excessively intrusive and outspoken. The therapist must be very aware of this in order to avoid being contaminated.

While masochistic insufficients unconsciously perceive themselves as submissive servants and the therapist as a dominant master, consciously they are always afraid of being too domineering and cruel to be loved by the therapist; that is, they repress and project their own masochism and deny and introject the therapist's (supposed) sadism.

SALLY: I don't know. I have this uneasiness. Maybe it is that I'm not feeling very comfortable working at the hospital. (*She is a psychiatrist.*) And I don't know why. Everybody is so kind, so warm. (*Pause*) Maybe it's that I'm very concerned with a very difficult patient. She was so anxious yesterday that I had to see her urgently last night—very late.

THERAPIST: What happened with her?

SALLY: It seems to me that her problem is that she doesn't know how to set limits on others. She doesn't know how to say no. Her boyfriend abuses her. Her roommate abuses her. Her parents abuse her. She's not safe anywhere and she has no space of her own. On top of that, you know how dangerous it is living in this city. Yesterday morning she was mugged. This was the last straw. She felt so anxious that finally she called me for an emergency session last night.

THERAPIST: Do you think that what you are saying about your patient can be somehow applied to yourself? Are your current anxiety and uneasiness at the hospital provoked by your own difficulty in setting limits on others? Look at what happened with this patient, for example. You "had" to see her very late in the evening.

SALLY: As a matter of fact, I can't stand Sharon *(one of her colleagues)*. You know how competitive and abrasive she is. On the other hand, the head nurse kept persecuting me all day long. She suddenly and unexpectedly stormed into my office and kept talking and talking for more than one hour. I felt so trapped that I could hardly breath. But it was my fault.

THERAPIST: *(In a tough tone)* Certainly yes! You are too soft! You behave like a little girl who is so weak that she cannot defend herself!

SALLY: You are so very right. I like it when you talk to me in this direct, clearcut, straightforward way. It is something that I must learn indeed. I'm such a coward. I'm so weak, so inhibited.

THERAPIST: Maybe you are doing it again. Maybe I have been too tough, too rude to you. But instead of pointing it out to me, you are encouraging me to be more aggressive with you.

SALLY: *(Smiling)* Right again, Doctor! Actually I felt that you were blaming me.

Masochistic insufficients idealize the therapist as a straight-forward, sincere, faithful reliable person, while putting themselves down as weak, insincere, unfaithful, unreliable, and demanding clients whom the therapist sooner or later will get tired of and abandon. And this is how they talk about themselves. But from time to time the quality of the therapeutic relationship suddenly changes in these clients' minds, and they start feeling that they can no longer stand the (supposed) blame or devaluation of the therapist. Maybe the therapist is right, but the client has had it and is not prepared any longer for such tactless mistreatment. At this moment such clients will flee—by not working in sessions or not showing up. This flight is usually not permanent, however. Whenever the therapist stops criticizing or blaming the masochistic insufficient, he or she tends to think that the therapist is already fed up and wants to quit the treatment. The client will then make every possible effort to make the therapist begin criticizing or blaming again (Bion, 1965).

Masochistic insufficients tend to attack their own memory, perception, and feelings and push the therapist into attacking them too. But during their cyclical periods of flight, they become aware of the real direction of domination and abuse. At this point the therapy tends to become something like a supervision of the client's unstable couple relationships. The therapist is asked to function as a couple counselor who is supposed to advise and train the client to be (even) more kind and tolerant with his or her porcupine fiancee or spouse, etc. Masochistic insufficients are completely unaware of the oversubmissive running-away behavior that generates the aggressive, jealous, intrusive behavior of their significant others.

Such clients are quite faithful to the therapist in the long run. The therapy is usually very long because of the client's reluctance to get involved in a more intensive and effective therapeutic interchange. The therapist must be patient and allow the client to progress very slowly. Only then will the client's resistance be overcome.

The masochistic insufficient tries to reach an unconscious agreement with the therapist. The client will absorb the therapist's unpleasure and a tactless and painful domination. They can suffer an affective crisis each time the therapist stops behaving sadistically and can experience claustrophobic anxieties—and actually run away—each time the therapist becomes too sadistic. But as soon as the therapist comes back to the "usual" degree of tactless, intrusive devaluation, the masochistic insufficient will return to treatment or will "improve."

Stepping into Socioeconomic Irrational Restriction

Such clients inform and include the therapist in fundamental socioeconomic decisions and responsibilities—but only partially, thus suggesting that the best way of dealing with them is not to get fully involved. In this way, neither therapist nor client is fully in charge of the treatment. The client tries to convince the therapist that it is better not to be ambitious in setting treatment goals. Moreover, each time the therapist tries to achieve a full commitment to the treatment, the masochistic insufficient will try to escape. Many times the therapist will get desperate because the client, on the threshold of a major positive achievement, will suddenly run away from all responsibilities. Moreover, the therapist feels unable to correct the negative effect that this compulsive avoidance behavior has on the client's prestige and possibilities. The client fears all entanglements and true responsibility.

Therapists of such clients never know when they can count on a particular therapeutic effort; the masochistic insufficient is a very slippery client who hates to truly support the therapist's efforts. It is essential that the therapist not count on the client. These constant and ruthless demonstrations of lack of commitment to the treatment disappoint the therapist. But when the therapist despairs, the client once again makes kind and intelligent efforts, until the therapist gets infatuated again, forcing the client to run away, and so on.

Masochistic insufficients can accept discussing socioeconomic issues but strongly censor analysis of their own shortcomings. On the contrary, they either rationalize or justify or even praise their middle-class socioeconomic trap and shortsighted restrictions. Or else they get depressed and take it "personally" whenever the therapist tries to comment on it.

DAVID: Peter offered me work with him. He says that he has an excellent opportunity, that there is a whole new world of possibilities if we work hard. Actually I think he is right because he has been working for a long time now in the same area: he knows very well what he is talking about. He is trying to include me because I talked to him about my low salary and lack of future. That's why he is pushing me into accepting this new opportunity. *(Pause)* But I don't know what to do with it. Maybe it is too demanding for me. I'm afraid I won't have time to attend my weight-lifting sessions. *(Pause)* He told me that initially we will have to be constantly in touch with what is going on, that sometimes we will have to have night meetings. I really don't know. Peter insists that I will get twice as much money and actual freedom than I currently enjoy. But still, I told him to start looking for another partner. *(Pause)* I go to the barber on Friday afternoon and play squash on Saturday morning. The idea of spending a Saturday morning discussing business scares me to death. I don't know if one would call that freedom.

THERAPIST: But you have been complaining for a long time about

how painfully limited your resources are. You insisted here also
that you have no future where you are working now, that your
boss is very mean and intrusive, that you would like to work on
your own.

DAVID: Oh yes, but I feel that what Peter is offering me will trap
me day and night. I won't have any independent life left, any space
free left for me.

THERAPIST: What you fear is what you are provoking with your
avoiding attitude. You are jeopardizing your chances of freedom
and well-being for reasons such as going to the barber on Fridays
and playing squash on Saturdays.

Masochistic insufficients try to reach an agreement with the
therapist to share superficial feelings of freedom and undercommitment as well as underlying feelings of claustrophobia and
restriction. The therapist is supposed to deny, and to help the client
to deny, all the frustrations derived from the client's irrational
restrictions.

These clients will suffer intolerable feelings of claustrophobic
dependence if the therapist is too controlling, and intolerable
feelings of claustrophobic overresponsibility if the therapist is too
dependent. But as soon as the therapist comes back to the "usual"
degree of devaluing and blaming ambiguity and undercommitment, the masochistic insufficient "improves" drastically.

The Sadistic Insufficient

Sadistic insufficients are overaggressive, tactless, tenacious people
who are able to take care of their own socioeconomic survival but
not to depend on or support others. Because they are constantly
irritating others they frequently experience rejection or abandonment. However, they are able to obtain some kind of precarious
affective and socioeconomic stability by being a qualified expert in

some specific area that is important for others (such as surgeon, accountant, etc.).

Testing the Therapist's Masochism and Insufficientism

Sadistic insufficients unconsciously select masochistic insufficients as therapists, that is, somebody who may be prone to submit interpersonally and do everything possible to please but, at the same time, will avoid being dependent or supportive at the socioeconomic level. This is the most common type in traditional psychoanalytic psychiatry.

Usually sadistic insufficients say that there is nothing that they hate in this world more than the manipulative, hypocritical, "diplomat" but, in fact, this is the only type of person who tolerates and is tolerated by them. Sadistic insufficients demand absolute truthfulness from others, but each time someone tells them some truth about themselves they get angry and start furiously blaming or devaluing the other (Epstein, 1979a).

These clients will make some initial attempts to overqualify themselves and to disqualify the therapist as well as to impose some irrational socioeconomic restrictions on the treatment (diminishing the weekly number of sessions, for example). If the therapist accepts these initial probes, then treatment will go ahead.

ELLA: I am very angry at my daughter-in-law. I'm sure that she keeps insinuating that I'm foolish or dishonest just to irritate and offend me. Seems to me that I'll have to speak to her very, very clearly, to confront her and point out some truths. For example, we went out to have tea with her yesterday, but she didn't pay her share. When I very angrily confronted her, she started complaining about how expensive the tearoom is. I told her she was saying that because she does not know how much this treatment costs. A treatment in which the client has to work, to do all the talking, while the therapist's activity is limited to making a few vague remarks per session.

THERAPIST: *(Angrily)* Just a few vague remarks?

ELLA: Let's face the truth. Your job is quite a comfortable one. It's very different from being a grandmother, for example. This morning my grandson was very harsh, very cool with me, very aggressive. I told him that he was a spoiled little brat. He became very angry with me. But he must learn to be nice to his grandmother. He enjoys putting me down, making me feel uncomfortable.

THERAPIST: Let us face the truth: you tend to be aggressive and harsh here with me. As if you enjoy putting me down—just like your daughter-in-law and your grandson.

ELLA: *(Very angry)* It seems to me that you are the one who is like my daughter-in-law and my grandson—the one who has to learn how to be nicer to your clients. Maybe you're trying to justify your fees.

THERAPIST: Maybe you're the one who is trying to justify the fact that you still haven't paid for last month's sessions even though we are now in the middle of the month.

Stepping into Domination and Abuse

Sadistic insufficients will try to seduce the therapist—especially those just starting out—into accepting their tactless, unpleasant domination in return for being a faithful, tenacious client. As long as the therapist tolerates these clients' aggressions they will not leave the treatment under any circumstances even if they apparently hold them in low esteem (Bion, 1963).

Because sadistic insufficients are used to being initially tolerated and then abandoned, they are very aware of the minor signs indicating that the therapist's patience has reached a limit. Consequently, as soon as these clients realize that the therapist has had it and is prepared to abandon the therapy, they will start apologizing for their aggressiveness, justifying it as an attempt at sincerity, and so forth. They will point to their need for treatment and the therapist's moral obligation to keep treating clients even if they are sometimes unpleasant. If not, what is psychiatry all about? If people didn't have symptoms, they wouldn't be asking for help.

Because this is partially right (and because young therapists can't afford to lose limited but stable sources of income), the therapist usually reassures the client and the vicious circle starts again.

In other words, the sadistic insufficient constantly invites the therapist to be overly tactful, ambiguous, tangential, indirect, diplomatic, etc., to match the client's sincere but tough, direct but crude, "realistic" approach.

Sadistic insufficients are frequently jealous and constantly threatened by abandonment or infidelity from their sexual partners. These clients are, consciously, afraid of being too servile, tolerant, or permissive. They repress and project their own sadism and rigidity while denying and introjecting the therapist's (supposed) masochism and overflexibility. They view themselves as tough, strong, sincere, honest, faithful, and reliable—entitled to judge, command, and be served by the therapist, who is weak, insincere, faithless, unreliable, excessively accepting, and servile. They fear that the therapist will someday betray them. They feel morally superior to all others.

DICK: My brother is extremely and stupidly competitive toward me. This bothers me very much. I invited him yesterday to the Museum of Modern Art, but he kept criticizing everything over and over, saying that the paintings were ugly and meaningless. I knew that the paintings were really very aggressive, but I told him in a very tough way that he and his friends were a bunch of ignoramuses. I patiently explained to him the symbolic meaning of the paintings, but he became very envious of my knowledge, and he insinuated that I was showing off. I became very angry and told him that he was attacking me with his insinuations. Then he said that I was a very difficult person to be with. Can you imagine that? After making ridiculous, offensive, vicious remarks and insinuations against me because I knew more about art than he, he started complaining about me! He really offended me very badly. He is very abusive and an ungrateful person.

THERAPIST: Do you remember that yesterday you were extremely critical of my interventions? Especially when I tried to explain the meaning of your aggressive behavior. Do you remember that you reacted very badly? Your associations today indicate that maybe you felt envious and competitive toward me because of my knowledge of psychology. Maybe you felt that I thought of you as a very abusive and ungrateful client.

DICK: (*Surprised*) You remind me of my neighbor. He is always contradicting me, instead of helping me keep the building clean. He constantly throws out garbage in the corridor, and when I confront him with it he starts screaming at me. Maybe because he's nuts. He makes fun of me. He irritates me. Tries to get into discussions with me. I try to tolerate him, but I won't be able to stand him much longer.

THERAPIST: You also keep contradicting me. Maybe you're "nuts"? Possibly you're afraid that I won't be able to tolerate you much longer.

From time to time the quality of the therapeutic relationship suddenly changes. This happens, as we said before, when the therapist starts sending unconscious messages that the relentless attacks of the client are becoming unbearable. These clients will then start apologizing for their "occasionally" unnecessary and involuntary rudeness. With the exception of these times, sadistic insufficients attack the therapist's memory, perception, and feelings.

Therapy usually is very long with sadistic insufficients, not only because they are reluctant to get involved in a more intense and effective therapeutic interchange but because they are so difficult to change (Freud, 1937). Even if they become aware of their compulsion to project and insult others, they keep doing it again and again. They usually become affectively dependent on the therapist because they know how difficult it is for them to be accepted and tolerated. They are quite conservative in affective relationships.

Thus an unconscious sadomasochistic agreement is reached. The therapist is constantly absorbing unpleasure and a tactless and painful domination, and the client is constantly injecting un-pleasure into the therapist (Winnicott, 1949).

Sadistic insufficients can suffer an intensive crisis of rage and indignation—and actually quit the treatment—if the therapist stops behaving masochistically. They experience fear of being abandoned if the therapist becomes too masochistic. As soon as the therapist comes back to the "usual" degree of undercommitted, tactful, and conciliatory masochism, the sadistic insufficient will "improve" clinically.

Stepping into Socioeconomic Irrational Restrictions

Such clients will inform and include the therapist in funda-mental socioeconomic decisions and responsibilities but only in a very partial way. They constantly suggest that it is best not to get excessively involved. There is a subtle difference between the socioeconomic policy of the masochistic insufficient and that of the sadistic insufficient. Masochistic insufficients tend to think of themselves as adolescents with limited resources who want to be free. Sadistic insufficients view themselves more as old retired people in need of security. They want to save rather than to invest. These fantasies of poverty and ruin tend to become true because sadistic insufficients—quite unlike their masochistic counter-parts—have a striking inability to generate new friends and socioeconomic relations. The social network is extremely re-stricted, scarce, and hostile. Consequently, they are alone in this world.

These clients try to convince the therapist that it is better not to be very ambitious about treatment goals. They attempt to keep the therapist's expectations in check each time the therapist gets enthusiastic by becoming overly aggressive or interrupting the weekly rhythm of the sessions. Often the therapist will get desperate because the client, on the very threshold of a major achievement, will suddenly attack those who are important to its success in a way that is suicidal. Because of these attacks, they are constantly weakening their socioeconomic network, which in turn diminishes their resources and increases their loneliness and isolation. This triggers further paranoid attacks, and the vicious circle continues.

BARBARA: It's very difficult to be a physician nowadays. Patients want to be cheated, and my colleagues enjoy cheating them. Such hypocrisy is something very difficult to swallow. *(Pause)* Yesterday Doctor Smith was giving a press conference about the functioning of the department of hematology. He's the director, as you know. Incredibly enough, he was bragging about the quality and quantity of research done in the department this year. A bunch of lies. How can he be such a demagogue. Finally I couldn't stand it any longer and openly contradicted him in front of the press. *(In a very proud tone)* When he talked about the importance of the research, I stood up and asked him in a loud voice if he was kidding. He was shocked. His staff was furious with me, but the press was very interested when I told them the whole truth about what was going on.

THERAPIST: Doctor Smith is the main source of referrals that you have, isn't he?

BARBARA: *(Morally outraged)* What are you trying to imply? Maybe that I should be overindulgent with his professional negligence and false propaganda just to selfishly protect my source of referrals? Do you want me to become a dishonest cynic?

THERAPIST: Not exactly. What I'm trying to tell you is that you are trapped between two false alternatives: you have to be either dishonest and hypocritical or compulsively and counterproductively "sincere." You think that you can only switch from being Ms. Justice into being Ms. Cynic and the only way of protecting your professional network is by being a selfish cynic. Consequently you become tactless and superhonest, regardless of the consequences of such an attitude.

BARBARA: Certainly yes, but I can't go against my ethical principles! Moreover, I don't "want" to go against such principles. I'm wondering what yours are? Do you have them at all? Where will we be if nobody cares about ethical standards in medical practice.

THERAPIST: You are very right. In fact, I am the one who has to "care about the ethical quality of your behavior" in the sense that I have the obligation to tell you that many of your "attacks of sincerity" against other people are motivated by your need to place the blame on others, blame that you are afraid to experience yourself. But you want to cheat yourself and have me cheat you by disguising your "immoral" projections onto others as moral integrity.

Because of their perceived poverty it is usually very difficult for sadistic insufficients to take on a traditional psychoanalytic contract of four or five sessions per week. A dynamic or behaviorally oriented psychotherapy of one or two sessions per week that will last forever is more feasible. This is also more expensive and less effective, but they don't realize that everything has a price; in this case, what is cheaper in appearance will be much more expensive in terms of happiness and success in the long run.

Sadistic insufficients short-circuit therapeutic attempts to analyze or change their socioeconomic patterns. On the contrary, they rationalize or justify or even praise their middle-class trap and irrational restrictions. They try to reach an unstated agreement with the therapist. The therapist is supposed to deny, and to help the client to deny, all the frustrations derived from the client's irrational restrictions.

These clients are threatened if the therapist becomes too controlling. They are overwhelmed if the therapist becomes dependent on them. But as soon as the therapist comes back to the "usual" degree of ambiguity and undercommitment, the sadistic insufficient "improves" drastically.

8

Treatment
Strategies

Strategic Goals

The therapist acts as a political conductor whose job is to understand and change the power structure on the individual, couple, family, and institutional levels. The objective in the micropolitical sphere may be a conservative restitution of the old balance of power, a mild reform, or a more ambitious qualitative transformation. The degree of change to which the therapist can aspire depends on the resources of the client, the therapist, and the environment. The therapeutic success very much depends on the power of the therapist, that is, his or her capacity to develop a consciousness of the need for change, a supporting consensus, and therapeutic alliances for the treatment effort.

The treatment plan is designed to change the client's psychological structure, actual behavior, microenvironment, and, to a much lesser degree, even the macroenvironment, in a gradual and progressive manner. This implies changes in the pathological interpretative paradigm and the defensive action plan with its accompanying social skills.

For our clients, the therapeutic process consists of successfully working through the transference neurosis and thereby modifying their intrapsychic, interpersonal, and socioeconomic situations in such a way that they achieve greater autonomy and happiness. To achieve these changes, our clients have to develop insight into their own psychological, behavioral, and environmental structure and process. We, as the therapists, must help them tear down the defenses that they have built up to keep their anxiety at bay; this is part of the process of working through. We must also support our clients' efforts to restructure and improve their life situations.

This intrapsychic reorganization takes place on a number of different levels. Self-perception is usually—but not necessarily—the first area to change. Clients gradually modify their rigid view of themselves as helpless or their insistence that they alone must shoulder the full financial burden of the family. This change in self-perception involves a new perception of others in the client's environment. Gradually the client's affect is also reorganized. Unjustified feelings of guilt and inferiority or moral entitlement and superiority are relinquished. The client is no longer caught in the iron grip of feelings of helplessness, lack of control, loneliness, depression, etc. Depressed, lethargic clients will become more energetic, while manic clients will discover a new calm. These changes, brought about by an intrapsychic restructuring, will also cause our clients to make modifications in their approach to interpersonal and socioeconomic relations. As they gradually move away from sadistic or masochistic stances or rigid adherence to their agent, patient, or insufficient roles, the positive reinforcement that they get from their environment (in the form of improved interpersonal relations and social status) will enable them to make further alterations in their self-perception and affective structures (Rangell, 1969).

As therapists we must remain flexible but in control of the treatment. We must act as a mirror which accurately reflects our clients' feelings, behavior, and unconscious desires and which constantly corrects our clients' distortions of reality. This is in contrast to the complementary mirroring of the clients' partners, who reinforce and reaffirm their defensive distortions (Watzlawick, 1976).

We lead clients up to the walls of defense that they have erected and encourage them to dismantle these defenses. We discourage inappropriate acting out and encourage new and positive forms of behavior in the client and in the micro- and macroenvironment. Of course, the therapy must be tailored to suit the client, and not the other way around. Drug therapy, for example, may be appropriate at one time for a client and not at another. Sessions five days a week may work well with a client with adequate resources and full environmental support but could prove impossible with an insufficient client or with a powerless masochistic patient in a hostile environment.

In summary, to the extent that it is possible, therapeutic power should concentrate on changing the client's patterns. To change implies correcting the client's defensive displacement, inversion, and narrowing. Correcting patterns of behavior vis-a-vis socioeconomic and interpersonal power is the precondition for modifying other variables: defensive qualifications, affect state, reality testing, centeredness, attitude towards organizations, and phenomenologic symptoms.

Tactical Stages

Treatment progresses through certain tactical stages. During the first stage the therapist should play the client's complementary role in the pathological dyad, thus promoting the transference and facilitating the therapist's ability to intervene in a crisis. It must be stressed that the therapist should consciously *play* but not blindly *take* the client's complementary role. In this way the therapist can control and conduct the treatment without becoming trapped in the countertransference (Barchilon, 1958). For example, the therapist of a masochistic patient should be assertive but not devaluing, firm but not blaming, tough but not abusive, etc. In this way the client, who is not yet ready to give up his or her masochistic-patient role, will feel supported by the (agent) therapist but not excessively controlled or attacked. And the client can learn from the therapist's example that there is an alternative to authoritarian sadism (Klein, 1957).

The second stage involves correcting the client's interpersonal abusive domination or sacrificed submission. The therapist should start by trying to overcome the client's excessive denigration and blame and excessive idealization—whether of self or of others—that are evident in the client's speech and attitudes. Excessive self-or other-centeredness and phenomenological symptoms related to distortions of interpersonal power must also be dealt with. In this second stage the main task is to overcome the defense mechanisms of narrowing and inversion (Turillazzi, 1979).

Once clients have changed their perception of interpersonal power, the therapist is in a better strategic position to initiate modification of the client's perception of socioeconomic power. This entails helping clients to overcome their defensive "personalization" and confront their excessive socioeconomic dependency, monopoly, or restriction, as well as the phenomenologic symptoms related to distortions of socioeconomic power.

In the final stages of treatment, clients become self-actualizing. They assume full responsibility for their own socioeconomic and interpersonal reality in equal relationships with others in their lives (Toffler, 1981). Initially they are supervised to avoid their tendency to regress when interacting with others who complement their historic position. Finally they stabilize and become autonomous.

Technical Procedures

The therapist should be able to apply either simultaneously or successively all the biological, psychological, and social means currently available in order to achieve the therapeutic goals already described.

On the one hand, the therapist should be flexible and open-minded enough to accurately apply a wide variety of therapeutic procedures. On the other hand, the therapist should be rigorous, knowledgeable, and responsible enough to be constantly aware and in control of what is going on with the client. The therapist must be aware in order to choose the appropriate tactical and technical procedures (Langs, 1973). In accordance with the therapeutic goals which have been previously determined in each tactical stage of treatment, the different therapeutic procedures must be systematically and coherently organized and applied.

The therapeutic interventions most often used can be classified into ten categories.

1. Therapeutic information about the client's conceptual, perceptual, and affective pathological defensive organization. To transmit this information and to give insight, the therapist may use *descriptions* of the defensive narrowing, inversion, and displacement in cognition and affect; *interpretations* of the unconscious sadomasochistic and socioeconomic paradigm; *reconstruction* of the family and/or cultural origin of these pathological paradigms of interpersonal and social understanding; *disauthorization* of the mutilated historical paradigm (it was designed for another age, other circumstances, etc.); and *opening* of new alternatives to organize the perceptual, conceptual, and affect aspects of current understanding.

2. Therapeutic information about the client's pathological and defensive organization of speech and action. In order to promote behavioral insight the therapist can use *contextual and sequential descriptions* which demonstrate displacement from a current socioeconomic problem to a stereotyped sadomasochistic interaction in which the relationship of domination and submission is described inversely to how it is acted. The naturalization of dependence, control, or restriction can also be described; that is, the acting-off, and counteracting-off defensive transactions are defined and explained. *Opening* to new speech and action alternatives is employed. Therapeutic acting-on and counteracting-on transactions are taught (Kohut, 1977).

3. Therapeutic information about the client's most significant partner and the micro- and macroenvironment. The therapist can use a descriptive outline of the general characteristics and stereotyped defensive action plan and pathological

paradigm characteristic of the client's partner, family, work environment, and community (Neri, 1978). To the degree that it can be given, environmental information about the structure and dynamics of the client's significant others should result in a realistic and complete picture of their environmental restrictions, possibilities, and pressures. Using Lacan's (1966) terms, the therapist shows the clients how they, as subjects, are "subjected" by society. However, this view should be provided only when the therapist is sure that clients will use it constructively and not destructively, or manipulatively with others (Gear & Liendo, 1980).

4. Therapeutic directions which modify the defensive action plan, replacing it with a therapeutic action plan. Proscriptions neutralize the client's acting-off behavior. Prescription promotes acting-on behavior. The directions are specific instructions for the client to overcome pathologic interpersonal behavior patterns of domination or submission and pathologic socioeconomic patterns of excessive dependence, control, or restriction (Lowenstein, 1954).

5. Therapeutic supervision to show clients how to help their partner, family, etc., to step out of the complementary role or neutralize their own defensive action plan, which contaminates the client. Specific *decontaminating* and *anticontaminating instructions* are given to interrupt the mirroring of one another's pathology (Langs, 1979).

6. Therapeutic reactions which specifically act to block the client's defensive acting-off behavior. Therapeutic counteracting on is executed while specifically avoiding counteracting off.

7. Therapeutic counterpressures. These are used when the therapist counters specific threats and promises of the client (Laruelle, 1978). Therapeutic counterthreats or counterpromises can be used either as *dissuasions* against the client's defensive action plan or *persuasions* to promote the therapeutic action plan.

8. Therapeutic contracts, which are used to work through and make evident the client's defensive action plans. The *therapeu-*

tic setting has two types of rules: those that deal with interpersonal authority and those which deal with socioeconomic control (Langs, 1979). Because the therapeutic contract constitutes the infrastructure which makes possible all other kinds of interventions, its rules should be as rigorous as possible without being counterproductive. The contractual rules of the treatment should be tailored according to both the types of client and their individual characteristics. For example, the contract designed to treat a manipulative psychopatic sadistic patient will be stricter than one designed to treat a fragile schizoid masochistic patient (Gear & Liendo, 1976).

9. Environmental therapy, used to promote awareness and therapeutic supporting consensus from the client's significant others. This therapy helps the others to respond with counteracting on rather than the counteracting off. It also deals with their own contaminating defensive action plan and acting-off behavior. This is achieved by *individual, family, or couple counseling, direct intervention, hospitalization, etc.* We have effectively used *environmental contracts* in which each partner avoids acting-off behavior while helping the other by specifically blocking the other's acting off and executing the other's counteracting on behavior. This increases therapeutic efficiency, since each functions as a cotherapist for the other and extends therapeutic help to the everyday situation.

10. Psychoactive drugs, which are used tactically to control the client's excessive aggression, depression, anxiety, etc., when these are so intense as to inhibit the therapeutic process. The drugs make it possible to work through the problem in therapy. When the neurohormonal imbalances go beyond a certain point, psychotherapy is ineffective.

In brief, we are recommending a multidimensional biological, psychological, and environmental technical approach aimed at multiplying therapeutic power and shortening the duration of treatment.

Therapeutic Reactions

The basic types of clients have distinctively different reactions to different types of therapeutic interventions (Langs, 1979). The positive or negative responses of each different client type to various interventions is shown in Table 5.

It is evident that the client most receptive to all the instruments of psychotherapy seems to be the masochistic insufficient, followed by the masochistic patient, the masochistic agent, the sadistic patient, the sadistic insufficient, and the sadistic agent.

We will now examine treatment strategies, tactical stages and technical procedures for the six basic client types.

The Masochistic Patient

The Therapist as Sadistic Agent

Because they feel weak and helpless, masochistic patients are usually addicted to cruel, tough, abusive, and controlling sadistic agents. By playing the role of sadistic agent the therapist accepts

Table 5

Positive and Negative Responses
of the Six Basic Client Types
to Different Therapeutic Interventions

Therapeutic Intervention	Masochistic Patient	Sadistic Agent	Masochistic Agent	Sadistic Patient	Masochistic Insufficient	Sadistic Insufficient
Intrapsychic information	+	−	−	−	+	−
Behavorial information	+	−	−	−	+	−
Environmental information	−	+	+	−	±	−
Directions	+	−	+	−	+	±
Supervisions	+	−	+	−	+	±
Reactions	+	+	+	+	+	+
Counterpressures	+	+	+	+	+	+
Contract	+	−	+	+	+	+
Environmental therapy	+	+	+	+	+	+
Drug therapy	+	+	+	+	+	+

the transference of the client's submission and dependence. However, while it is important that the therapist be tough, firm, and assertive, he or she must avoid abusing, blaming, or deningrating the client. The therapist must also *appear* able and willing to take responsibility for the client's socioeconomic survival and major decisions; however the therapist should not assume such responsibilities unless the client is going through an acute psychotic episode (Daniels, 1969).

Working through Interpersonal Submissiveness

Once treatment has begun and a transference relationship has been established, the therapist can begin to point out the client's tendency to act out a particular sadomasochistic sequence over and over again—a sequence in which the client portrays himself or herself as an abusive dominant master and others (the therapist included) as submissive servants, when in fact the opposite is the case. The therapist must work first to correct the faulty perception and then to improve the client's self-image (Adler & Myerson, 1973).

The therapist must show these clients that their behavior stems from their ingrained masochistic way of thinking. They think that the only way to obtain protection, acceptance, and relief from anxiety is to submit to others. Failure to submit is to experience not only irrational guilt but also rejection and abandonment. The therapist should point out how they have allowed their sadistic partners to isolate them socially, thus making themselves more vulnerable to emotional blackmail and abuse.

Once these clients' fundamental masochistic approach to interpersonal relations has been fully delineated in the transference, it is generally useful to help clients reconstruct their family origins. As we have already noted, the client's same-sex parent usually played the complementary—that is, sadistic—role, while the opposite-sex parent usually played the masochistic role. It is also important to discuss the social origins of the client's masochism, for example, the effect of sex, class, religious, or ethnic prejudices (Freud, 1937a).

At this point the therapist can actually begin to rectify distortions within the therapeutic relationship, both by giving the client specific therapeutic instructions and by relinquishing the tough, aggressive manner adopted early in the transference in favor of a more permissive, open style. This forces the client to assume a more assertive manner. If the client still adheres to a rigid complementary conception of interpersonal authority, he or she may temporarily switch to the alternative position of sadistic agent with respect to the therapist. Further work will then be required to help the client break this alternate pattern (Freud, 1914).

The therapist must also help these clients modify their relationships with sadistic others. The therapist can best do this by helping clients to understand the characteristics and motives of these others. During this stage, the therapist acts as a type of supervisor.

However, if the client is very young or very psychotic and, consequently, incapable of modifying these interpersonal relations, the therapist should take a more direct approach, in the form of couple, family, or peer therapy. If these relationships cannot be changed, the client can be taught certain protective measures or the relationships can be ended altogether.

Because masochistic patients have a defensive need to idealize the therapist, their resistance can often take an indirect form. For example, they may unconsciously manipulate their sadistic others to sabotage the therapy. The therapist must always bear in mind that the masochist is a masochist and not a "good guy" with "bad guy" partners. The real enemies of the treatment at this stage are the client's masochism and the sadism of the significant others (Segal, 1967).

The following transaction shows how a masochistic patient expresses her negative transference by inducing her husband to attack the treatment.

JOANNE: I had a real hard time with my husband. He was furious with you. He said that you were making me too aggressive and independent, that women are supposed to remain at home because they are born to be housewives. I don't know why he was so angry.

Maybe he's right—but I had an anxiety attack when he told me to stop the treatment right away because he wouldn't pay for it anymore.

THERAPIST: Did you discuss with him something about what is going on in the treatment?

JOANNE: (*Thinking carefully*) Well, yes. I just told him what you said about how bad it was for me to be so dependent on him the way I was on my bossy mother. Maybe that was it! Oh, how stupid I am! I'm so sorry.

THERAPIST: Possibly you unconsciously wanted him to react against the treatment?

JOANNE: (*Very sad*) Oh, I'm so sorry. I'll always be a loser. Please forgive me, Doctor. Maybe it was because I was so shocked after watching this terrible movie. Do you remember *Psycho*? It's a movie about a crazy young man who falls in love with a beautiful girl who stays at the motel that he and his mother run. His mother is pathologically jealous. But the really shocking thing is that the mother was actually dead. The man had a split personality. He was both the lover and the murderously jealous mother at the same time. I was terrified.

THERAPIST: So am I. It seems that you're telling me that you have a split personality.

JOANNE: (*Concerned*) How is that?

THERAPIST: According to your associations, it seems that you are, at the same time, a devoted patient and a very controlling mother-husband who is jealous enough to want to "murder," to interrupt the treatment.

JOANNE: (*Confused*) Could you please explain more about this splitting?

THERAPIST: It seems that you are warning me to be more aware of your own aggressive jealousy that is split off from your consciousness but enacted by your husband.

JOANNE: (*Smiling*) Do you think so? It seems very clear. Actually it reminds me of what we were talking about—how I made my mother very jealous each time my father approached me.

THERAPIST: Yes, but this happened after you yourself experienced jealousy because you saw that your mother and your brother were on excellent terms. Remember that when you were leaving last time, you saw my other patient who came earlier to his session?

The therapist must try to build a therapeutic coalition with the client with respect to the sadistic agent, a coalition that is not against the agent per se but against the pathological sadism (Bienner, 1979). The client then becomes a kind of go-between, on the one hand acting in the manifest service of the sadistic agent, and on the other hand working with the therapist to understand the motives behind the sadistic behavior. Masochistic patients must learn that the agents cannot change suddenly and that tact is required in transmitting information and in changing the relationship. If the therapist is successful in handling this delicate and crucial stage of the treatment, the sadistic agent may decide to seek treatment.

Working through Socioeconomic Dependence

Once a client's masochistic approach to interpersonal authority has been somewhat modified, the therapist can start working on the client's crippling socioeconomic dependence. The therapist does so by describing in general and in particular all the ways that the client maintains his or her dependence on others and forces others to assume control over his or her life (Searles, 1973).

But every time the therapist tries to confront such clients with their infantile, dependent behavior, they repeatedly change the focus of attention. The therapist must point out this defensive maneuver and help their clients work it through. Once they are able to acknowledge their dependence, the therapist can then begin to work with these clients on their need to maintain a posture of infantile helplessness in order to avoid being abandoned. The family and social origins of this behavior can then be uncovered and worked through. As with the interpersonal relationship, the therapist can start rectifying the client's socioeconomic dependence by giving the client specific therapeutic instructions and by progressively demanding from the client a more equal, less dependent relationship. As in the case of sadomasochism, the client may switch to the complementary role of agent for a time, particularly if the client has not really modified his or her intra-psychic pattern vis-à-vis socioeconomic reality (Boutang, 1978).

The therapist must also help these clients modify their relationships with the agents in their lives. These clients must be fully aware of their own socioeconomic dependence. The therapist must, for a time, supervise the clients' relationships with their controlling significant others—as was done during the earlier working through of sadomasochism. These agent others may be brought into the therapy to help the client work on this stage. If a complete therapeutic transformation of these patient-agent relationships is not obtainable, the client should choose between reestablishing, in better terms, the old patient-agent agreement or creating some protective distance, or, if there is no other viable solution, ending the relationship altogether.

The therapist can expect considerable resistance to changes in this area—both passive resistance on the part of the client and active sabotage—threats involving payment refusal, etc.—from the agent partner. If the therapist is successful in overcoming these resistances, a new, healthy agreement will then be achieved between the client and the former agent. Unfortunately, things do not always work out this way. If clients are extremely dependent on their sadistic agents, they will probably leave treatment sooner or later. The only way to avoid this is to transform the psycho-analysis into chronic counterproductive "psychodialysis" (Freud, 1937b). The therapist limits his or her activity to listening to the chronic complaints of the masochistic patient—who never im-proves—and no longer attempts any deep interpretation or change in the patient-agent system. Naturally, this is not healthy for the patient or for the therapist; but sometimes—more often than one cares to think—this degradation of the analysis is unavoidable. The therapist must decide whether to end the therapy altogether or continue on a long-term basis in the hope of later change (Langs, 1980).

Achieving Autonomy

Once masochistic patients start to seek out and obtain healthy forms of security and pleasure—either from new or from modified old relationships—a whole new world will open up for them. They will achieve much greater autonomy and will learn to be interdependent in a mature way with many other people (Kernberg, 1976).

However, when faced with situations similar to those that transformed them into masochistic patients in their childhood, these clients may regress to their earlier posture. Therefore, the treatment should train clients to detect their anxiety in order to abort this behavior at an early stage. Finally, in order to stop being masochistic patients, they must develop new interpersonal and socioeconomic patterns and skills. It is not enough to *want* to change; one must also be able to act in a different way.

The Sadistic Agent

The Therapist as Masochistic Patient

Because they need to confirm their feelings of omnipotence, sadistic agents are usually addicted to helpless, weak, naive, submissive, dependent masochistic patients. By playing the role of a masochistic patient the therapist accepts the transference of the client's domination and monopoly. However, while it is important that the therapist appear "weak," that is, not aggressive, he or she should not act overly submissive or self-denigrating. Without really doing so, the therapist should also appear willing to give up socioeconomic responsibilities and to depend on the client for his or her own socioeconomic survival (Haley, 1966).

Working through Interpersonal Domination

Once treatment has begun and a transference relationship has been established, the therapist can begin to point out the client's tendency to perceive and act out a particular sadomasochistic story over and over again—a story in which the client appears to be a submissive servant, and others (the therapist included) as abusive domineering masters—when in fact the opposite is the case. The therapist must correct the client's faulty perception of reality, that is, the client's self-idealization and sense of superiority. The therapist assumes the role of a respected professional who is entitled to exercise specific authority over the client's treatment. That is, the therapist "knows better" than the client what is going on and what to do about it in the treatment (Freud, 1913).

If the sadistic agent can tolerate this switch in interpersonal authority, the therapist can start fighting more openly against the abuse and emotional blackmail that the sadistic client unconsciously tries to impose. However, this struggle for authority in the therapeutic relationship is usually rather complicated and delicate (Frank, 1961). Clients can threaten to quit treatment; they may accuse the therapist of being a sadist, etc.

The therapist must show these clients that their behavior stems from their ingrained sadistic thinking. That is, they think the only way of obtaining any pleasure in life is to dominate and abuse others into letting them have their own way. The therapist should point out how they have unconsciously isolated their masochistic partners in order to control and blackmail them (Gear, Grinberg & Liendo, 1976).

Once these clients' fundamental sadistic approach to interpersonal relations has been fully delineated in the transference, it is useful to help the client reconstruct its family origin. It will become evident that this was the best form of behavior for the client as a child. The child usually imitates the pattern of the opposite-sex parent while assuming the role of complementary other to the masochistic-patient same-sex parent. The therapist should reconstruct not only the family matrix of the client's sadism but also its psychosocial and sociological matrix, the effect of sex, class, religious, or ethnic prejudices (Strachey, 1934).

At this point the therapist can actually begin to rectify distortions within the therapeutic relationship, both by giving the client specific therapeutic instructions and by progressively relinquishing the soft, kind, "weak" manner adopted earlier while assuming a tougher, more assertive style (Bramson, 1981).

The therapist must also help these clients modify their relationship with their masochistic others. The therapist can best do this by helping the clients to understand the characteristics and motives of their others. During this stage, the therapist acts as a type of supervisor.

However, sometimes clients are incapable of modifying these interpersonal relationships by themselves and the therapist should adopt a more direct approach by instituting couple or family therapy. If a complete transformation of these sadomasochistic relationships is not obtainable, the client can either reestablish the old sadomasochistic agreement on better terms, or establish greater distance, or end the relationship altogether.

Because sadistic agents have a defensive need to maintain their illness, they are usually quite resistant to the therapist's suggestions. They often become paranoid and hypomanic—defenses that are usually very hard to overcome because they tend to close the client's psychic system to any new information. Usually it is very difficult for the therapist not to overreact with anger and rejection when facing the chronic and intense negative transference of the sadistic agent. Therapists may also mistakenly pity their clients' helpless partners (Menaker, 1942).

At this point the therapist must try to build a therapeutic coalition with the clients in regard to the others in their lives, a coalition that is not against the others themselves but against their pathological masochism. The client then works with the therapist in an "antimasochist" way, after being carefully prepared to understand that others are not able to change all of a sudden. The client must be advised to tactfully and gradually stop being sadistic in such a way that the masochistic patients will not get panicky; they will have to understand that the therapist is not really "against" them personally but merely trying to change the pathogenic system in which they are included as abused followers.

In all probability the sadistic agent's most significant masochistic patients are already in therapy. If not, the gradual change of the client's sadism will motivate them in that direction (Jackson, 1959).

Working through Socioeconomic Control

Once a client's sadistic approach to interpersonal authority has been somewhat modified, the therapist can start working on the client's infantilizing socioeconomic control of his or her dependent others (including the therapist).

The therapist does so by describing in general and in particular all the ways that the client excludes others from socioeconomic power and turns them into dependents. But every time the therapist tries to confront these clients with their infantilizing, monopolistic socioeconomic behavior, they repeatedly change the focus of attention. The therapist must point out this defensive maneuver and help their clients work it through (Bion, 1977). Once they are able to acknowledge their controlling behavior, the therapist can then explain why they have such a need to infantalize others. They feel that if they don't control others, they will be faced with a catastrophic loss of control because they are—and perceive themselves to be—surrounded by extremely helpless ineffective children (Chertok, 1968). As with the interpersonal relationship, the therapist can start rectifying the client's socioeconomic monopoly by giving the client specific therapeutic instructions and by progressively demanding from the client a more equal, less controlling relationship. As in the case of sadomasochism, the client may switch to the complementary role of patient for a time, particularly if he or she has not sufficiently altered the intrapsychic pattern vis-à-vis socioeconomic reality (Dewald, 1976).

The therapist must also help these clients modify their relationships with the patients in their lives. These clients must be fully aware of their own socioeconomic monopoly. The following vignette shows how a sadistic agent starts working through the negative interpersonal and socioeconomic effects of his domination and control over others.

JIM: I was talking yesterday with Michael, a friend of mine. I was telling him how foolish he is to act like a boss with his family. He's raising his children to be stupid, unreliable, obedient puppets. I reminded him that we were no longer in the Middle Ages.

THERAPIST: Wouldn't you say that something similar could be happening to you?

JIM: Don't jump to easy conclusions, Doctor. It's true that I'm strict with my children. But I'm doing this because I don't want to spoil them.

THERAPIST: It seems that you're the one who indulges in easy explanations. Remember that I was trying to show you yesterday how you overstress others' failures but don't recognize their achievements? how you compulsively criticize your family as you just did with my intervention?

JIM: But you aren't recognizing my achievements either. I thought that I showed you how I changed my behavior in this respect. But if my family insists on behaving stupidly, it's not my fault.

THERAPIST: Hold on. I showed you that I was able to recognize your improvements whenever they happened. But you are insisting now on denying it.

JIM: *(Smiling)* I think that you have a point there.

THERAPIST: Yes, I have another point. You are risking transforming members of your family—and me—into stupid, unreliable, obedient puppets who won't be able to help you when you need it—and who won't be able to share in your success or happiness either. We were talking last week about your feelings of loneliness, and your family's lack of understanding of your position.

JIM: Sometimes it is **very** difficult for me to tolerate their silliness. They don't care. They are always concerned about stupid small things. *(Smiling)* OK! OK! There I go again. See? I'm improving. As a matter of fact, I'm very worried about getting sick or something. What will happen to our organization and their future without me?

THERAPIST: *(Jokingly)* I was also quite worried about the future of our therapeutic organization—and about your future if you keep behaving like a boss.

The therapist must temporarily supervise the clients' relationships with their infantile others—as was done during the earlier working through of sadomasochism. It may be advisable to do some couple or family therapy at this stage to help other members change. If a complete therapeutic transformation of these patient-agent relationships is not obtainable, the client should choose between reestablishing, in better terms, the old patient-agent agreement, putting some distance between them, or if there is no other possibility, ending the relationship.

The therapist will encounter considerable resistance to change—both direct and indirect (Dickes, 1967). If these resistances can be overcome, the agent and his or her patients will be able to achieve a new, healthy agreement. Unfortunately, things do not always happen this way, and sometimes divorce or total rupture of the relationship occurs.

Achieving Autonomy

Once sadistic agents are able to give up their pathological attacks on and control over others, they will start to find healthy sources of security and pleasure and will be in a much better position to neutralize the subtle masochistic blackmail of the patient in their lives (Deutsch, 1968). They will be able to offer real security and pleasure to others as well. However, in order for the treatment to be truly successful, sadistic agents must be able to recognize situations that are similar to those childhood experiences which originally forced them into the pathological mode. At an early stage, they must learn to abort tendencies to engage in sadistic behavior or to retreat from socioeconomic anxiety. Only when they recognize these "triggering" situations and prevent regression can they be considered cured (Freud, 1910). For this reason, therapeutic supervision is necessary until the gains are stabilized and the client becomes truly autonomous.

──────────── **The Masochistic Agent** ────────────

Masochistic agents are usually tactful and overprotective people who like to take care of and spoil their sadistic dependents. They appear even more masochistic than the masochistic patient because they protect their torturers even though they don't need them for survival. They seem to have received a strong message from their parents that they are unlovable and hence must buy the company of others by overprotecting them.

Usually masochistic agents start treatment because they are no longer able to deal with their dependents. The latter are beyond control because they are becoming either more independent or more destructive. Sometimes they are threatening suicide or homicide. Masochistic agents are usually good clients—not as insightful or cooperative as masochistic patients, but much more psychologically minded than sadistic agents or patients.

The Therapist as Sadistic Patient

Because they feel unworthy, unlovable, and guilty, masochistic agents are usually addicted to selfish, abusive, manipulative, and omnipotent sadistic patients. By using the role of sadistic patient the therapist accepts the transference of the client's submission and monopolistic control and acts like a spoiled, demanding child. The therapist should not be outrightly abusive or blaming, however. The therapist must also appear needy and helpless with respect to socioeconomic matters and willing—even eager—to hand over these responsibilities to the client (Gill & Muslin, 1976).

Working through Sacrificed Submission

Once treatment has begun and a transference relationship has been established, the beginning stages of treatment can proceed as with the masochistic patient. The client's distorted and stereotyped view of interpersonal reality is uncovered and worked through. The origins of the client's masochism, both in the family and in the social matrix, are discussed. The client and therapist form a coalition to modify the other's sadism. Couple or family therapy is initiated to modify the client's masochism. Various active and passive forms of resistance are dealt with.

When treating a masochistic agent it is particularly important that the therapist assume the role of a "respected professional" who is entitled to exercise technical authority over the client's treatment. This is necessary because, unlike masochistic patients, who tend to idealize the therapist to an excessive degree, masochistic agents sometimes fear the therapist—viewing the therapist more as a blaming prosecutor. They have a tendency to devalue the prosecutor-therapist, however; they may view the therapist—at least covertly—as stupid, rigid, naive, and easily fooled. Therefore, the therapist's technical expertise must be asserted (Greenson, 1965).

In delineating these clients' masochism, the therapist must help them uncover their terrible fear of being abandoned, a fear which stems from their conviction that they are unlovable. It is this basic fear that makes them so vulnerable to the accusations and threats of their spoiled dependents.

Because masochistic agents have a compulsive need to take care of their spoiled dependents (to buy their affections, but also to control them), these clients will be highly resistant to seeing themselves as in need of treatment. Consequently, they will tend to listen politely and respectfully to the therapist's interventions but without really taking them to heart unless they can be used to help them take better care of their dependent others (Heimann, 1956). Thus the supervisory stage is crucial for these clients, as masochistic agents can be irritatingly obtuse in recognizing their dependents' sadism and their own role in the pathological relationship. Being aware of the masochistic agent's need for love and terror of abandonment will help the therapist understand their client's perverse loyalty to the sadistic patients in their lives. Through the systematic use of a rigorous therapeutic contract, the therapist can help masochistic agents to finally overcome their pervasive other-centered mirrorism.

Working through Socioeconomic Control

Once a client's masochistic approach to interpersonal authority has been somewhat modified, the therapist can start working on the client's infantilizing socioeconomic control of his or her spoiled dependents. The treatment approach at this stage is similar in many respects to that of the sadistic agent. The client's need for socioeconomic control and consistent choice of dependent partners is discussed, both in its present manifestation and in its original form in the familial and social matrix (Ticho, 1971). The transference is worked through, and the therapist's authority as a professional is reiterated. The various active and passive forms of resistance on the part of the client and his or her others is dealt with (Masterson, 1978).

Masochistic agents will try to exercise control over the therapist, but in the guise of "helping" their spoiled dependents. For example, they may withhold payment for the therapy because their dependents have once again gotten themselves into financial hot water and naturally turn to their caretakers to bail them out. Thus the client is temporarily "unable" to pay the therapist. This kind of situation, involving both socioeconomic control of the therapist and masochistic submissiveness to the unrealistic demands of the sadistic other, needs to be thoroughly analyzed (Heimann, 1950).

Masochistic agents eventually have to give up their control over their sadistic-patient others—thus forcing these others either to become more independent or to find a new caretaker. Resistance to change will be very strong indeed on the part of these others. They may make a serious suicide attempt or precipitate some other major crisis. Clients in this stage will need much therapeutic support in order to resist the hysterical manipulation of their others (Neri, 1979). In the following vignette we see how a masochistic agent works through the histrionics of his sadistic-patient son.

PAUL: My son had another bad temper tantrum this morning. And, again, I didn't know what to do with him. He kept saying that I was being selfish because I wouldn't give him money to buy marijuana. He told me that I really enjoyed torturing him, that I was a coward, old-fashioned. But I know that if I give him money he will buy marijuana or any other drug available. He'll stop studying and start destroying himself again, going out with his damn friends.

THERAPIST: Well? What did you finally do?

PAUL: Well, you know. (*Smiling, ashamed, like a very warm person who cannot resist another's suffering.*) I'm very soft-hearted. I'm a fool. I felt so guilty that I finally gave in. I gave him the money for his damn junk. I felt that in some way he was right, that I was being too strict, and, on top of that, that I was largely responsible for his difficulties in facing reality. I taught him to be passive and dependent. I felt that I didn't have the right to frustrate him again. Thinking things over, maybe I was wrong, but he is so convincing, you know?

THERAPIST: You're very convincing as well—in rationalizing and giving excuses for indulging yourself and following what we know is the easier alternative for you, but very destructive for you and your son. Instead of facing your guilty feelings and fighting your son's manipulative reproaches, you surrendered to them. It's easier to spoil than to educate.

PAUL: Oh! I'm sorry! I'm terribly sorry! I feel extremely guilty now. I feel as if I failed you. It's my fatal weakness again! Oh my God! You showed me this so many times before, and here I am doing the same again!

THERAPIST: I'm not "blaming" you—not like you said your son blamed you. I'm just trying to point out that you are addicted to your son's dependence, just as he is addicted to drugs when he has to face reality.

PAUL: I see your point.

THERAPIST: Please don't blame yourself again now, because this is not useful at all. Not for your son or for you. The point is that by overprotecting your son you are really responsible—not guilty— for keeping him a social cripple, so to speak.

PAUL: I know that. But it is so difficult for me not to feel pity for him. And at the same time I know that I am keeping him dependent on me. And in some strange way this makes me feel that as long as he needs me, he won't abandon me. You see, he seems to hate me so much.

THERAPIST: It's because you despise yourself that you are so frightened of not being loved by others.

Achieving Autonomy

In the final stages of treatment the masochistic agent must be able to recognize situations that trigger the old pathological fear of being unlovable and the need to spoil others by "buying" their affection. If the client is able to recognize and abort these reactions at an early stage with the help of the therapist, he or she will then be able to achieve true love, security, and pleasure in equal, interdependent relationships with others and to stabilize in this new autonomous position.

The Sadistic Patient

Briefly, a sadistic patient is an interpersonally blaming and/or devaluing or devalued abusive dominant type who tends to depend socioeconomically on sacrificed submissive masochistic agents. The sadistic patient could be blaming and devaluing, of the hypochondriac, histrionic, or antisocial-delinquent subtypes; or blaming but devalued, of the paranoid-depressive, dissociative-explosive, or schizophrenic-paranoid subtypes. The blaming and devaluing subtypes are mostly borderlined because their spoiling others tend to distort or disavow their perception of socioeconomic reality; but they can be, simultaneously, neuroticizing or psychoticizing because they distort and/or disavow the perception of interpersonal reality of their blamed and devalued compulsive depressive masochistic agent. The blaming but devalued subtypes are mostly neuroticized or psychoticized because their blamed but devaluing compulsive hypomanic masochistic agents tend to distort and/or disavow their perception of interpersonal reality.

Sadistic patients are usually demanding, charming, unpredictable, and spoiled. They can switch suddenly from seductive idealization of others to paranoid or hysterical denunciations. In a peculiar way, they feel entitled to ask for protection, tolerance, and infinite patience from others without giving anything in return except their periodically charming company.

The Therapist as Masochistic Agent

Usually sadistic patients begin therapy at the urging of their masochistic-agent partners because their destructive behavior is getting out of control. The more they try to overcome their devastating dependence on others, the more destructive they become. The therapist is therefore faced with a client who is a very volatile and dangerous mixture of blackmail and terror. The therapist's initial role is to serve as a crisis manager who must be able to neutralize and disarm explosive situations and make possible a more civilized type of interpersonal negotiation (Kanzer, 1975).

Because they need to confirm their feelings of omnipotence, sadistic patients are usually addicted to spoiling, overprotective, and controlling masochistic agents. By playing the role of masochistic agent, the therapist accepts the transference of the client's domination and dependence. In this role, the therapist must appear able and willing to take responsibility for the client's socioeconomic survival and for big decisions, without really doing so unless the client is going through an acute psychotic episode. The therapist must be warm, quiet, tolerant, and persuasive, but able both to cope with the client's threats and seduction and to cool off dangerously volatile situations (Klauber, 1968).

Working through Interpersonal Domination

Once treatment has begun and a transference relationship has been established, the beginning stages of therapy can proceed as with the sadistic agent. This will involve uncovering and correcting the clients' distorted and stereotyped view of interpersonal authority—their tendency to play the role of abusive master while seeing themselves as submissive servants—and tracing the various origins and facets of the clients' sadism in the family and social matrix and in present situations. The therapist can, at this point, start demanding less spoiled behavior of the client, who may temporarily resort to the role of masochist. The source of the client's sadism—anxiety stemming from a fear of interpersonal manipulation—will be worked through, and if the therapy is successful, these clients will begin to develop less sadistic, less histrionic relationships with those close to them (Jackson, 1956).

Working through Socioeconomic Dependence

Once a client's sadistic approach to interpersonal authority has been somewhat modified, the therapist can begin working on the client's infantile socioeconomic dependence on others. The treatment at this stage is similar in many respects to that of the masochistic patient. The client's refusal to assume socioeconomic responsibility and consistent refusal to confront this issue are slowly worked on in therapy. Resistance will be great, as sadistic patients fear utter abandonment if they are forced to be independent.

The following transaction shows how a sadistic patient tries to run away from the emotional impact of a socioeconomic blow by presenting himself as the helpless victim.

GEORGE: Yesterday I fought with my father again. He started bothering me on the phone very late at night, and I was extremely tired after a very boring meeting with my boss. I was so bored that I left the meeting before it ended.

THERAPIST: What was the meeting about?

GEORGE: Well, nothing really important—the same old thing. They're cutting the budget, and they decided to cut our salaries by one third. I wasn't interested. But when I came back home I called Mommy to say good night, and there was my father asking me about what happened in the meeting. I didn't want to talk about it, but he kept insisting. You know how bossy he is.

THERAPIST: In any case, if your salary has been reduced by one third. . .

GEORGE: (*Interrupting*) Yes, this was exactly what my father was telling me. He told me that I should have stayed in the meeting and fought against the cutback. But I didn't want to know anything more about it. He kept suggesting different ways of compensating for the economic loss, but I got very mad at him. He was treating me like a little boy. He had to explain everything to me, what was important and how to fight it.

THERAPIST: But actually if your salary is reduced you won't be able to travel to California. And maybe you won't be able to keep up your treatment schedule either.

GEORGE: (*Smiling*) There would be no problem about that, actually, because I got so upset last night that my father finally apologized to me and told me not to worry about it. He'll take care of the expenses of my trip and my treatment, if necessary. He felt

so guilty that he does not know how to deal with this thing
properly.

THERAPIST: It seems that you don't know how to deal with your
financial problems either. Or better, when you have to deal with
urgent economic matters, you run away from them and have a
fight with somebody else instead, so that he or she will feel guilty
and take care of your financial needs.

GEORGE: Actually, that's quite true. I was feeling guilty because I
didn't stay in the meeting and fight like everyone else did. But it is
still impossible for me to face hard economic facts and difficult
negotiations. They make me extremely anxious. I feel impotent,
like a total failure, stupid and small.

As soon as sadistic patients realize that their masochistic
caretakers are growing tired of their dependence, these clients
react impulsively and violently. They threaten to kill themselves—and others—if the status quo is not immediately restored.
This is usually a very critical and dangerous stage of the treatment,
because the timing must be right and the therapist and the client's
caretaker must have the courage and the flexibility to resist the
client's manipulative threats and pleas (Langs, 1979c). Suicide is a
real possibility, so the client, who is like an unexploded bomb,
must be very gradually and progressively neutralized in such a way
that the final decisive therapeutic confrontation does not turn into
a tragedy. This type of client provokes the highest rate of burn-out
in therapists (Freudenserger, 1980).

At this stage the therapist should analyze the vicious circle
that locks the client and his or her partner into an impossible bind.
Specific actions to break up this explosive sadomasochistic alliance
should be made. If this proceeds correctly, the client's behavior
will change from sweet, cute, helpless, and childishly overdemanding to bitter, nasty, blaming, and bossy. If the therapist is
successful, the sadistic patient will transfer his or her dependence
from the masochistic agent to the therapist.

While analyzing the changing transference, therapists should
show the sadistic patient that they are not going to be blackmailed

hostages and that neither charm nor threats will push them into pathogenic overprotection. When therapists successfully resist their client's pressures, they are themselves able to change. Through the systematic use of a rigorous therapeutic contract and counterpressures the therapist can help sadistic patients in finally overcoming their pervasive self-centered narcissism.

Achieving Autonomy

Sadistic patients, like other types of clients, will have to learn to recognize "triggering" situations at an early stage so they can regain control over their own anxiety and act in a way that ensures positive, healthy pleasure and support from others. In this phase therapeutic supervision is valuable. They will also have to learn life skills to enable them to become truly independent and self-reliant (Langs & Searles, 1980). Once this is learned they have achieved autonomy.

————— The Masochistic Insufficient —————

The Therapist as Sadistic Insufficient

Because they are so desperate to please others—at the same time that they keep running away from them—masochistic insufficients are usually addicted to intrusive, mean, aggressive, irritating, tenacious, sadistic insufficients. By playing the role of sadistic insufficient, the therapist accepts the transference of the client's submission and restriction. However, while it is important that the therapist be somewhat abrasive, at times painfully "honest," and even somewhat controlling, he or she must avoid blaming or denigrating the client. The therapist must also appear unwilling or unable to offer socioeconomic support to the client unless the client is going through an acute anxiety attack (Winnicott, 1956).

Working through Interpersonal Submissiveness

Once treatment has begun and a transference relationship has been established, the therapist can begin to point out the client's tendency to act out a particular sadomasochistic sequence over and over again—the same sequence that we have observed in both the masochistic patient and the masochistic agent. As with these other clients, the therapist must work to correct the client's faulty, inverted self-perception as an abusive—and, in this case, intrusive—master, with others acting as submissive, avoidant servants.

Treatment then proceeds as with other types of masochistic clients. The client's ingrained masochism and inferiority complex are discussed, together with its origins in the social and family matrix, its current manifestations in the client's current environment and in the transference, and so forth (Klein, 1952). The therapist forms a coalition with the client to fight against the other's sadistic behavior, and possibly a coalition with others in the form of family or couple behavior to fight the client's masochism.

It is especially important that the therapist show these clients how they initially try to be excessively pleasing to others (including the therapist) and when this submissiveness becomes intolerable, experience extreme claustrophobia and run away. Hysteric masochistic insufficients usually manage to arouse jealousy in their paranoid sadistic-insufficient partners. The cycle begins when the masochistic insufficient starts hiding his or her true thoughts and feelings, fearing the anger of the partner. Somehow the hysteric gives the paranoid subtle indications that he or she is actually hiding something. The paranoid then becomes extremely suspicious and intrusive, thus arousing anxiety in the hysteric—who engages in further distancing behavior, thus perpetuating the cycle. Eventually the hysteric feels overwhelmed and runs away. But in time the masochistic insufficient "forgets" the partner's irritating intrusiveness and gets closer again.

Working through Socioeconomic Restriction

Once the client's masochistic and avoidant approach to interpersonal authority has been somewhat modified, the therapist can start working on the client's irrational socioeconomic restrictions. The therapist does so by describing in general and in particular all the ways that the client compulsively avoids both depending on and supporting his or her significant others. The therapist will have to point out all the manifestations of this undercommitment, the ways in which the client prevents any real commitment to the therapy on the part of both therapist and client, the ways that the client punishes those who attempt to be dependent, and so forth. These clients portray themselves as eternal adolescents, switching from one job to another, doing just enough to get by but not enough to get "saddled" with responsibility.

It is very important that these clients come to understand how their apparently light and unconcerned attitude toward work and money tends to make those around them adopt the role of very conservative "advisers," who constantly make gloomy predictions about the future.

Masochistic insufficients are quite reluctant to fully commit themselves to treatment. For example, when establishing the therapeutic contract, they ask for the minimum number of sessions. They use different rationalizations like lack of time, financial squeeze, etc. If the therapist naively agrees to this avoidant contract, he or she will be therapeutically restricted, and the treatment will be ineffective and interminable (Langs, 1975a). But every time the therapist tries to confront such clients with their adolescent, irrationally undercommitted socioeconomic behavior, they repeatedly try to change the focus of attention. The therapist must point out this defensive displacement and help their clients work it through (Rosenfeld, 1978).

Once these clients are able to acknowledge their socioeconomic restrictiveness—which results from a fear of being forced to assume more responsibility than they can handle and a simultaneous fear of being overly controlled by others—the therapist can begin to work with them on overcoming their irrational restrictiveness. The socioeconomic undercommitment is analyzed in all its manifestations—in the client's family of origin, current family and work situation, etc. At times the therapist may adopt a supervisory role vis-a-vis the client's relations with his or her socioeconomic "advisers." At other times, couple or family therapy may be useful in helping insufficient dyads to work through their excessive avoidant-intrusive behavior.

Establishing a permanent protective distance from some of the client's most "toxic" and irritatingly intrusive others is usually the most feasible therapeutic alternative for the masochistic insufficient. This is especially true when treating the closest relatives. For example, it is not functional to cut off relations with parents, but there should be enough protective distance to prevent a major rupture. If resistance to change is too great—if the shift to greater commitment is too threatening—the therapy will continue without progress indefinitely. If the therapist is able to overcome the client's resistance—and enable the client to overcome the resistance of others in his or her life—there will be dramatic changes for the better in the client's life (Stone, 1973).

The following transaction shows how the masochistic insufficient's phobic anxieties are treated:

IRENE: I'm thinking of quitting my job. It makes me so anxious. It is really impossible for me to tolerate the anxiety any longer. I don't know why I experience such uneasiness with my boss. I feel as if he's watching me all the time. Everything I do seems to be wrong. He is constantly making remarks about my work. He's not exactly unfriendly, but I feel completely trapped, unable to do things in my own way. However, they are actually satisfied with me. As a matter of fact, they want to raise my salary—provided I do some overtime and take on more responsibility. But I don't think it's worth it. It will take away my free time. I won't be able to go jogging, go to the hairdresser. And on top of that, I can't stand my boss! He's not a bad man, but he butts in all the time.
THERAPIST: But you told me that you badly need to improve your position at the office—not only because of the money. . .
IRENE: (Interrupting) Please, Doctor, don't ask me to stay there any longer. I don't want to lose my freedom.
THERAPIST: I'm not taking away your freedom. I'm not your boss. I'm just reminding you of your own needs.
IRENE: (Very anxious) Oh yes! That's true! But, I don't know—it's just too much for me. I feel trapped, overwhelmed. I don't want to be a prisoner of my work. I want to have my own life. You know. I can hardly breath just thinking about it. Can you imagine?
THERAPIST: Yes, I can imagine your anxiety. But let me remind you that you are doing something very similar to what you have done in your two previous jobs. As soon as they accepted you and

gave you more responsibility you felt trapped, imprisoned. And instead of facing your anxiety—analyzing and overcoming it—you preferred to run away.

IRENE: *(Still very anxious)* Yes, yes, I knew you would say all this. But you can't imagine how my boss is constantly at me. You're behaving like my mother.

THERAPIST: And you are behaving like your father. Actually you're the one who is getting at me right now. You are interrupting me all the time, jumping to conclusions—as you have always done when talking with your mother, whom you repeatedly describe as an intrusive woman. She was constantly complaining because your father always quit his jobs. Listen carefully and calmly. It seems quite possible that if you run away again from your boss-mother, you will deeply regret it afterward. You always get very depressed after you escape and miss good opportunities.

I realize that you are overwhelmed by anxiety and claustrophobia, but I feel if you escape now, both your treatment and your professional future will be going backward again.

IRENE: So do you think that I should wait and see—give them a chance? Is this what you want? OK, you win. I'll try.

THERAPIST: It's not what I want—or what you must do. I'm not your mother pushing your father. It's just convenient for your treatment that, as far as you can, you stop running away from adult commitments and responsibilities because you become depressed when you have to start all over again.

Achieving Autonomy

Once masochistic insufficients stop running away from responsibilities and start looking for and obtaining real security and pleasure, they will be able to be interdependent in a mature way. They will break their unhealthy undercommitted bonds with sadistic restrictors.

The treatment should train masochistic insufficients to detect, as soon as possible, those situations and people that trigger their anxiety (Watzlawick, 1965). In this way they can prevent themselves from submitting to others and sacrificing themselves in a masochistic way. They can also prevent themselves from slipping into socioeconomic restrictions when confronted with critical socioeconomic decisions and responsibilities. This usually requires therapeutic supervision. Finally, they must develop new interpersonal and socioeconomic skills so that they will be able to act on their desire for change.

The Sadistic Insufficient

The Therapist as Masochistic Insufficient

Because they are such tactless, compulsively irritating people, sadistic insufficients are usually addicted to avoidant, soft, nice, ambiguous masochistic insufficients. By playing the role of masochistic insufficient, the therapist accepts transference of the client's intrusive domination and restriction. However, although the therapist should be diplomatic, tactful, and pleasant, he or she should not act in a blamed or devalued manner, or devalue the client.

The therapist must appear unwilling and unable either to depend on or to support the client, unless the client is going through an acute paranoid episode (Macalpine, 1950).

Working through Interpersonal Domination

Once treatment has begun and a transference relationship has been established, the therapist can begin to point out the client's tendency to act out a particular sadomasochistic sequence over and over again—the same sequence that we have observed in both the sadistic agent and the sadistic patient. As with these other clients, the therapist must work to correct the client's faulty, inverted self-perception as a submissive—and in this case, avoidant—servant, with others acting as abusive, intrusive masters.

Treatment then proceeds as with other sadistic clients. The client's ingrained sadism and sense of superiority are discussed as they originated in the family and social matrix and as they appear in current relationships, in the transference, and so forth. The therapist forms an alliance with the client against the other's masochism, and with others (in family or couple therapy) against the client's sadism (Racker, 1968).

It is especially important that the therapist show these clients how they try to be excessively "straightforward" with others and how their intrusive and tactless behavior becomes more and more intolerable until they are abandoned by others who are close to them. They do not run away because the client is too "sincere" but because he or she is overly aggressive and outspoken (Rangell, 1968).

Paranoid sadistic insufficients compulsively and blindly establish a vicious circle of aggression, jealousy, and abandonment with their hysteric masochistic-insufficient partners. They become relentless in their blaming and suspiciousness, until the partner becomes completely upset. But instead of realizing that they are causing the other's rejection, they think the other is unfaithful, unreliable, and consequently infatuated with someone else. This is often the case because of the type of partner the client chooses. When things get too bad, the partner will back off entirely for a while, and the sadistic insufficient will cease harassing the partner for a while. Then the cycle begins again.

As with all clients working through interpersonal authority, when the therapist first steps out of the pathological complementary role, the client steps into it. This inversion of the interpersonal positions can be observed in the following transaction involving a paranoid sadistic insufficient:

MATT: Seems to me that Mr. Peters *(a very important and powerful politician)* will never be a great man. He is excessively concerned about small details at the very moment that he should be thinking about the most important political matters. Did you read that he delayed his trip to the Middle East to continue the negotiations about the South Lebanon border crisis just because the plane that the White House gave him wasn't luxurious enough? He waited six hours for another! He is so worried about his personal status that he forgets that he is representing one of the countries involved in an international dispute. And this is precisely what undermines his personal and political status. My God! When will he realize that and stop fighting about petty issues and making everybody mad!

THERAPIST: In any case Mr. Peters is already a very important and powerful person. It seems to me that you are also concerned about yourself. Do you remember the tremendous to-do you had with me last week because I was five minutes late?

MATT: *(Sarcastically)* Don't take it personally, Doctor. I was just making a point. I didn't want to offend you. Everybody can make mistakes—even you.

THERAPIST: *(Insisting)* I'm not taking it personally. You insist that I'm offended—that I'm so presumptuous that I am not able to admit my mistakes. That's just what you said about Mr. Peters. But what about you? Instead of listening to my interpretations, you're fighting with me about who made what mistakes. And this is not the point.

MATT: Oh yes! But you're the one who was late. And now you're trying to place the blame on me.

THERAPIST: That's not correct. I'm not placing blame on you or on me. The point is that you are not able to listen to my remarks about how you undermine your own economic or social status because your concern about blame and petty issues keep you focused on small details instead of analyzing and thinking about more important and urgent matters.

MATT: *(Very softly and kindly)* My apologies, Doctor. I didn't realize that. I've been very nasty with you.

THERAPIST: Thank you very much. But I still don't think you get the point. I'm not only saying that you should respect me, but that you should stop trying to fix blame. The crucial issue here is why and how your quarrelsome behavior interferes with or jeopardizes your personal and social achievements and well-being.

Working through Socioeconomic Restriction

Treating the client's insufficiency follows essentially the same pattern as with the masochistic insufficient. Both are afraid of having others depend on them, of taking too much away from them, of not having enough. Both feel the need to conserve scarce resources. But while the masochistic insufficient sometimes appears to be a flighty, skittish adolescent, the sadistic insufficient seems like a ponderously gloomy, extremely conservative old person. These two types of insufficients feed on each other, the intrusiveness of the sadist making the masochist more skittish and the apparent flightiness of the masochist rendering the sadist even more gloomy and ponderous. This is a sort of grasshopper-and-ant dyad.

Achieving Autonomy

The therapist will have to use similar tactics in helping the sadistic clients overcome their insufficiency and resistance to change. And, as with other clients, treatment must make them able to identify situations and relationships that "trigger" their old modes of reactions so they can avoid these traps and maintain equal, interdependent relationships with others. There is therefore a period of supervision until the newly learned action plans and skills become stable and autonomy is achieved.

9

The Typology in
Three of Freud's
———————— Cases ————————

In this chapter and the next, we will sum up both the theory and the treatment strategy developed in this volume. Both can be synthesized in a cross-sectional and sequential strategic formulation, which can be applied to the individual client to arrive at a diagnosis and treatment plan. This technical instrument could be defined as a synthetic but comprehensive phenomenologic description, dynamic explanation, and strategic prediction for planning treatment.

Once this new systematization of the clinical data, which stresses the critical variables of production and distribution of power and pleasure, is fully analyzed, we will apply the format to three of Freud's best-known clinical histories: "Dora," the "Rat Man," and the "Wolf Man." Freud's amazing capacity for clinical description immediately shows the reader how some subjects not only drove their complementary others into obvious mental illness but also tried to involve Freud in their pathogenic manipulations. For example, Freud wrote about the spoiled Dora, who was projectively sent into treatment by her demagogic father, who had previously left his own treatment with Freud; the charming Wolf

Man, who tried to manipulate Freud and others into overprotecting him as if he were a little prince; and the extremely intrusive and anxiety-provoking father of Little Hans, who actively and projectively transformed his son into an avoidant phobic with the "help" of Freud.

Strategic Formulation

As we have seen, mental illness is the result of a failure in the production and distribution of interpersonal and socioeconomic power and pleasure that the subject experiences because of a mutilation of his or her cognitive structure. This failure seems to be both cause and effect of a pathogenic and pathologic organization of the subject's perception, thoughts, feeling, actions, and environment.

By using the multiaxial diagnostic decision sheet (MADDS) we have already systematized the diagnosis of the client's strategic, structural, and environmental organization according to nine strategic variables. Now we will use some biographical data to determine the specific predisposing, precipitating, and perpetuating factors and to forecast and plan the treatment and prevention of the client's mental illness.

The strategic formulation covers the following dimensions: identifying data, strategic diagnosis, structural diagnosis, diagnosis of the environment, operational diagnosis, and treatment plan.

Identifying Data

The client's *objective status* (sex, age, education, occupation, income, etc.) and *presenting complaint,* as well as the predisposing, precipitating, and perpetuating (biological, psychological, and social) factors of the *present illness* are all identified, thus allowing the therapist to make a tentative diagnosis.

Strategic Diagnosis

This stage, based on the client's situation with respect to the seven strategic axes analyzed by the MADDS, involves diagnosis of (1) socioeconomic control (patient, agent, or insufficient), (2) interpersonal authority (sadist or masochist), (3) defensive mis-qualification (blame and/or devaluation), (4) affect states (elated, depressed, angry guilty, distrustful, or anxious), (5) reality testing (neurotic, psychotic, or borderline), (6) centeredness (narcissistic or mirroristic), (7) attitude toward organizations (joiner-bu-reaucrat or lonely maverick), (8) clinical phenomenology (22 subtypes and DSM-III).

Structural Diagnosis

This stage, based on the client's unique individual speech and action structure (and that of the significant others), involves diagnosis of the client's *defensive acting off* (defensive avoidance of problems involving socioeconomic dependence, monopoly, or restriction by focusing on interpersonal domination or submission, the perception of which is inverted and stereotyped), the *client's counteracting off* (complementary defensive structure which the client tends unconsciously to induce in significant others), the *client's therapeutic acting on* (the therapist must deduce what should be done by analyzing the individual manner in which the client displaces, inverts, and stereotypes his or her perception, speech, and actions, and from this, design the specific treatment needed to help the client work through his or her resistance), and the *therapeutic counteracting on* (which should be executed by the signifi-cant others to correct the client's acting off).

Environmental Diagnosis

The therapist should make a brief formulation of (1) the client's *most significant others* (control, authority, misqualification, affect state, reality testing, centeredness, attitude towards organi-zations, phenomenology, acting off and counteracting off; (2) *microenvironmental* (family, for example) *myth,* or pathologic paradigm, and defensive action plan; and (3) *macroenvironmental* (work place and community, for example) myth, or pathologic paradigm, and action plan. The analysis of the environmental power organization involves also the diagnosis of its power axes, coalitions, hierarchical structure, and the situation of the client with respect to them. The client is considered an unconscious "spokesperson" of the underlying dynamics of the organizations in which he or she participates.

Operational Diagnosis

In order to be able to predict the client's reaction to different therapeutic procedures and to design a treatment plan, the therapist should test the receptivity of the client and his or her environment to *therapeutic, behavioral and environmental information, directions, supervisions, reactions, counterpressures, contract, environmental therapy* and *psychoactive drugs.*

Treatment Plan

This stage involves the design of the client's treatment: (1) *strategic goals* (overcoming excessive socioeconomic dependence, control, or restriction and excessive interpersonal domination or submission), (2) *tactical stages* (playing the role of the client's interpersonal and socioeconomic complement; working through and overcoming the client's excessive interpersonal domination or submission; working through and overcoming the client's excessive socioeconomic dependence, control, or restriction; achieving interpersonal and socioeconomic autonomy), and (3) *technical procedures* to be specifically used in each stage of the treatment to achieve the goals determined for the client.

We believe that the following strategic formulation can be applied to all types of clients. It is especially helpful in enabling mental health professionals to maintain control over the therapy because it shows them how to avoid being unwittingly manipulated by the countertransference. In fact, using our typology and strategic formulation, therapists are able to conduct their clients' very illness so that it works in the service of a successful treatment.

STRATEGIC FORMULATION

- IDENTIFYING DATA
  Objective status
  Presenting complaint
  Present illness
- STRATEGIC DIAGNOSIS
  Socioeconomic control
  Interpersonal authority
  Defensive misqualification
  Affect state
  Reality testing
  Centeredness
  Attitude toward organizations
- STRUCTURAL DIAGNOSIS
  Defensive acting off
  Counteracting off
  Therapeutic acting on
  Therapeutic counteracting on
- DIAGNOSIS OF THE ENVIRONMENT
  Significant other
  Microenvironment
  Macroenvironment
- OPERATIONAL DIAGNOSIS
  Reaction to therapeutic interventions
- TREATMENT PLAN
  Strategic goals
  Therapeutic tactics
  Treatment procedures

———————— Strategic Formulation of Dora ————————

Dora was treated by Freud and described in "Fragment of an analysis of a case of hysteria" (1905). She was reanalyzed by Felix Deutsch.

Identifying Data

Objective status. Dora is the 18-year-old daughter of an upper-middle-class industrialist. She is totally economically dependent and is neither working nor studying formally.

Presenting complaint. Dora was brought to Freud by her father after an episode of loss of consciousness and memory. She had written a suicide note, stating that she could no longer endure life. Other complaints included depressed spirits, dissatisfaction with herself and others, an uncooperative attitude toward her mother, and abuse directed toward her father.

Present illness. Dora suffered a "neurotic disorder" (dyspnea) at age 8. At age 12 she had migraines and aphonia. At age 16 she was first seen by Freud at her father's request because of a cough and aphonia. She had been resistant to all attempts at treatment and had grown accustomed to "laugh at the efforts of doctors" and in the end to renounce their help entirely.

Health concerns were common in Dora's family. An aunt, Dora's role model, had been severely neurotic; an uncle was a hypochondriac. Freud considered that the family history demonstrated a predisposition to neurotic illness.

Dora's relationship with Herr and Frau K was significant; they were family friends and Frau K was romantically involved with Dora's father. Herr K courted Dora for two years, sending flowers daily, etc. Later he had openly declared his love for her and desire to divorce his wife and marry Dora. When he proposed, Dora slapped him and fled. She complained at once to her father, demanding that he break off all relations with the K family. "She pressured in all possible ways, begging, pressing, and accusing" (p. 26). Dora sought to create circumstances which would confirm her paranoid hypothesis that she was the sexual victim of others. Her father's insincere, manipulative, and infantilizing relationship with her tends to perpetuate her problem.

The hysterical structure of the Viennese society and its tendency to relegate women to concerns with the trivial also reinforced and perpetuated her pathology.

Strategic Diagnosis

Socioeconomic control.   Dora's socioeconomic relations are controlled by her father. She is dependent, does not study, and does not help at home. Her time is occupied by intrigue, conferences for ladies, sexual reading material, etc. Dora is a *patient.*

Interpersonal authority.   Dora claims to be the victim of Herr K, her father, the former governess, her mother, and Frau K. She makes strong attempts to manipulate, using suicidal notes and illness to impose her will. Dora is a *sadist.*

Defensive misqualifications.   Dora chiefly blames others. Freud says "Before I could answer she put the blame on her father" (p. 75). She places total responsibility and blame on Herr K. She sees others as bad, manipulative, and egotistical. Dora is a *blamer.*

Others devalue Dora. For example, Herr K disregards her accusations and qualifies her as a silly and disturbed adolescent excessively interested in sex. Dora is *devalued.*

Affect state.   Dora feels morally superior to her father, the K family, and the governess. Although she apparently complained of depressed spirits and wrote a suicide note, her chief emotion was anger. The depression seems to have been a response to her inability to get her own way and a momentary confrontation with her inferior competence. The inferior competence and moral superiority give a sense of distrust. Dora is principally *angry* and *distrustful.*

Reality testing.   Dora's interpersonal reality perception is severely attacked by her father, who denies her perceptions of his relationship with Frau K as well as the abnormality of permitting Herr K such a prolonged and potentially intimate relationship with his young daughter. He also behaves as if "Dora's tale of the man's immoral sugggestions is a phantasy that has forced its way into her mind" (p. 18).

Dora's socioeconomic relations are characterized by a rather spoiled expectation that she be free of social responsibility; that is, there is a naturalization of the patient paradigm, but within this context socioeconomic reality testing is intact.

Dora is *neuroticized* (with a potential to be *psychoticized* by her father). Her own behavior is *neuroticizing;* for example, her perception of her own sexually seductive behavior is denied.

Centeredness.   Dora's point of reference is herself. An example would be that in her visit to the K family at the death of one of their children, she used this painful moment to take her revenge on them, blaming and accusing them both in regard to the former "affairs." She is therefore contaminating, making others answer her accusations and deal with her pathology. Dora is a *contaminating narcissist.*

Attitude toward organizations.   Dora is not a joiner and is socially isolated. She is unable to understand even the cooperative nature of household work. Dora is a *lonely maverick.*

Clinical phenomenology.   Dora is destructive, as is evidenced by her continual attacks on the K family and on her governess. She is dominant, using blame and manipulation to impose herself. At the same time she is socioeconomically dependent. Dora is a *sadistic patient.*

Within this group, Dora is irritable and blaming and has a history of somatic and paranoid preoccupations. She is also capable of provocation and seductive behavior. This histrionic style was very characteristic of Victorian times, whereas the underlying paranoid behavior seems to have been more characteristic of Dora. Dora belongs chiefly to the *paranoid depressive* subtype of sadistic patient.

Structural Diagnosis

Defensive acting off.   Dora talks monothematically about how she is victimized: sexually manipulated, cheated, and used by insincere seductors. She claims to be a frustrated victim of others, while she seduces, frustrates, and victimizes others, claiming all right to moral pleasure. She represses and projects her own sadistic seduction and denies and introjects the other's acceptance of her seductive role. She therefore acts rather than confronting her interpersonal problem of excessive blaming and moral entitlement. She naturalizes her socioeconomic problem of excessive dependence and replaces it in perception and thought by sadomasochistic personalization.

When Dora was seen by Deutsch (1957) twenty years later she presented the same defensive acting-off behavior and the same monotheme. This time, however, her paranoid attacks were in relation to her son.

Counteracting off. Herr K accepts that he is the sexually manipulative, insincere seducer who cheats and uses Dora and victimizes and frustrates her, while he is, in fact, frustrated and victimized, losing all moral pleasure. He represses and projects his masochistic seduced position and denies and introjects the position of sadistic seducer.

He therefore counteracts the interpersonal problem of exessive blaming and moral entitlement rather than confronting current problems. He naturalizes and accepts his own role of excessive socioeconomic control, fomenting continued excessive dependency in Dora, while replacing perception and thought about the socioeconomic with the acting off of her sadomasochistic personalization.

Therapeutic acting on. Dora first recognizes her own insincere manipulative seductive behavior. She controls the sexual seduction and blaming behavior and looks to develop new realistically trusting and nonmanipulative respectful relationships with others. She discusses her naturalized excessive spoiled dependency on her family and others. She instruments herself, develops, and puts into action plans to overcome this dependency.

Counteracting on. Herr K recognizes that he himself has been seduced and then blamed by an insincere and manipulative Dora. He controls his automatic reaction of acceptance that he is an insincere seducer and enters into a sincere nonblaming relationship with her.

He discusses openly and objectively her naturalized excessive socioeconomic dependence. He refuses to accept the controlling role and encourages her in her development of greater autonomy.

Diagnosis of the Environment

Significant other.   Herr K will be taken as Dora's choice of a complementary partner. Her father was similar to Dora and only partially complementary.

Herr K has comparative socioeconomic control in relation to Dora, his wife, his children, etc. Herr K is an *agent*.

He is said by Dora to be a dominating victimizer, but he tends to be the submissive victim. For example, he allows Dora her discharge of blame, his wife is unfaithful, Dora slaps him and denounces him, etc. Herr K is a *masochist*.

He is *blamed* by Dora and at the same time is also somewhat ironic and *devaluing* when Dora denounces him. He is morally attacked, and his affect is chiefly *depression*.

His interpersonal reality testing is poor, but his socioeconomic reality testing is preserved. Herr K is *neuroticized*. At the same time he accepts Dora's distortions of interpersonal reality and mildly attacks her socioeconomic reality testing. Herr K is a *neuroticizer* to Dora.

He centers his attention on Dora and answers her accusations rather than being the one to define the situation. Herr K is *contaminated and mirroristic*.

Information is not available in regard to his organizational relations. He was likely a *bureaucratic joiner*.

In his relationship with Dora he was chiefly mirroristic, protective, and somewhat controlling although submissive. Herr K is a *masochistic agent*. Within this group he is ironic and devaluing when exposed by Dora and is probably of the *compulsive-hypomanic subtype*.

His natural acting-off position approximately coincides with the complementary position to Dora's defensive acting off.

Microenvironment.   Dora's natural position of alliance was with her father, while her mother and brother were in alliance in the complementary power pole. The men—father and brother—

were allowed greater socioeconomic control, whereas the women—mother and daughter—were expected to be dependent. The father and Dora were the dominant personalities.

Dora and her father were sexual seducers who blamed others. Their family acting off was to insincerely seduce others while denying it and blaming these others. This was done with the K family, the governess, the English teacher, etc.

Macroenvironment. Vienna in the late 1800s was a restricting, inhibiting society where sexual freedom and socioeconomic autonomy were especially censored in women. Preoccupation with the trivial and the interpersonal was very much fostered.

Operational Diagnosis

Reaction to therapeutic interventions. Because she accepts her father's pressures to come into treatment, even if she mistrusts his explanations about her need for treatment, it can be said that, initially at least, she is openly resistant to intrapsychic, behavioral, and environmental therapeutic information and to therapeutic directions and supervisions. By the same token she seems to be more receptive to therapeutic reactions, counterpressures, contracts, and environmental therapy.

However, Freud is able to overcome some of her initial resistances to therapeutic information. When this happens, Dora's father reacts negatively; he feels "betrayed" by Freud and cuts off his support of the treatment.

Treatment Plan

Strategic goals. It is critical for Dora's treatment that she work through and overcome her excessive socioeconomic dependence, and its defense of displacement by paranoid personalization, as well as her excessive interpersonal abusive blaming domination, and its defense of inversion and narrowing.

Therapeutic tactics. The first tactical stage of Dora's treatment would be for the therapist to play the complementary narcissistic role: to step into the position of a compulsive-depressive masochistic agent.

The second tactical stage of Dora's treatment would be the working through and overcoming of her interpersonal abusive, intrusive, blaming domination as well as its defense by inversion and narrowing of perception and speech about it. Actually, Freud was initiating this second stage when the treatment was interrupted.

The third tactical stage of Dora's treatment—not even reached during Dora's eleven weeks of treatment—would be the working through and overcoming of her excessive socioeconomic dependence (or restriction) on others and its defense by displacement into protective paranoid interpersonal blaming. It is precisely Dora's infantile dependence which allows her father to manipulatively interrupt her treatment when Freud does not follow the father's psychopathic guidelines. Freud himself makes some connections between this premature interruption and both money and jealousy.

The fourth tactical stage of Dora's treatment would be supervision with respect to the prevention of possible regressions to histrionic dependent seduction and paranoid, blaming, sadistic-patient pattern each time her environment tempts her. The fifth tactical stage would be her self-conduction in a new autonomous relationship.

Technical procedures.   Because of Dora's dependence on her father it seems critical to directly work with Dora's microenvironment, that is, to build a therapeutic consensus through family therapy or, at least, through renewed treatment of Dora's father.

Once the basic misunderstanding that Freud could be acting as an ally or puppet of Dora's father is clarified, therapeutic information and supervisions about how to behave with respect to her environment could be most useful. In turn, this environmental information could be reinforced by therapeutic reactions, counterpressures, and the use of contracts.

Once Dora's suspiciousness about a possible plot against her interpersonal and socioeconomic perception is aleviated, therapeutic information about Dora's perceptive, cognitive, affective, and behavioral organization, as well as therapeutic directions, could be more fruitfully used.

Strategic Formulation of the
"Rat Man"

This case was treated by Freud and described in "A Case of Obsessional Neurosis" (Freud, 1909).

Identifying Data

Objective status. Paul is a 30-year-old unmarried university graduate in law. He is related to a rich industrial family through his mother. His father was of a lower class origin but obtained a good position as a result of the marriage.

Presenting complaint. Paul consulted Freud with the complaint of "obsessions" since childhood, more acute in the last four years, and intensified by his recent military service.

> The chief features of his disorder were fears that something might happen to two people of whom he was very fond—his father and a lady whom he admired. Besides this he was aware of compulsive impulses—such as an impulse, for instance, to cut his throat with a razor; and further he produced prohibitions, sometimes in connection with quite unimportant things (p. 192).

Present illness. Paul dates the onset of his problem to his early infancy when he recalls incidents of a sexual nature with two governesses, Fraulein Peter and Fraulein Lina. He was convinced of his own "badness" and the "wrongness" of what he was doing. Although the governesses were provocative, he felt himself to be the instigator of the sexual play and felt guilt and humiliation, guilt for his "badness" and humiliation because they found him inept and quite inferior to his brother.

Paul perceived himself as very aggressive and relates an incident of jealous rage at his brother. Although his fantasies were very aggressive, his actual behavior tended to be submissive and accepting of the aggression of others.

He thus had "wasted years in fighting against these ideas and in this way had lost much ground in the course of his life" (p. 183). For this reason he graduated in law at the age of 30 and was not sufficiently established to consider marriage to his girlfriend of the last eight years. His fantasies about how to obtain economic independence included the death of his father or marriage to a rich lady rather than a successful career.

In the service he had a severe exacerbation of his symptoms, and his time and attention became totally occupied with obsessive thoughts.

Paul's physical and social inferiority to his more developed, more handsome, and more favored brother predisposed him to jealousy, envy, and aggressive impulses. His exposure to servants, themselves frustrated in their general development and more able to teach sexual preoccupations than socioeconomic skills, was an important developmental factor. The interpersonal and the sexual were all that was emphasized and valued as important by them. His father, a man of interpersonal rather than socioeconomic skills, solved his socioeconomic problems by using a pleasant interpersonal style (marriage to the mother, a friend to pay his army debts, etc.).

Precipitating factors in his illness seem to have included the death of his father, which increased the real possibility of being more economically dependent because the mother, with her access to connections and money, took a more active, protective role. Also, his guilt increased, since his fantasies had included death wishes and aggressions toward his father.

His military service also exposed him to sadistically aggressive behavior—as with the Captain of the Rat Incident (p. 171), and further confused him in regard to the frightening violence which he felt himself capable of.

His conflict was made more acute by the existence of a candidate for marriage who would assure his future (a rich cousin), and at the same time confirm that he was exactly like his father, a dependent person marrying for money.

Perpetuating factors in the problem included the use of trivialization or personalization. He failed to solve his socioeconomic problems and instrument himself adequately because he did not address these problems, but rather replaced them with sadomasochistic preoccupations. His love relationship with "his lady" kept him in a situation which emphasized his lack of independence and which was a frequent source of feelings of humiliation with her. Also, he was trapped in the sadomasochistic and did not have to solve the problems of adult commitment and responsibility.

Real socioeconomic advance was hindered by his father's excessive expectations, although his father served as neither a disciplinarian nor a role model. The expectation was for some kind of outstanding greatness "a great man or a great criminal" (p. 185).

Strategic Diagnosis

Socioeconomic control. Paul is restricted in his relations to socioeconomic reality. He left his studies and then half-heartedly returned to them for many years, finally achieving an adequate preparation. He does not have the economic resources for marriage, nor does he accept the "patient" position of a marriage to a rich woman. He is in a love relationship of undercommitment, in which both parties avoid marriage. Paul is an *insufficient*.

Interpersonal authority. Paul sees himself as an aggressive victimizer of his girlfriend, his brother, his father, etc. For example, he considers himself the aggressor who victimized the governesses (p. 161), while in fact he was the victim of their aggressive sexual abuse. Paul is a *masochist*.

Defensive misqualifications. Paul is devalued by his lady friend and by the governesses. With his lady his devaluation is so dramatic that the father warns him that he is making a public fool of himself. Paul also blames himself, giving moral entitlement to the other. Paul is chiefly *devalued*.

Affect state. Paul feels incompetent in relation to others' expectations of him. He also feels somewhat inferior morally, although this is not the issue given most importance in his environment. Paul is principally *depressed and anxious;* secondarily he is *guilty.*

Reality testing.   Paul's defensive distortions periodically passed the neurotic limits and both interpersonal and socioeconomic reality would become severely distorted (for example, he thought that his parents could hear his "unspoken thoughts"). The distortions were defended with magical primary-process thinking rather than rationalization. This magical thought process was also typical of his mother. Most of the time his interpersonal reality testing was severely distorted and his socioeconomic reality testing moderately so. He is therefore at times *psychoticized* and more frequently *neuroticized*. His overvaluing of others confirmed their hypomanic neurotic paradigm. Therefore, Paul is at times *neuroticizing* to others.

Centeredness.   Paul's point of reference is the other. He is concerned about his lady friend, tries to understand her reactions, worries about the effect of his aggressive thoughts, etc. His point of reference is also his father. Paul is therefore *contaminated and mirroristic*.

Attitude toward organizations.   Paul is too avoidant and under-committed to be much of a joiner. He is a lover. He tends to escape when anxious. He is aware, however, of interpersonal power as a goal and is not distrustful of group goals. On the contrary his fantasies are very altruistic. The leadership structure which he understands is demagogic. Paul is a *bureaucratic follower*.

Clinical phenomenology.   Paul belongs to the type characterized by anxious avoidant and submissive behavior in which he is in control of his own socioeconomic reality. Paul is a *masochistic insufficient*. Within this group Paul is inhibited, depressed, insecure, and placating, with great difficulty in the expression of aggression. Paul belongs to the *avoidant depressive* subtype of masochistic insufficient.

Structure Diagnosis

Defensive acting off.   Paul talks monothematically about how he is a potentially aggressive, destructive victimizer, while he denies that he is being treated aggressively and destructively by others (by their devaluing attitude). The other is given all right to moral and hedonic pleasure. Paul represses and projects his own masochistic acceptance of aggressive devaluation and denies and introjects the other's acceptance of a sadistic position of personal overvaluation.

He therefore continually acts out his interpersonal problems of excessive self-devaluation and other overvaluation with its corresponding personal loss of moral and hedonic entitlement. He naturalizes his socioeconomic problem of excessive restriction and replaces socioeconomic consideration in perception and thought with the defense of personalization and trivialization, presenting only the sadomasochistic problem.

Counteracting off.   The other accepts or actively implies that he is the victim of destructive aggressions, while he frustrates Paul and victimizes him with destructive, devaluing aggressions, taking an excessive share of moral and hedonic pleasure. He represses and projects his sadistic aggressive position and denies and introjects the position of the masochistic abused.

He therefore counteracts, or even initiates, the interpersonal problem of excessive aggressive devaluation, with its accompanying retention of hedonic and moral pleasure for himself.

He naturalizes and foments the existence of excessive socioeconomic restrictions in Paul, replacing perception and thought about current socioeconomic problems with trivial considerations and the acting out of sadomasochistic personalization. (Paul at one moment states that he would like to show how much he knows and how much he can take. However, he always ends up showing only how much he can take.)

Therapeutic acting on.   Paul first recognizes his own aggressively self-devaluing and other-overvaluing behavior. He controls the overvaluing behavior and tries to develop a realistic appraisal of his own and others' value, recognizing that a realistic sense of worth is related to a healthy assertive attention to current problems.

He discusses the naturalized excessive socioeconomic restrictions related to his avoidant undercommitted behavior, identifying and analyzing socioeconomic problems.

He instruments himself, develops, and puts into effect plans to overcome the socioeconomic restrictions and to solve the socioeconomic problems.

Counteracting on.   The other recognizes that he himself has engaged in aggressive devaluations toward Paul, leaving Paul with a sense of low self-worth and guilt. He controls his automatic reaction of acceptance of the overvalued position given to him by Paul and insists on a realistic or respectful and mutually valuing relationship.

He discusses openly and objectively the naturalized tendency to excessive socioeconomic restriction accompanied by an avoidant undercommitted attitude. He refuses to accept the undercommitted, invasive, restricting role and encourages Paul in the development and use of greater socioeconomic skills.

Diagnosis of Environment

Significant other.   Let us take his relationship with his lady friend as the most complementary relationship to his preferred structure.

The lady has control over her own socioeconomic status; she is neither controlling nor dependent. She is concerned with security and is avoidant and undercommitted. She is an *insufficient.*

The lady claims to be a submissive victim of a jealous Paul, while she compulsively devalues him with hostile teasing. The lady is a *sadist.* She is *devaluing* in speech and especially in her actions. Her affect state should be *elation.* Her interpersonal and socioeconomic reality testing is mildly distorted. She is *neuroticized.* With Paul she mildly attacks his interpersonal reality testing. She is *neuroticizing.* She centers on herself, her feelings, her ambitions, and Paul talks about her as his point of reference. She is *contaminat-*

ing and narcissistic. No clear information is given by Freud about her organizational relations. She is probably *bureaucratic.*

In her relationship with Paul she was disagreeable and dominant with control only over herself. She is a *sadistic insufficient.* She fomented jealousy and was somewhat exhibitionistic (her treatment of Dick in front of Paul) and narcissistic, with a tendency to devalue. Her subtype is *intrusive hypomanic.* Her natural acting-off position coincides approximately with Paul's counteracting-off position.

Microenvironment.   Paul's family was demagogic in its organization. The father, probably in alliance with Paul's brother, was in the sadistic-patient pole—interpersonally dominant but socioeconomically dependent. The mother was in the masochistic-agent pole, interpersonally sacrificing and devalued but socioeconomically powerful, and related to the agentism of her relatives. Paul was like her in masochism, but avoidant rather than submissive. She attempted to complement rather than to form an alliance with him, that is, to treat him as a patient. She suggests a marriage to solve his socioeconomic problems, pays for treatment, etc. He did not want to complement his mother and form an alliance with his father, and he consistently rejected both of these possibilities. He was in conflict with the family paradigm.

Macroenvironment.   We have already commented on the importance of servants in terms of Paul's early sexual stimulation.

In the authoritarian environment of the army Paul had the role of agent thrust upon him because of his social class and education. This resulted in a crisis of competence and displacement into obsessive-compulsive behavior. In this macroenvironment Paul selected out people who did not devalue him. The macroenvironment did not allow his mother to be a true agent who could teach him agentism. She was apparently superstitious and, although economically powerful, was not skilled enough to transmit her agentism, which was acquired from her family's power rather than achieved by her own skill.

Operational Diagnosis

Reaction to therapeutic interventions.   Paul was open to intra-psychic therapeutic information, and Freud used this abundantly. Freud gives the reader therapeutic behavioral information (interprets the symptom as a way of evading socioeconomic reality). Paul was likely receptive to this, since he decided to leave treatment to deal more energetically with his socioeconomic problems. Freud also gives information about the effect of the behavior of his lady friend.

There is no record of behavioral directions or environmental supervisions by Freud, but Paul's friend does do this to some degree after the rat incident. Paul would have been open to this, as long as the style was persuasive and not authoritarian. Paul was sensitive to social pressure (public opinion, consensus, etc.), as is seen in his concern that "his lady" had devalued him publicly. Drugs were not used. The therapeutic contract was used very effectively to keep him on task.

Treatment Plan

Strategic goals.   Upon making the diagnosis of masochistic insufficient, we are able to define in general terms the ideal therapeutic goal. Paul must work through and overcome his excessive socioeconomic restriction (and slide toward dependence) with its defense of displacement by depressive personalization, as well as his excessive stereotyped interpersonal avoidant and abused behavior, with its defense of inversion and narrowing.

Therapeutic tactics.   The first tactical stage has the objective of entering the system and containing or stabilizing it before initiating the process of change. The therapist will therefore play a complementary narcissistic role in the interpersonal and socioeconomic.

The second tactical stage of Paul's treatment was the working through and overcoming of his initial avoidant, frustrated interpersonal relations, with the defense of inversion and narrowing of perception and speech. An example of reversion of the inversion occurs when Freud indicates to Paul his reason for ambivalent behavior toward his lady, that is, her rejecting and frustrating behavior toward him.

In his behavior Freud rejects Paul's induction to treat him sadistically when he analyzes rather than responds to Paul's aggressions.

The third tactical stage of the Rat Man's treatment would be the working through and overcoming of his excessive socioeconomic restriction and its defense of displacement into hypomanic interpersonal aggressive devaluation and guilt because of the related aggressive thoughts.

Freud was initially accepting of displacement by trivialization and personalization. He, however, used the setting to pressure Paul to overcome his resistance. It is obvious that Freud considered the symptom an evasion which had strongly prejudiced Paul's life.

Paul left treatment before the fourth and fifth tactical stages were completed. These would have included the supervision of the stabilization of his new behavior patterns and finally, autonomy and self-conduction in the nonmasochistic position with the capacity for an adult committed relationship to socioeconomic reality.

Technical procedures.   Since Paul is avoidant and not dependent, the mother and woman friend would not be involved directly in treatment, but rather Paul would be "supervised" while he undertook "treatment" of his environment. Supervision of his dealings with his social environment would be extremely important.

Paul is open, intelligent, and verbal, with a good symbolic capacity; therefore, he should (and did) receive therapeutic information about his perceptive, cognitive affect and behavioral organization. Therapeutic directions had to be given in a democratic way with reasons, since Paul does not respond to authoritarian impositions.

Strategic Formulation of the
——————————"Wolf Man"——————————

This case was treated by Freud and described in "From the History of an Infantile Neurosis" (1918). He was reanalyzed first by Ruth Mack Brunswick and later by Muriel Gardiner. He also wrote an autobiography, "The Wolf Man by the Wolf Man" (*The Wolf Man,* 1971).

Identifying Data

Objective Status.   The client is a 23-year-old, extravagantly dressed Russian aristocrat, with an elegant and expensive secondary-school education. He is living in Vienna and comes to see Freud accompanied by his private physician and his valet.

Presenting complaint.   Muriel Gardiner makes the following observation (*The Wolf Man,* 1971, p. 38): "When the Wolf Man consulted Freud he was totally incapacitated and completely dependent on others." We are told that he couldn't even dress himself alone. He could not study, nor was he prepared for any type of work. He did not have a satisfactory relationship with any woman, nor a true friendship with any man or woman. (unless one considered his relation with his sister a friendship). He was gravely incapacitated in three of the most important areas of his life: work, love, and the assumption of responsibility.

He personally associates his need to seek treatment with the recent development of gonorrhea. He had grown up in the superstitious belief that he had been born to be favored by fortune. The gonorrhea dramatically deprived him of his omnipotence.

Present illness.   The Wolf Man's history of psychological problems dates back to infancy. Freud records that at the age of 3½ he underwent a dramatic change in character, becoming "irritable and violent" (Freud, 1918, p. 14). At about this time he was seduced by his sister, saw his parents having sexual relations, and was under the care of a cruel governess. His sister, who committed suicide at a young age, had been a very precocious, active, and intelligent child. Two years his senior, she had outdone him in most fields. She apparently delighted in his fear reactions and particularly enjoyed his distress when she repeatedly showed him a picture of a wolf in a story book. Her death brought conflicting emotions to the Wolf Man. He was depressed, and at the same time he was pleased with the increase in his inheritance.

Significant also was his dedicated nurse Nanya who, more than anyone else, raised and taught him. She was a simple, loving, rigidly religious person, who had lost a child of her own and replaced this child with her love for the Wolf Man. Freud attributes the Wolf Man's choice of love objects as having been influenced by his strong love for Nanya. These were always with people of origin very inferior to his own. For instance a precipitating cause of the illness which made him seek out Freud was a love affair with a servant girl, which had ended in a case of gonorrhea. His wife Teresa was also of an inferior social class. She was a nurse.

The Wolf Man's father, a lawyer, suffered manic-depressive episodes. He was hospitalized on various occasions. He died—probably by suicide—when the Wolf Man was 21. As other predisposing factors to his illness we have his extremely spoiled and sheltered childhood, and the father's favoring of his older sister.

His illness was perpetuated by his extraordinary ability to make others responsible for his material support. Also his initial lack of social skills and the spoiling care of his micro- and macroenvironment, which endured until the Russian Revolution, changed his socioeconomic reality.

Strategic Diagnosis

Socioeconomic control. The Wolf Man was socioeconomically dependent when he initiated the treatment process. The following quotations confirm his dependent condition.

"His shrinking from a self-sufficient existence was so great as to outweigh all the vexations of his illness" (Freud, 1918, p. 11). "Freud took up a collection from among his patients to help to maintain the Wolf Man in Vienna" (Jones, 1955, p. 240). The Wolf Man is a *patient*.

Interpersonal authority.   The Wolf Man considered himself a victim of dominating exploiters, while he was an exploiting, dominating victimizer of others. For example, the Wolf Man claimed to be the victim of his mother, whom he dominated and abused to obtain more money from her. He was frightened of animals, but in fact he hurt and tortured the animals that he feared. He, not the animals, was behaving in a frightening way. He confided to Mack Brunswick that he felt misguided and exploited by Freud, while he felt totally entitled to the money that Freud collected for him. The Wolf Man is a *sadist.*

Defensive misqualification.   The Wolf Man is both blaming and devaluing toward others. He blames his mother, and he blames Freud for meanness. His expectation that others meet his every need is evidence of a sense of personal superiority and hedonic entitlement. The Wolf Man is *blaming and devaluing.*

Affect state.   The affect of the Wolf Man is characterized by anger with those who do not do his bidding and a sense of elation related to an unrealistic and unjustified sense of superior worth. When he is frustrated, and when socioeconomic reality intrudes on him in spite of the protection of others, he became depressed and anxious. At these times he sought treatment. His affect at times of treatment was chiefly *depressed and anxious or angry.*

Reality testing.   The Wolf Man's interpersonal reality testing is severely impaired. He attacks projectively both his mother and Freud. His socioeconomic reality testing was severely impaired, especially in regard to the consequences of behavior. He was borderlined by spoiling, protective others. The Wolf Man is *borderlined.* At the same time his interpersonal attacks were strong. He was himself a *neuroticizer* (or could inspire a suicidal psychotic depression).

Centeredness.   The Wolf Man was extremely self-centered and contaminating. He took the death of his sister with some satisfaction because it improved his economic reality. He made his mother excuse and justify herself in regard to his allowance. He felt entitled to the benefits which he received from Freud, etc. The Wolf Man is *contaminating and narcissistic.*

Attitude toward organizations.   When first seen by Freud the Wolf Man was too dependent and self-centered to interest himself in organizations. After treatment he became a successful employee of an insurance company. He became a *bureaucratic joiner.*

Clinical phenomenology.   The Wolf Man was destructive in his attacks on his mother. His wife committed suicide. He is dominating, using blame and manipulations (for example, insincere withholding of information from Freud). At the same time he was dependent socioeconomically. The Wolf Man is a *sadistic patient.* He is emotionally labile, exhibitionistic, vascillates between seductive softness and blaming and threatening behavior. It is true that at a point of crisis in his life he manifests hypochondriacal, paranoid behavior; however, his subtype is principally *histrionic.*

Structural Diagnosis

Defensive acting off.   The Wolf Man talks monothematically about being frightened of terrifying, sadistic, self-interested "monsters." He claims to be the victim of these frightening others, while he frightens and victimizes or alternately seduces them, claiming all right to moral and hedonic pleasure. He represses and projects his own terrifying sadistic aggressiveness of his "sweet seductions" and denies and introjects the others' acceptance of his position of frightened victim or seduced servant.

He therefore acts, rather than confronting, his interpersonal problem of blaming, devaluing, or seduction with an accompanying excessive entitlement. He naturalizes his socioeconomic problem of dependence and replaces it in thought and perception by this historic sadomasochistic personalization.

Counteracting off.   The other accepts that he is the frightening, sadistically aggressive, self-interested monster or the seducer who frightens, seduces, and victimizes the Wolf Man, while this other is himself frustrated, frightened, attacked sadistically, or seduced by the self-interested monster. As a consequence the other loses all moral and hedonic pleasure.

He represses and projects his own masochistic attacked and seduced position and denies and introjects the position of the sadistic aggressor.

He therefore counteracts the interpersonal problem of excessive attacks of aggressive blaming and devaluation alternating with manipulative seduction. He naturalizes and accepts his own role of excessive socioeconomic responsibility and control, fomenting a continued excessive dependency on the Wolf Man. He replaces perception of socioeconomic problems with the acting out of the historic sadomasochistic problem.

Therapeutic acting on.   The Wolf Man must first recognize his own aggressive, sadistic, egoistic attacks or seductions. He controls the attacking, devaluing, blaming, or seducing behavior and looks to develop mutually respectful, responsible, and reasonable relationships with others whom he realistically values. He discusses the naturalized excessive spoiled dependency of his mother, Freud, Teresa and others.

He instruments himself, develops, and puts into action, plans to overcome the dependency.

Counteracting on.   The other recognizes that he himself has been unfairly attacked, blamed, devalued, or seduced by the frightening and aggressive Wolf Man. He controls his automatic reaction to justify and excuse himself and enters into a mutually respectful, realistically valuing relationship with the Wolf Man.

He discusses openly and objectively the naturalized excessive socioeconomic dependence. He refuses to accept the controlling role and encourages the Wolf Man in his attempts to develop greater autonomy.

Diagnosis of the Environment

Significant other.   Teresa, the Wolf Man's wife will be taken as his most significant complementary other. Teresa maintained the Wolf Man. She managed his life. She nursed him and looked after him physically. Even her suicide note is advice to him about how to handle his affairs. She is an *agent*. Teresa is dominated and victimized by the Wolf Man, while she fears that she may somehow fail him, that is, victimize him. She is a *masochist*.

She is *devalued and blamed* by the Wolf Man. Teresa is attacked in her social worth and her affect, as, for instance, when the Wolf Man discards her. Her affect is therefore chiefly *depressive*.

The Wolf Man severely attacks her interpersonal reality testing while her socioeconomic reality testing is intact. When the attacks on her worth are strong and persistent she could become psychotically depressed, as she does when left by the Wolf Man. Teresa is therefore chiefly *neuroticized* but in danger of being *psychoticized*. She herself accepts the distorted definition of the Wolf Man in terms of his interpersonal worth, and she protects him from socioeconomic consequences. She is *borderlining*.

Teresa completely centers her thoughts on others and most especially the Wolf Man. Her suicide centers on him, she was his devoted nurse, etc. She is *contaminated and mirroristic*. In her relations with the Wolf Man she is chiefly mirroristic, protective, and controlling. She is a *masochistic agent*. She is empty, lonely, and emotionally inhibited. She is of the *compulsive-depressive subtype*.

Her natural acting-off position is approximately the complement to the Wolf Man's defensive acting off, that is, his counteracting off.

Microenvironment.   It seems that the Wolf Man's father exercised an artificially acquired socioeconomic control over the rest of the family while he was alive. After his death, it was the mother—not the Wolf Man—who replaced the father in the role of the spoiling caretaker. The spoiling protection of the Wolf Man's parents was very much reinforced by the servants of his aristocratic wealthy family. Because of the Wolf Man's position as a dependent, demanding, sadistic patient within his family, he is concerned and ambivalent about his sister's death. On the one hand he loves her, but on the other hand her death leaves him with a bigger share of their father's wealth.

Macroenvironment.   The Wolf Man has as his group of reference and belonging the Russian agricultural aristocratic upper class, where his dependant and sadistic attitude is not only tolerated but admired and rewarded as in all young "true" aristocrats of his time. Once this aristocratic agricultural structure was dissolved, the Wolf Man tried to rebuild it among his acquaintances and friends in Switzerland and Austria, as many other Russian aristocrats did at this time. But the restitution of his lost grandeur is just an illusion, because he really begins to live in a middle-class context, where he survives by "selling" his refined charm and culture.

It is a tribute to his therapist that the Wolf Man was finally able to incorporate himself into this middle-class context, get a job, and assume responsibility for others, that is, to finally overcome his "patientism."

Operative Diagnosis

Reaction to therapeutic interventions.   Because of the Wolf Man's basic manipulative, dependent attitude—regarding Freud as a new protector—it seems that, initially at least, the client is deeply resistant to intrapsychic, behavioral, and even environmental therapeutic information, as well as to therapeutic directions and supervisions. By the same token, he seems to be more receptive to therapeutic reactions, counterpressures, social consensus, and contracts.

The threat of interrupting the treatment and the redefinition of its setting produce an amazing therapeutic improvement in the Wolf Man: "his fixation to the illness gave away" (Freud, 1918, p. 11). They seem to be the only viable type of antimanipulative intervention powerful enough to overcome the client's pervasive dependent attitude; that is, to "assail his obliging apathy" (Freud, 1908, p. 11).

At one moment Freud failed to recognize the exploiting manipulative behavior of the Wolf Man because he withheld information from Freud (the jewels and the continuing collection of money for him). As a result of this the Wolf Man regressed dramatically and was reanalyzed by Mack Brunswick, who confronted him consistently and forcefully.

The consistent "antipatient" measures resulted in the Wolf Man's development of his own capacity to relate to socioeconomic reality and even to be an agent to his own dependent others.

Treatment Plan

Strategic goals. It is critical for the Wolf Man's treatment that he work through and overcome his excessive socioeconomic dependence—and its defense of displacement by histrionic personalization—as well as his excessive interpersonal abusive blaming and devaluing domination—and its defense of inversion and narrowing.

Therapeutic tactics. The first tactical stage of the Wolf Man's treatment would be for the therapist to play his complementary narcissistic role: to step into the position of a compulsive-depressive masochistic agent.

The second tactical stage would be the working through and overcoming of his interpersonal abusive demagogic and blaming domination, as well as its defense by the inversion and narrowing of his perception and speech. Freud is aware of the Wolf Man's interpersonal sadistic seduction and blaming behavior and points it out to him, but it is easy to become seduced by such an "interesting case" and to look after him out of compassion.

For instance, Freud had analyzed the Wolf Man's sadistic relationship with his mother in regard to money. The Wolf Man received generously but distorted his perception, saw himself as a victim, and blamed his mother. All of this was interpreted by Freud. He himself gave generously to the Wolf Man—attention, importance, understanding in the first analysis, and money in the second. The Wolf Man's response was to more forcefully invert his perception in the second analysis and to require a further reanalysis to resolve this transference problem. An important part of the information given by Mack Brunswick has to do with this point. She resisted great seductive pressures. She detected his hypocrisy and desire to evade what was to be corrected while talking about the avoiders of analysis, the precision of its techniques, etc. She insisted that he leave his role of "favorite son" at the same time as he "fooled, denounced, and abused" the father.

The third tactical stage of the Wolf Man's treatment would be the working through and overcoming of his excessive socioeconomic dependence on others and its defense by displacement into demagogic interpersonal seduction and projective blaming.

Freud successfully reaches this stage at some point when he establishes a fixed date for ending the treatment regardless of the Wolf Man's manipulative maneuvers to defend his dependence. At this time Freud reports a spectacular general improvement of the Wolf Man's inhibitions and symptoms, as well as his collaboration in treatment (Freud, 1918, p. 11).

There was strong pressure to fail in these efforts because the Wolf Man did not completely leave his old position, and he therefore pressured for the analyst to continue the spoiling behavior. The person who seems to have best resisted this was Mack Brunswick. It would appear that Muriel Gardiner treated him with an overprotective attitude. For example, "she undertook the arduous task of placing the unconnected sequence [of the Wolf Man's autobiography] in order" (*The Wolf Man*, 1971, p. 3).

The fourth tactical stage of the Wolf Man's treatment would be his supervision with respect to preventing possible regressions to his demagogic dependent sadistic-patient pattern each time his environment tempted him to do so again. The fifth tactical stage would be his self-conduction in his new role.

Technical procedures. Because of the Wolf Man's clear manipulative motivation for coming into treatment—to obtain a new spoiling caretaker—it seems critical to start applying therapeutic reactions, counterpressures, and contracts from the very beginning. Moreover, the client's demagogic approach should also be neutralized by doing microenvironmental therapy with the Wolf Man's more significant other; they should have clarified the pathogenic effect on him of their spoiling overprotection.

Once the demagogic alliance between the Wolf Man and his environment is under acceptable therapeutic control, the therapist can start informing the client about his perceptive, cognitive, affective, behavioral, and environmental organization, as well as giving the client therapeutic directions—how to transform his acting off into a therapeutic acting on—and therapeutic super visions—how to transform his environmental, interpersonal, and socioeconomic pathogenic structure into a more fruitful and effective behavior.

The Outcome of Treatment of the ————————————"Wolf Man"————————————

Muriel Gardiner's evaluation of the outcome of the Wolf Man's treatment by Freud is an eloquent argument in favor of what our model as a whole stands for.

> After his analysis with Freud the Wolf Man completed his studies in a brief period of time. He graduated in law and was received at the bar. After leaving Russia and losing all that he possessed he obtained work in an insurance company, beginning in a low position, something difficult to accept for a man who had been so rich and had been served all his life. He progressed continually in his work, and he became interested in it; he was capable of maintaining his wife and looked after her for the twenty three years of their marriage. Also he took a real and affectionate interest in Theresa's daughter and he mourned her early death. After the suicide of his wife the Wolf Man lovingly looked after his mother for fifteen years, and after her death he faithfully protected Fraulein Gaby, who had done so much for him before becoming ill and therefore dependent. (*The Wolf Man,* 1971, p. 285)

10

Some Fundamental
——————Issues——————

In this final chapter we will clarify certain fundamental issues and answer some basic questions often asked of us.

——————Emphasizing the Socioeconomic——————

Why is there so much emphasis on the socioeconomic parameter? Why do we say that subjects displace from consciousness only their social pathological rather than the interpersonal paradigm? Is it not possible that another area of conflict is displaced, and that the same may be true for that which does the displacing? Could it not be, for example, that subjects escape from painful and difficult interpersonal situations by focusing on the socioeconomic situation, which they manage with greater skill and resources? Surely this is the case with many competent executives who feel incompetent and powerless in their family situation. Or, it is argued, subjects may become fixated on socioeconomic trivia in order to avoid their vital problems.

The concept of displacement of a painful mental representation by a less painful one is basic to psychoanalytic thinking, and most especially to the hypothesis of repression. For example, Freud (1915) thought that certain socially censored sexual fantasies were most painful, since they produced great anxiety. Subjects tended to use condensations and displacements as less painful substitutes.

Klein (1957) believed that the greatest anxiety was aroused by a subject's fantasies of aggression toward some vital object, who was thereby endangered. Consequently, the subject employs the defense mechanisms of splitting and projective identification. The aggression is perceived as being in the other. Thus, it seems less painful and it is definitely less dangerous. The needed object is protected from the subject's unconscious aggression. In addition, the aggression may be substituted in consciousness by an idealized representation of the object.

Bion (1977) also developed a theory of the repressed; he argued that what is displaced is consciousness of the painful representation of the subject's psychosis. For this reason subjects tend to attack their whole symbolic process and employ the defense of evacuation and projective identification.

Otto Rank (1928) thought, on the other hand, that what is most painful, and therefore displaced from consciousness is the representation of the subject's own birth trauma, whereby the subject suddenly loses the protection of the instantly gratifying and containing uterus. The trauma of birth is displaced by a fantasy in which the subject, still unborn, is protected by the uterus.

Jacques Lacan (1966) focused on the subject's representation of social impotence; this tends to be substituted by an imaginary narcissism. This is why the Lacanian subject is an imaginary one (Rossel, 1982).

Each school of psychoanalysis and each generation of analysts has its own hypothesis about what is most painful, most repressed, displaced, and substituted. For this reason we could say that there are dynamic therapists who are "fetalists," "oralists," "analists," "urethralists," "genitalists," "aggressivists," and "omnipotentists," in accordance with what each one considers to be most deeply rooted in the unconscious and most painful to remember or experience.

According to this conceptualization, then, we could be classified as "socioeconomists." However, we do not by any means consider this to be an accurate interpretation of our hypothesis. Our theory is an integrating theory, borrowing concepts from psychoanalysis, semiology, the theory of power, cognitive theory, and problem-solving theory in order to unite them on another level of understanding. What we consider to be most anxiety-provoking and painful—and therefore most often displaced and substituted—are vital problems of dimensions and complexity which exceed the possibility of resolution within the restrictions of the subject's personal "problem space." Subjects displace survival problems which they cannot either deal with effectively or totally avoid. These survival problems could be those that are proposed by Freud (sexual), Klein (aggression against the needed object), Rank (the sudden loss of a passive-dependent solution), Bion (an inadequate and psychotic system of representation), or Lacan (the development and representation of social and interpersonal power). Put simply, our clients have developed a narrow, stereotyped, and currently inadequate problem-solving space, structured by and shared with the family and the macroenvironment. The greatest deficiencies, and those which are accompanied by totally inadequate instrumentation, tend to be the socioeconomic. Historically, these complex problems have been inadequately understood and acted upon. They are large problems forced into narrow paradigms and inadequate problem spaces.

This is not to deny that subjects can and do substitute complex, insoluble, and painful interpersonal problems for less painful social ones, or that current interpersonal problems may be substituted by narrow, stereotyped enactments of historic interpersonal problems. These propositions are possible but not usual. In general terms, then, our unifying hypothesis is that subjects avoid facing impotence and failure in a vital, complex, unknown problem, which is displaced by a simpler, known problem. When the theory and problem space is inadequate to solve a current problem, subjects simply displace it, substituting it for an historic—usually interpersonal—problem for which an understanding and an action plan—albeit inadequate—already exist. Thus, instead of engaging in productive problem-solving behavior, subjects return to activity which confirms existing theory.

The Dyadic Model and Polyadic
———————————— Relationships ————————————

Can the dyadic model be applied to the oedipal triangle and to other polyadic relationships? This question recognizes the narcissistic mirroring of the basic human unit, the man-woman dyad. If the partners cannot move beyond their narcissism, which leads them to an inverted perception of themselves in others, it is impossible for them to accept others as real. If the dyadic narcissism is not overcome, they will only perceive and use others as an endless series of new mirrors, which form a closed, confirming consensus for what is already believed and perceived. Such is the case with the nymph Echo, who forms a consensus with Narcissus, which confirms and reinforces what Narcissus projects. A narcissistic triangle is formed by Narcissus, the water mirror, and Echo, just as the oedipal triangle is formed by the child, the mother, and the father.

In this sense we are in accord with Klein (1957), who said that to enter into the oedipal triangle the subject must overcome the dyadic splitting of the schizoparanoid position. There must be a dyad which is free of narcissism before there can be a triad. The subject must overcome the interpersonal—and *then* the social. Also we are in accord with Jacques Lacan (1966) in the sense that the subject must overcome the imaginary mirrored dyadic relationship "between the fetus and the uterus" to be able to accept his or her birth and the symbolic presence of the social law (phallus).

The passage from the schizoparanoid position to the depressive position, or from the imaginary order to the symbolic—which permits the narcissistic dyad to pass to the oedipal triangle—can only occur when both the sadomasochistic interpersonal and the agent-patient-insufficient problems are overcome. This is the theory behind the transference of narcissistic mirrored dyadic pathology.

———————————— Treating Psychotics ————————————

How does the technique work with psychotics? The mechanisms of displacement, substitution, inversion, and narrowing cannot be detected and corrected in nonexistent or incomprehensible speech, since there is no detectable plot or sequence. When verbal communication cannot be understood, the therapist must turn to the client's nonverbal, paraverbal, and contextual communication. When analyzing these levels of communication, the therapist will discover that the client is applying the same defense mechanisms and making the same mistakes at the social and interpersonal level. Even the most disintegrated and incoherent psychotics communicate that they are victims or victimizers as they avoid the problem of excessive socioeconomic dependence through nonverbal, paraverbal, or contextual communication. This is detectable not only in the paranoid schizophrenic but also in the simpler forms of schizophrenia; even apparently meaningless or simple gestures convey that the client is a victim or victimizer (Amati, 1978).

Generally a regressive psychotic crisis tends to result from a crisis of competence in the social sphere. In the following case, a paranoid-schizophrenic sadistic patient had improved in treatment to the point of being released from the hospital and had obtained a job interview, which was scheduled three hours before the therapy session. The family advised the therapist that the patient was canceling the session and would be there the following day.

In spite of this the therapist went to his office as usual, arriving late. To his surprise he found the patient there, already seated and in a very aggressive pose. He was eccentrically dressed in old dirty clothes—as in his time of crisis—and was talking alone in an arrogant, accusing attitude.

The therapist opened the door. The patient entered, took out a large watch, and extended it at arms length so that the hour was clearly visible to both. Then he remained very still, offering his cheek to the therapist and saying:

PETER: Now, the other cheek!
THERAPIST: You are accusing me of arriving late.
PETER: *(Starts crying, showing suffering in his face)* It was written . . .
THERAPIST: You're trying to confirm again your idea that I don't like you.
PETER: *(Turns his head and looks openly accusatory)*
THERAPIST: But you were the one who made sure I was advised that you wouldn't be here. Why are you trying to blame me now?

PETER: *(Smiles sarcastically, as if he had caught the therapist trying to justify himself by a trick.)*

THERAPIST: Possibly I'm not the one justifying himself. From what I see, there was a problem with the new work, and you feel accused by me.

PETER: *(Changes dramatically; leaving his psychotic attitude, he now angrily addresses himself to the therapist)* You son of a bitch, always thinking of how you're not to blame for what happens.

THERAPIST: It's possible, Peter. Maybe. But please think over what I say to you. Maybe you're afraid of being a failure and are trying to justify yourself by blaming me. Remember how your mother says that you are lazy, a parasite. Now, can you tell me about the interview.

PETER: *(Smiling sadly)* Just a bit too much.

THERAPIST: So it was too difficult for you. Now you're afraid of going home and confronting your family.

PETER: I'll try to explain. But my mother . . .

THERAPIST: It's not only your mother. It is also you. You must accept and understand your current situation, stop blaming yourself, and prepare yourself. Maybe you could practice interviewing.

PETER: Thinking clearly is harder than it seems.

THERAPIST: Especially if you're blamed instead of taught.

—————————Inverted and Direct Speech—————————

Does the client always speak and act in reverse? When must the therapist invert the discourse, and when can it be understood directly? When clients have an unresolved problem, their speech is the inverse of their acts. When they are trying to resolve such a problem, as happens when they improve their understanding in treatment, they will rectify their own perception and speak directly. The therapist must, of course, distinguish between these circumstances. If one stays with the discourse alone, this rectification is impossible to determine. When the discourse is taken in relation to the action language (nonverbal and paraverbal) and reviewed by the therapist, who is aware of his or her own affective response to what is happening, then the therapist has the necessary means to determine the relation of the discourse to action and therefore to the client's unconscious structure and meaning. We disagree with Lacan (1966), who said that the context of validation of the client's speech is within the client's speech itself. We believe that the meaning is clear when we go to the therapeutic context and the relation to action, which the client's discourse is describing. To be understood, what is being symbolized is more broadly contextualized. Therefore, coming back to the speech, actions, and affects within the therapeutic context seems to be the way to break the client's narcissistic closure.

───────Detecting Contaminated Speech───────

How can one tell if the subjects' speech reflects their own pathology and not that of contaminating others? If subjects seem to be justifying themselves, answering or accepting accusations or devaluations which originate from the other, they are being contaminated by the pathology of the other. Also, when their monotheme is replaced by another narrow, stereotyped monotheme, and their apparent pathology changes, we can consider that they are contaminated by the pathology of the other. This is especially common in masochists, and most especially in masochistic psychotherapists, who are exposed to a series of sadistic clients. Masochists are more contaminated, sadists more contaminating.

The very idea of *folie a deux* seems to be based on the dyad of a contaminating narcissist and a contaminated mirrorist. The mirrorist is totally paralyzed by the narcissist's definition of the situation; consequently, both function as a pathological duet, like Narcissus and Echo. This attack on the other's identity constitutes one of the main ways of closing dyadic narcissistic systems and of transmitting mental illnesses. The other ceases to be a lucid, autonomous witness and becomes only a confirming mirror.

We believe that this is one reason why the concept of identification has progressively been substituted for the concept of projection in psychoanalytic theory. When using projection, subjects perceive their own image in neutral others. When they use projective identification, this projection is complemented and reinforced by introjective identification. The narcissistic closure becomes even more impregnable. It is akin to a labyrinthine fun house, with infinite reflecting mirrors. These narcissistic "mirrors" can disorient, trap, and contaminate the therapist, unless he or she continuously reconnects the client's speech and actions within the therapeutic context and relates their content to the client's interpersonal and social reality. That is, the therapist pulls the client back to reality from the infinitely elusive and imaginary world.

An example of this is Marilyn, a compulsive, depressive, mirroristic masochistic agent with a strong tendency to be contaminated by the other's definition of the situation. She "disappears" from the session, swallowed up by her contaminating, narcissistic, sadistic-patient husband. Only after repeatedly decontaminating therapeutic interventions is the client able to return to her own narcissism, so to speak.

Here is a typical decontaminating transaction in which a clinical evaluation can be made as to when the client is expressing her own theme and when she is contaminated by the monotheme of others.

MARILYN: I'm just coming from the doctor. I consulted him because of my dyspepsia. He told me that maybe I have parasites. (Pause) I don't know what to think. I don't think I'm a cheater or a thief, but who knows? It is very difficult for me to be absolutely clear about that, you know. One never wants to admit one's own mistakes. However, I don't know. Bernard (the husband) insists that I'm not telling him the truth, that I cheat him, that I steal money from his pocket—it's terrible! I've never done anything like that before. Actually this is what his mother always did to his father, but maybe I'm unconsciously like his mother. Who knows?

THERAPIST: Don't you think that if this has never been your concern or your behavior, and if it's something that happened very often between Bernard's parents, it seems quite possible that these repetitive preoccupations are more Bernard's own problems than yours? Maybe you are "parasited" by his preoccupations.

MARILYN: Well, what I actually think is that maybe Bernard keeps telling me those things because I'm so damn unworthy, so boring and unattractive. Maybe he's trying to wake me up or something. But I don't think he will really get much out of me. At least my mother failed in trying to teach me how to have a more attractive personality. Even as your client, I know that I'm so boring.

THERAPIST: Now we are talking about *your* preoccupations. Now you are the one who is identifying Bernard and myself with your mother, who kept saying such things as what a boring daughter she had.

MARILYN: You are always trying to support me. Beyond my mother's opinion I was, and still am, really very boring.

THERAPIST: Maybe that is why you even prefer being accused of being an "interesting" cheater or "thief" than a boring honest person?

MARILYN: *(Smiling)* Well . . . I think that you've got something there, you know.

——————————Levels of Intervention ——————————

Must therapists work only at the concrete level of the client's problem? Since socioeconomic problem is what subjects should finally work through, this could lead to the idea that the therapist must become a money manager and that the secret to happiness lies in the possession of money and social power. Obviously this is a very concrete interpretation of our model.

Although Freud accentuated the importance of the sexual as that which is repressed, and therefore what the subject must work through in therapy, this does not transform the therapist into a sexual manager. Nor does it imply that happiness depends wholly on good sexual relations, an interpretation which some more concrete analysts might give—and have erroneously given to Freud's theory. Nor would we expect that Otto Rank's (1928) emphasis on the importance of the birth trauma as the fundamental repressed situation signifies that the therapist has to become an obstetrician, or that happiness depends on a good delivery, or perhaps, on not being born at all. And we, like Freud and Rank, are speaking metaphorically and in broad terms.

What we emphasize is that the therapist is a collaborator in the working through, one who helps the client confront complex vital problems and points out and avoids their displacement onto the exclusive perceptions of historic interpersonal sadomasochistic or trivial problems. The therapist must avoid personalization, which results from interpreting all behavior within the inter- personal paradigm and inducing the client to speak about and analyze only the interpersonal. The therapist would then be avoiding the social sphere.

The therapist, rather than working only with the concrete acts as an epistemologist, or expert in thought and understanding, and as a problem-solving technician, who discovers the obsolete, narrow, stereotyped, and inappropriate paradigm of understand- ing, with its corresponding stereotyped affect "fixation." There is a corresponding inadequate action plan for problem solving. The therapist helps to develop an effective relevant paradigm of understanding, with its corresponding action plan and affect organization, and the necessary skills which allow solution of the vital problem.

We think also that the subjects' happiness depends in great part on the quality and sophistication of their symbolic and metasymbolic capacity, that is, on the accuracy and sophistication of their perception, thinking, and corresponding affects, which allow them to use effective action plans with social intelligence and relevant skills.

In this sense we coincide with Bion (1977), in that the effort and hope of the therapist is to improve the thinking apparatus in general and not only certain concrete thoughts or actions in determined areas of reality.

We think that the therapist is a specialist—in Freud's terms— whose task is to improve the quality and complexity of our clients' psychic apparatus and thus help them understand the external world more completely and have appropriate affects with a more complex sophisticated and effective action plan.

Briefly, this process of improving the "intelligence" of the client by an intelligent, relevant therapy would correspond to the specific development of the part of the psychic apparatus destined to understand the organization of perception, affect, concepts, and action plans of this apparatus. It is the meta-apparatus which realizes the function of "metasemiosis."

However, as all clients are not initially prepared to dedicate themselves to analyze how they perceive, think, and feel—and therefore how they act and what their environment is like—the therapist ought, in the beginning, to choose the communication mode to which the client is open and responsive (for example, directions, counterpressures, actions, environmental therapy) and later to go to intrapsychic information about perception and cognitive structure, behavior or environment.

The therapeutic task is an epistemological effort, which terminates by transforming clients into epistemologists for themselves as well others. Client and therapist think about thinking; that is, they develop a metaepistemology.

Strategic Stages

Could you summarize your treatment strategy? In our approach the psychic apparatus is reorganized in five stages to give the subject a new relationship with the other and to social reality; general understanding changes, and the general problem-solving capacity is improved. Both therapist and client are thinking on the metalevel (Brunner, 1964).

In order to function effectively on the symbolic and meta-symbolic level therapists must have, and be perceived as having psychological, interpersonal, and socioeconomic power. Only in this way can they be true "agents" of mental health, as opposed to "insufficient" unresolving therapists or problem-perpetuating "patients" themselves.

The first stage of the technique is to contain the clients' anxieties and prepare for coming operations. This is the restorative phase, where the system is restored to balance within its old defensive pattern, and the conditions for further operations are prepared.

Defenses are analyzed in the second stage. Clients are made conscious of their displacement, narrowing, and inversion which result in the stereotyped behavior that provides the therapist with the raw material for analysis.

In the third stage clients are exposed to new information and perceptions, and memories are reorganized. New experiences facilitate the development of an enhanced cognitive and affective understanding of the social and interpersonal aspects of the clients' relationship to the world. This process requires information from the preconscious, unconscious, and transconscious dimensions of reality. As a result, clients pose new problems that they now wish to resolve and master rather than defensively reacting or coping more effectively within their defensive perceptions. Instead of merely improving their ability to achieve old goals clients actually change their life objectives.

The fourth stage is one in which these different life objectives are accompanied by the development of a long-range plan with operational procedures to assure its achievement. This requires that specific learning has taken place in prior stages, and that clients have now achieved new skills and the capacity for general planning, subplans, etc.

The last stage is that of stabilization of gains. The clients consult with the therapist to detect and balance external pressures which tend to reinforce their acting off and defensive organization, until they have achieved a routinization of their new cognitive system. Tactically, these stages are worked upon first in the interpersonal sphere and then in the socioeconomic spheres. The therapeutic goal is accomplished when they have stabilized with a new autonomy and awareness.

References

Adler, G., & Myerson, P. *Confrontation in psychotherapy.* New York: Jason Aronson, 1973.

Amati, S. Recit d'une analyse ou il s'agit de toute puissance. Paper presented at the Swiss Psychoanalytic Society, Geneva, Nov. 1978.

American Psychiatric Association. *Diagnostic and statistical manual of mental disorders* (3rd ed.). Washington, D.C.: A.P.A., 1980.

Anderson, C. Report on cases of induced insanity. *Illinois Medical Journal,* 1974, *65,* 357–358.

Asch, S. E. Effects of group pressure upon the modification and distortion of judgements. In H. Guetzkow (Ed.), *Groups, leadership and men.* Pittsburgh: Carnegie Press, 1951.

———. *Social psychology.* Englewood Cliffs, N.J.: Prentice-Hall, 1952.

Atwood, W. G. *The lioness and the little one.* New York: Columbia University Press, 1980.

Bales, R. F., & Slater, P. E. The role of differentiation in small decision-making groups. In T. Pearson and R. F. Bales (Eds.), *Family, socialization and interaction process.* New York: Free Press, 1955.

Balint, A., & Balint, M. On transference and countertransference. *International Journal of Psychoanalysis, 1939, 20,* 223–230.

Bander, R., & Gunder, J. *The structure of magic.* Palo Alto, Calif.: Science & Behavior Books, 1975.

Barchilon, J. On countertransference cures. *Journal of the American Psychoanalytic Association,* 1958, *6,* 222–236.

Bateson, G. The group dynamics of schizophrenia. In L. Appleby, J. M. Scher, & J. Cumming (Eds.), *Chronic schizophrenia: Exploration in theory and treatment.* Glencoe, Ill.: Free Press, 1960.

————— & Ruesch, J. *Communication: The social matrix of psychiatry.* New York: W. W. Norton, 1945.

Bem, D. J. Self-perception: An alternative interpretation of cognitive dissonance phenomena. *Psychological Review,* 1967, *74,* 183-200.

Bienner, C. Working alliance, therapeutic alliance, and transference. *Journal of the American Psychoanalytic Association,* 1979, *27,* 137-159.

Bion, W. R. Differentiation of the psychotic from the nonpsychotic personalities. *International Journal of Psychoanalysis,* 1957, *38,* 266-275.

—————. *Learning from experience.* New York: Basic Books, 1962.

—————. *Elements of psychoanalysis.* London: Heineman, 1965a.

—————. *Transformations.* New York: Basic Books, 1965b.

—————. *Seven servants.* New York: Jason Aronson, 1977.

Bird, B. Notes on transference: Universal phenomenon and hardest part of analysis. *Journal of the American Psychoanalytic Association,* 1972, *20,* 267-301.

Blau, P. M. *The dynamics of bureaucracy.* Chicago: University of Chicago Press, 1955.

—————. *Exchange and power in social life.* New York: Wiley, 1964.

Bogen, J. E. The other side of the brain II: An oppositional mind. *Bulletin Los Angeles Neurological Society,* 1969, *34,* 135

Bonacich, P. Secrecy and solidarity. *Sociometry,* 1976, *39,* 200-208.

Boutang, P. *Reprendre le pouvoir.* Paris: Saggitaire, 1978.

Boyer, L. B. Countertransference with severely regressed patients. In L. Epstein & A. H. Feiner (Eds.), *Countertransference.* New York: Jason Aronson, 1979.

Bramson, R. M. *Coping with difficult people.* New York: Anchor, 1981.

Bruner, J. S. The course of cognitive growth. *American Psychologist,* 1964, *19,* 1-15.

Bruner, J. S. *Beyond the information given.* New York: W. W. Norton, 1973.

Chertok, L. The discovery of the transference: Toward an epistemological interpretation. *International Journal of Psychoanalysis,* 1968, *49,* 560-576.

Christodoulou, G. N. Two cases of *folie a deux* in husband and wife. *Acta Psychiatrica Scandinavica,* 1970, *46,* 413-419.

Cohen, H. *The nature, method, and purpose of daignosis.* Cambridge, Eng.: Cambridge University Press, 1943.

Cohen, M. B. Countertransference and anxiety. *Psychiatry*, 1952, *15*, 231–243.

Cook, K. S. Expectations, evaluations, and equity. *American Sociological Review*, 1975, *40*, 372–388.

———. Power, equity, and commitment in exchange relations. *American Sociological Review*, 1978, *43*, 721–739.

Corrao, F. Struttura poliadica e funzione gamma. *Gruppo e Funzione Analitica*, 1981, *2*, note 2.

Courtright, J. A., Millar, F. E., & Rogers-Millar, L. E. Domineeringness and dominance: Replication and expansion. *Communication Monographs*, 1979, *46*, 179–192.

Crown, D. M., & Marlow, D. The approval motive. *Studies in evaluative dependency*, 1964, *40*, 224–30.

Dahrendorf, R. *Conflict after class*. London: Longmans Green, 1967.

Daniels, R. S. Some early manifestations of treatment: Their implications for the first phase of psychoanalysis. *Journal of the American Psychoanalytic Association*, 1969, *17*, 995–1014.

Della Fave, L. R. The meek shall not inherit the earth. *American Sociological Review*, 1980, *45*, 955–972.

Deutsch, F. A footnote to Freud's "Fragments of an analysis of a case of hysteria." *Psychoanalytic Quarterly*, 1957, *26*, 2.

Deutsch, K. W. *The analysis of international relations*. Englewood Cliffs, N.J.: Prentice-Hall, 1968.

Deutsch, M. *Folie a deux* and reality testing. *Psychiatry*, 1938, *33*, 390.

Dewald, P. A. Folie a deux and the function of reality testing. *Psychiatry*, 1970, *33*, 390–395.

———. Transference regression and real experience in the psychoanalytic process. *Psychoanalytic Quarterly*, 1976, *45*, 213–230.

Dickes, R. Severe regressive disruptions of the therapeutic alliance. *Journal of the American Psychoanalytic Association*, 1967, *15*, 508–533.

Dohrenwend, B. P., & Dohrenwend, B. S. *Social status and psychological disorders*. New York: Wiley, 1969.

Dornbusch, S. M., & Scott, W. R. *Evaluation and the exercise of authority*. San Francisco: Josey-Bass, 1975.

Eco, V. James Bond: Une combinatoire narrative. *Communications*, 1966, *8*, 24–33.

Ellis, D. G. Relational control in two group systems. *Communication Monographs*, 1979, *46*, 153–166.

Elon, A. *Between enemies.* New York: Random House, 1974.

Emerson, R. Power-dependence relations. *American Sociological Review,* 1962, *27,* 31–41.

Epstein, L. The therapeutic function of hate in the countertransference. In L. Epstein & A. H. Feiner (Eds.), *Countertransference.* New York: Jason Aronson, 1979a.

———. Countertransference with borderline patients. In *Countertransference,* op. cit., 1979b.

Etzioni, A. A comparative analysis of complex organizations: On power, involvement and their correlates. New York: Free Press, 1961.

Ferreira, A. J. Family myth and homeostasis. *Archives of General Psychiatry,* 1963, *9,* 457–463.

Festinger, L. *A theory of cognitive dissonance.* Evanston, Ill.: Row-Peterson, 1957.

Fox, W. S., Payne, D. E., Priest, T. B., & Philliber, W. W. Authority position, legitimacy of authority, and acquiescence to authority. *Social Forces,* 1977, *55,* 966–973.

Frank J.D. *Persuasion and healing.* Baltimore: John's Hopkins, 1961.

Freud, S. (1895) Project for a scientific psychology. In *Standard edition of the complete psychological works of Sigmund Freud* (Vol. 1). London: Hogarth Press.

———. (1905) Fragments of an analysis of a case of hysteria. *Standard Edition* (Vol. 7). London: Hogarth Press.

———. (1908) Character and anal eroticism. *Standard Edition* (Vol. 9). London: Hogarth Press.

———. (1909a) Analysis of a phobia in a five-year-old boy. *Standard Edition* (Vol. 10). London: Hogarth Press.

———. (1909b) Notes upon a case of obsessional neurosis. *Standard Edition* (Vol. 10). London: Hogarth Press.

———. (1910) The future prospects of psychoanalytic therapy. *Standard Edition* (Vol. 11). London: Hogarth Press.

———. (1912a) The dynamics of transference. *Standard Edition* (Vol. 12). London: Hogarth Press.

———. (1912b) On beginning the treatment. *Standard Edition* (Vol. 12). London: Hogarth Press.

———. (1913) On beginning the treatment. *Standard Edition* (Vol. 12). London: Hogarth Press.

———. (1914a) On narcissism: An introduction. *Standard Edition* (Vol. 14). London: Hogarth Press.

————. (1914b) Remembering, repeating and working through. *Standard Edition* (Vol. 12). London: Hogarth Press.

————. (1915a) Observations on transference love. *Standard Edition* (Vol. 12). London: Hogarth Press.

————. (1915b) Repression. *Standard Edition* (Vol. 14). London: Hogarth Press.

————. (1916) Some character types met with in psychoanalytic work. *Standard Edition* (Vol. 14). London: Hogarth Press.

————. (1918) From the history of an infantile neurosis. *Standard Edition* (Vol. 17). London: Hogarth Press.

————. (1922) Some neurotic mechanisms in jealousy, paranoia, and homosexuality. *Standard Edition* (Vol. 18). London: Hogarth Press.

————. (1923) The id and the ego. *Standard Edition* (Vol. 19). London: Hogarth Press.

————. (1924a) The loss of reality in neurosis and psychosis. *Standard Edition* (Vol. 19). London: Hogarth Press.

————. (1924b) The economic problem of masochism. *Standard Edition* (Vol. 19). London: Hogarth Press.

————. (1937a) Analysis terminable and interminable. *Standard Edition* (Vol. 23). London: Hogarth Press.

————. Constructions in analysis. *Standard Edition* (Vol. 23). London: Hogarth Press.

————. (1938) An outline of psychoanalysis. *Standard Edition* (Vol. 23). London: Hogarth Press.

Freudenserger, H. J. *Burn-out.* New York: Anchor, 1980.

Friedman, L. The therapeutic alliance. *International Journal of Psychoanalysis,* 1969, *50,* 139–153.

Gamson, W. A. Coalition formation. In D. L. Sills (Ed.), *International encyclopedia of the social sciences,* (Vol. 2). New York: Macmillan, 1968.

Gear, M. C., Grinberg, L., & Liendo, E. C. Group dynamics according to a semiotic model based on projective and counterprojective identification. *Group therapy,* New York: Stratton Intercontinental, 1976.

Gear, M. C., Hill, M. A. & Liendo, E. C. *Working through narcissism.* New York: Jason Aronson, 1981.

Gear, M. C. & Liendo, E. C. *Semiologie psychoanalytique.* Paris: Minuit, 1975.

————. Psychoanalyse de la communication familiale. *L'Evolution Psychiatrique,* 1976, *2,* 240–272.

————. *Action psychoanalytique.* Paris Minuit, 1979.

———. *Psicoterapia della coppia e del gruppo familiare.* Florence: Del Riccio, 1980.

———. *Therapie psychoanalytique de la famille.* Paris: Dunod, 1981.

———. Metapsychology of sadism and masochism. A bipolar semiotic model. *Psychoanalysis and Contemporary Thought,* 1981, *4,* 207–250.

Gill, M., & Muslin, H. Early interpretation of transference. *Journal of the American Psychoanalytic Association,* 1976, *24,* 779–794.

——— The analysis of the transference. *Journal of the American Psychoanalytic Association,* 1979, *27,* 263–288.

Giovacchini, P., Kernberg, P., Masterson, J., & Searles, H. *New perspectives on psychotherapy of the borderline adult.* New York: Brunner/Mazel, 1980.

Glauser, D. La naturalization symbolique. Doctoral dissertation, Universite de Geneve, 1978.

Glover, E. *The technique of psychoanalysis.* New York: International Universities Press, 1955.

Gralnick, A. *Folie a deux:* The psychosis of association. *Psychiatric Quarterly,* 1942, *16,* 230.

Green, K. J., Taylor, M. G. Social expectancy and self-presentation in a status. *Journal of Experimental Social Psychology,* 1969, *5,* 79–92.

Greensberg, M. P. Crime and *folie a deux. Journal of Mental Science,* 1956, *102,* 772.

Greenson, R. The working alliance and the transference neurosis. In R. Greenson (Ed.), *Explorations in psychoanalysis.* New York: International Universities Press, 1978.

Greimas, A. J. *Semantique structurale.* Paris: Larousse, 1966.

Grinberg, L. On a specific aspect of countertransference to the patient's projective identification. *International Journal of Psychoanalysis, 1962, 43,* 436–440.

——— Contribucion al estudio de las modalidades de la identification proyectiva. *Revista de psicoanalisis* (Vol. 4). Buenos Aires: Argentine Psychoanalytic Society, 1969.

——— Projective counteridentification and countertransference. In L. Epstein & A. H. Feiner (Eds.), *Countertransference.* New York: Jason Aronson, 1979.

Grinker, R. R., Sr. Changing styles in psychoses and borderline states. *American Journal of Psychiatry,* 1973, *130,* 151–160.

——— Werble, B., & Drye, R. C. *The borderline syndrome.* New York: Basic Books, 1968.

Gunderson, J. G., & Singer, P. Defining borderline patients. *American Journal of Psychiatry,* 1975, *132,* 1-10.

Haas, E. G. *The web of interdependence.* Englewood Cliffs, N.J.: Prentice-Hall, 1970.

Haley, J. *Strategies of psychotherapy.* New York: Grune & Stratton, 1966.

Haywood, R. C. & Bourne, L. E. Attribute and rule learning aspects of conceptual behavior. Psychological Review, *1965, 72,* 175-95.

Heinmann, P. On countertransference. *International Journal of Psychoanalysis,* 1950, *31,* 81-84.

Heimann, P. Dynamics of transference interpretation. *International Journal of Psychoanalysis,* 1956, *37,* 303-310.

Henderson, S. The social network, support and neurosis: The function of attachment in adult life. *British Journal of Psychiatry,* 1977, *131,* 185-191.

Henderson, S., et al. Social bonds in the epidemiology of neurosis: A preliminary communication. *British Journal of Psychiatry,* 1978, *132,* 463-466.

Inheler, B., & Metalon, B. The study of problem solving and thinking. In P. H. Musen (Ed.), *Handbook of research methods in child development.* New York: Wiley, 1960.

Jackson, D. D. Countertransference and psychotherapy. In F. Fromm-Reichmann & J. L. Moreno (Eds.), *Progress in psychotherapy* (Vol. 1). New York: Grune & Stratton, 1956.

———. Family interaction, family homeostasis, and some implications for conjoint family therapy. In J. Masserman (Ed.), *Individual and familial dynamics.* New York: Grune & Stratton, 1959.

———. The monad, the dyad, and the family therapy of schizophrenics. In A. Burton (Ed.), *Psychotherapy of the psychoses.* New York: Basic Books, 1961.

Jacobson, E. Interaction between psychotic partners: Manic-depressive partners. In V. W. Einstein (Ed.), *Neurotic Interaction in Marriage.* New York: Basic Books, 1959.

———. The paranoid betrayal conflict. Paper presented at the Los Angeles Psychoanalytic Society, November 1966.

———. *Psychotic conflict and reality.* New York: International University Press, 1968.

Johnson, M. P. Commitment: A conceptual structure and empirical application. *Sociological Quarterly,* 1973, *14,* 395-406.

Jones, E. *Sigmund Freud: His life and work.* London: Hogarth Press, 1955.

Kadushin, C. The friends and supporters of psychotherapy: On social circles in urban life. *American Sociological Review,* 1966, *31,* 786-802.

Kallman, F. J., & Mickey, J. S. The concept of induced insanity in family units. *Journal of Nervous and Mental Disease,* 1946, *104,* 303⅞315.

Kant, O. The problem of psychogenic precipitation of schiophrenia. *Psychiatric Quarterly,* 1942, *16,* 341-350.

Kanzer, M. The therapeutic and working alliances: An assessment. *International Journal of Psychoanalytic Psychotherapy, 1975, 4,* 48-68.

Katz, E., & Lazarsfeld, P. F. *Personal influence.* Glencoe, Ill.: Free Press, 1955.

Kernberg, O. Notes on countertransference. *Journal of the American Psychoanalytic Association,* 1965, *13,* 38-56.

————. Borderline personality organization. *Journal of the American Psychoanalytic Association,* 1967, *15,* 641-47.

————. *Borderline conditions and pathological narcissism.* New York: Jason Aronson, 1975.

————. *Object relations theory and clinical psychoanalysis.* New York: Jason Aronson, 1976.

Kessler, R. C. Stress, social status, and psychological distress. *Journal of Health and Social Behavior,* 1979, *20,* 100-108.

Kiraly, S. J. *Folie a deux:* A case of "demonic possession" involving mother and daughter. *Canadian Psychiatric Association Journal,* 1975, *20,* 223-227.

Klauber, J. The psychoanalyst as a person. *British Journal of Medical Psychology,* 1968, *41,* 315-322.

Klein, M. Notes on some schizoid mechanisms. *International Journal of Psychoanalysis,* 1946, *27,* 99-110.

————. *Developments in psychoanalysis.* London: Hogarth Press, 1952a.

————. The origins of transference. *International Journal of Psychoanalysis,* 1952b, *33,* 433-438.

————. On identification. In Klein, M. & Riviere, J. (Eds.), *New directions in psychoanalysis.* London: Tavistock, 1955.

————. *Envy and gratitude.* London: Tavistock, 1957.

Kohut, H. *The analysis of the self.* New York: International University Press, 1971.

————. *The restoration of the self.* New York: International Universities Press, 1977.

Komarita, S. S., & Chertkoff, J. M. A bargaining theory of coalition formation. *Psychological Review,* 1973, *80,* 149-162.

Kuhn, T. S. *The structure of scientific revolution* (2nd ed.). Chicago: University of Chicago Press, 1972.

Lacan, J. *Ecrits*. Paris: Editions du Seuil, 1966.

Laing, R. D., & Esterson, A. *Sanity, madness, and the family* (Vol. 1). London: Tavistock, 1964.

Lane, R. E. The fear of equality. *American Political Science Review*, 1959, *53*, 35–51.

Langs, R. *The technique of psychoanalytic psychotherapy* (Vol. 1). New York: Jason Aronson, 1973.

————. Therapeutic misalliances. *International Journal of Psychoanalytic Psychotherapy*, 1975a, *4*, 77–105.

————. The therapeutic relationship and deviation in technique. *International Journal of Psychoanalytic Psychotherapy*, 1975b, *4*, 106–141.

————. *The bipersonal field*. New York: Jason Aronson, 1976a.

————. *The therapeutic interaction* (2 vols.). New York: Jason Aronson, 1976b.

————. On the formulation and timing of interventions. *Journal of the American Academy of Psychoanalysis*, 1979a, *7*, 477–498.

————. *The supervisory experience*. New York: Jason Aronson, 1979b.

————. *The therapeutic environment*. New York: Jason Aronson, 1979c.

————. Some interactional and communicative aspects of resistance. *Contemporary Psychoanalysis*, 1980, *16*, 16–52.

————, & Searles, M. *Intrapsychic and interpersonal dimensions of treatment. A clinical dialogue*. New York: Jason Aronson, 1980.

Larson, E. Why do some people outperform others? *The Wall Street Journal*, January 13, 1982, p. 33.

Laruelle, F. *Au-dela du principe de pouvoir*. Paris: Payot, 1978.

Lasch, C. *The culture of narcissism*. New York: W. W. Norton, 1979.

Laseque, C., & Falret, J. La folie a deux ou folie communiquee? *American Journal of Psychiatry*, 1964, *4*, 1–23.

Layman, W. A., & Cohen, L. A modern concept of *folie a deux*. *Journal of Nervous and Mental Disorders*, 1957, *125*, pp. 412–20.

Lefcourt, H. M. *Locus of control: Current trends in theory and research*. Hillside, N.J.: Erlbaum, 1976.

Leslie, G. R. *The family in the social context*. New York: Oxford University Press, 1979.

Levi-Strauss, C. *Structural anthropology*. New York: Basic Books, 1963.

Little, M. Countertransference and the patient's response to it. *International Journal of Psychoanalysis*, 1951, *32*, 32–40.

Loberg, T., Marlat, G. A., & Nathan, P. E. *Psychoanalysis of drug dependence.* New York: Brunner/Mazel, 1980.

Loewenstein, R. Some remarks on defenses, autonomous ego, and psychoanalytic technique. *International Journal of Psychoanalysis,* 1954, *35,* 188–193.

Luchins, A. S. & Luchins E. H. New experimental attempts at preventing mechanization in problem solving. *Journal of General Psychology,* 1950, *42,* 279–97.

Macalpine, I. The development of the transference. *Psychoanalytic Quarterly,* 1950, *19,* 501–539.

Mack Brunswick, R. A supplement to "From the history of an infantile neurosis." *International Journal of Psychoanalysis,* 1928, *9,* 439.

Mahler, M. S. *On child psychosis and schizophrenia: Autistic and symbiotic infantile psychoses.* New York: International University Press, 1952.

Manderscheid, R. W., Rae, D. S., McCarrick, A. K., & Silbergeld, S. Relational control in dyadic interaction. *American Sociological Review,* 1982, *46,* 62–74.

Masterson, J. *The borderline patient.* New York: Brunner/Mazel, 1978.

———. *Psychotherapy of the borderline adult.* New York: Brunner/Mazel, 1979.

McNeil, J. N., et al. Folie a deux in the aged. Review and a case report of role reversal. *Journal of the American Geriatric Society,* 1972, *20,* 316–323.

Meier, R. F., & Johnson, W. T. Deterrence and social control: The legal and extralegal production of conformity. *American Sociological Review,* 1977, *42,* 292–304.

Menaker, E. The masochistic factor in the psychoanalytic situation. *Psychoanalytic Quarterly,* 1942, *9,* 171–186.

Mensh, I. N. Personality structure in *folie a deux. American Journal of Orthopsychiatry,* 1950, *20,* 806.

Merloo, J. A. Mental contagion. *American Journal of Psychotherapy,* 1959, *13,* 66–70.

Miller, G. A., Gallanter, E., & Pribram, K. *Plans and the structure of behavior.* New York: Holt, Rinehart & Winston, 1960.

Mischel, W. Toward a cognitive social learning: Reconceptualization of personality. *Psychological Review,* 1973, *80,* 252–283.

Money-Kyrle, R. Normal countertransference and some of its deviations. *International Journal of Psychoanalysis,* 1956, *37,* 360–366.

Neri, C. Una mappa. *Gruppo e funzione analitica,* 1978, note. 2.

————. Representazione, construzione, interpretazione nel gruppo. *Gruppo e Funzione Analitica,* 1979, *1,* note 1.

Newell, A., & Simon, H. A. *Human problem solving.* Englewood Cliffs, N.J.: Prentice-Hall, 1972.

Nye, J. S., & Koohane, R. O. *Power and interdependence.* Boston: Little, Brown, 1977.

Ofshe, R., & Ofshe, L. Choice behavior in coalition games. *Behavioral Science,* 1970, *15,* 337–349.

Parkinson, C. N. *Parkinson's law and other studies in administration.* Boston: Houghton Mifflin, 1957.

Patchen, M. Models of cooperation and conflict: A critical review. *Journal of Conflict Resolution,* 1970, *16,* 389–407.

Perez, J. F. *The family roots of adolescent delinquency.* New York: Brunner/Mazel, 1979.

Potter, S. *Oneupmanship.* Harsmondsworth, Eng.: Penguin, 1947.

Prins, S. A. A case of conjugal psychosis. *Psychiatric Quarterly,* 1950, *24,* 324–335.

Pulver, S. E., & Brunt, M. Y. Deflection of hostility in *folie a deux. Archives of General Psychiatry,* 1961, *5,* 527–565.

Racker, H. The meanings and uses of countertransference. *Psychoanalytic Quarterly,* 1957, *26,* 303–357.

Racker, H. *Transference and countertransference.* New York: International Universities Press, 1968.

Rangell, L. The psychoanalytic process. *International Journal of Psychoanalysis,* 1968, *49,* 19–26.

Rangell, L. The intrapsychic process and its analysis: A recent line of thought and its current implications. *International Journal of Psychoanalysis,* 1969, *50,* 65–77.

Rank, O. *Le traumatisme de la naissance.* Paris: Payot, 1928.

Rappaport, A., & Wallsten, T. S. Individual decision behavior. *Annual Review of Psychology,* 1972, *23,* 131–176.

Reich, A. Empathy and countertransference. In Reich, A. & Sandler, J. (Eds.), *Psychoanalytic contributions.* New York: International Universities Press, 1966.

Reid, W. M. *The psychopath.* New York: Brunner/Mazel, 1980.

Robinson, R. V., & Bell, W. Equality, success and social justice. *American Sociological Review,* 1978, *43,* 125–143.

Rogers, L. E. Dyadic systems and transactional communication in a family context. *Dissertation Abstracts International*, 1973, *33*, 6450A.

Rogers-Millar, L. E., & Millar, F. E. Domineeringness and dominance: A transactional view. *Human Communication Research*, 1979, *5*, 238–246.

Rokeach, M. *The open and closed mind.* New York: Basic Books, 1960.

Rosecrance, R. N., & Stein, A. A. Interdependence: Myth or reality? *World Politics*, 1973, *26*, 1–27.

Rosenberg, M., & Pearling, L. I. Social class and self-esteem among children and adults. *American Journal of Sociology*, 1978, *84*, 53–77.

Rosenfeld, H. Some therapeutic factors in psychoanalysis. *International Journal of Psychoanalytic Psychotherapy*, 1978, *7*, 152–164.

Rossel, Y. *Les sujets de la psychiatrie.* Doctoral dissertation. Universite de Geneve, 1981.

Savage, G. Cases of contagiousness of delusions. *Journal of Mental Science*, 1881, *26*, 563–566.

Schachter, S. *The psychology of affiliation.* Stanford, Calif: Stanford University Press, 1959.

Sandler, J. Countertransference and role-responsiveness. *International Review of Psychoanalysis*, 1976, *3*, 43–47.

Sandler, J., Dare, C., & Holder, A. *The patient and the analyst: The basis of the psychoanalytic process.* New York: International Universities Press, 1973.

Searles, H. F. The schizophrenic's vulnerability to the therapist's unconscious processes. *Journal of Nervous and Mental Disease*, 1958, *127*, 247–262.

———. The effort to drive the other person crazy. An element in the etiology and psychotherapy of schizophrenia. *British Journal of Medical Psychology*, 1959, *32*, 1–18.

———. Concerning therapeutic symbiosis. *Annual of Psychoanalysis*, 1973, *1*, 247–262.

———. The patient as therapist to his analyst. In P. Giovacchini (Ed.), *Tactics and techniques in psychoanalytic therapy* (Vol. 2). New York: Jason Aronson, 1975.

Segal, H. Depression in the schizophrenic. *International Journal of Psychoanalysis*, 1956, *37*, 339–343.

———. Melanie Klein's technique. *Psychoanalytic Forum*, 1967, *2*, 197–211.

———. Countertransference. *International Journal of Psychoanalytic Psychotherapy*, 1977, *6*, 31–38.

Seligman, M. E. P. *Helplessness: On depression, death and development.* San Francisco: Freeman, 1975.

Sewell, W. H., & Hauser, R. M. *Education, occupation and earnings: Achievement in the early career.* New York: Academic Press, 1975.

Sluzki, C. E., Beavin, J., Tarnopolsky, A., & Vernon, E. Transactional disqualification. *Archives of General Psychiatry, 273* 1967.

Solomon, J. G., Fernando, T. G., & Solomon, S. M. Mother-son *folie a deux. British Journal of Psychiatry,* 1977, *125,* 230–235.

Soni, S. D., & Rockley, G. J. Socioclinical substrates of *folie a deux. British Journal of Psychiatry,* 1974, *125,* 230–235.

Stone, L. On resistance to the psychoanalytic process: Some thoughts on its nature and motivations. In B. Rubinstein (Ed.), *Psychoanalysis and contemporary science* (Vol. 2). New York: Macmillan, 1973.

Strachey, J. The nature of the therapeutic action of psychoanalysis. *International Journal of Psychoanalysis,* 1934, *15,* 127–159.

Sturges, S. G. *Folie a deux* in husband and wife: A case of *folie simultanee. Bulletin of the Menninger Clinic,* 1967, *31,* 343–351.

Tauber, E. Exploring the therapeutic use of countertransference data. *Psychiatry,* 1954, *17,* 331–336.

The Wolf Man. *The Wolf Man by the wolf man.* New York: Basic Books. 1971.

Tieho, G. Cultural aspects of transference and countertransference. *Bulletin of the Menninger Clinic,* 1971, *34,* 313–326.

Todorov, T. *Theorie de la litterature: Textes des formalistes russes.* Paris: Editions du Seuil, 1965.

Toffler, A. *The third wave.* New York: Bantam, 1981.

Trivers, R. L. The evolution of reciprocal altruism. *Quarterly Review of Biology,* 1971, *46,* 35–57.

Tucker, L. S. Mother and son *folie a deux:* A case report of attempted patricide. *American Journal of Psychiatry,* 1977, *134,* 1146–1147.

Turillazzi Manfredi, S. *La linea d'ombra delle psicoterapie.* Florence: Del Riccio, 1979.

Wason, O. C., & Laird, P. N. (Eds.). *Thinking and reasoning.* Middlesex, Eng.: Penguin, 1968.

Watts, A. W. *Psychotherapy, east and west.* New York: Pantheon, 1961.

Watzlawick, P. Paradoxical predications. *Psychiatry,* 1965, *28,* 368–374.

———. *How real is real?* New York: Vintage, 1976.

———. *The language of change.* New York: Basic Books, 1978.

———, Beavin, J., & Jackson, D. D. *Pragmatics of human communication.* New York: W. W. Norton, 1967.

————, Weakland, J., & Fish, R. *Change: Principles of problem formulation and problem resolution.* New York: W. W. Norton, 1974.

Webster, M. J., & Sobieszek, B. *Sources of self-evaluation: A formal theory of significant others and social influence.* New York: Wiley, 1974.

Winnicott, D. W. Hate in the countertransference. *International Journal of Psychoanalysis,* 1949, *30,* 69–75.

————. On transference. *International Journal of Psychoanalysis,* 1956, *37,* 386–388.

Wynne, L. C., Rychoff, I. M., Day, J., & Mirsch, S. I. Pseudomutuality in the family relations of schizophrenics. *Psychiatry,* 1958, *21,* 233–247.

Young, O. R. *The politics of force: Bargaining during international crisis.* Princeton, J.N.: Princeton University Press, 1969.

Index

Acting off, 14, 141–142
  to acting on, 147–148
  dynamic explanation of,
    144–147
  transference and, 200–201
Acting on, 142
  acting off to, 147–148
Adler, G., 246
Affect states, diagnosis of,
  104–105
Agents, 8, 102
  containing function of, 9n
  high performers as, 20–21
  masochistic, *see* masochistic
    agent
  sadistic, *see* sadistic agent
Amati, S., 309
Anderson, C., 35
Anger, 105
Anka, P., 112
Anxiety, 105

Asch, S.E., 19, 38
Atwood, W., *The Lioness and the*
  Little One, 68–70
Authoritarian dyad, 12, 22–44,
  103
  analysis and diagnosis of,
    154–167
  breaking of, 40–41
  cognitive structure of, 39–40
  complementarity in, 39–41
  consultation with, 41–44
  subtypes of, 135
Authority, diagnosis of, 102–103
Autonomy, 251, 256, 260, 265,
  269, 273

Bales, R.F., 59
Balint, A., 200
Balint, M., 200
Bander, R., 61
Barchilon, J., 240

Bateson, G., 28
Beavin, J., 9, 11, 47, 103
Bell, W., 87
Bem, D.J., 61
Bienner, C., 249
Bion, W.R., 9n, 67, 147, 227,
    232, 254, 306, 314
Bird, B., 196
Blame, 9-10
Blamed, 103
Blamed devaluers, 103
Blamer-blamed dyad, 104
Blamers, 103
Blau, P.M., 6, 49
Bonacich, P., 80
Borderlines, 105
Borderline syndrome, 15, 17
Borderlining, 107
Boutang, P., 250
Boyer, L.B., 202
Bramson, R.M., 252
Bruner, J.S., 67, 315
Brunswick, R.M., 295
Brunt, M.Y., 39
Bureaucracy
    and masochistic agents, 49
    sadistic patient's intolerance
        of, 60
Bureaucrats, 111

Centeredness, diagnosis of,
    108-111
Chertkoff, J.M., 85
Chertok, L., 254
Chopin, F., 68-73
Christodoulou, G.N., 19
Clients
    scripts of, 14
    types of, 8-10
Clinical interview
    with masochistic agent, 46-47

with masochistic insufficient,
    75-76
with masochistic patient,
    23-24
with sadistic agent, 31-32
with sadistic insufficient,
    84-85
with sadistic patient, 58
Cognitive structure
    of authoritarian dyad, 39-40
    of demagogic dyad, 66-67
    in undercommitted dyad,
        93-94
Cohen, H., 11
Cohen, M.B., 207
Complementarity
    in authoritarian dyad, 39-41
    degree of, 143-144
    in the demagogic dyad, 65-67
    in the undercommitted dyad,
        93-95
Container, infantilizing, 9n
Contamination, 144
Contract, "adult," 58
Control, diagnosis of, 102-103
Cook, K.S., 5, 87, 124, 132
Corrao, F., 6
Counteracting off, 14, 142
    to counteracting on, 148-149
Counteracting on, 142
Countertransference, 195-196
Courtright, J.A., 9, 27, 103, 107
Crown, D.M., 66

Daniels, R.S., 196, 246
Dare, C., 206
Days, J., 52
Defenses
    in acting off, 144-145
    basic, 13-14
    interpersonal, see
        interpersonal defenses

intrapsychic, *see* intrapsychic
    defenses
of masochistic agent, 53-54
of masochistic insufficient,
    80-81
of masochistic patient, 29-30
of sadistic agent, 36-37
of sadistic insufficient, 89-90
of sadistic patient, 61-62
Defensive action plan, 195-202
Della Fave, L.R., 5, 103
Demagogic dyad, 12, 45-73, 103
    analysis and diagnosis of,
        167-182
    breaking of, 67
    cognitive structure of, 66-67
    complementarity in, 65-67
    Sand and Chopin as, 68-73
    subtypes of, 135
Denial, 13n, 145
Dependence, 205-207, 249-250,
    263-265
Depression, 105
Depressive position, 7n
Deutsch, F., 278, 282
Deutsch, H., 34, 256
Devaluation, 9-10
Devalued, 103
Devalued blamers, 103
Devaluer-devalued dyad, 104
Devaluers, 103
Dewald, P.A., 29, 106, 254
Diagnosis, 140-192, 276-278
    of affect states, 104-105
    of attitudes toward
        organizations, 111-113
    of authoritarian dyad, 42-44
    axes of, 101-102
    of centeredness, 108-111
    of control and authority,
        102-103
    differential, 10-12

of phenomenologic subtypes,
    113-134
of qualification, 103-104
of reality testing, 105-107
of speech and action, 141-149
of undercommitted dyad,
    98-100
Dickes, R., 256
Disavowal through
    displacement, 13
Distrust, 105
Dohrenwend, B.P., 5
Dohrenwend, B.S., 5
Domination, 251-253, 262,
    270-272
Dora, 14, 143, 148-149
    strategic formulation of,
        278-285
Dornbusch, S.M., 22
Drugs, 244
Drye, R.C., 67, 125
Dyadic typology
    and DSM-III, 134-139
    and polyadic relationships,
        308
Dyads
    authoritarian, *see*
        authoritarian dyad
    blamer-blamed, *see* blamer-
        blamed, dyad
    complementarity in, 143-144
    contamination in, 144
    demagogic, *see* demagogic
        dyad
    devaluer-devalued, *see*
        devaluer-devalued dyad
    pathological, 11-12
    undercommitted, *see*
        undercommitted dyad

Eco, V., 142
Elation, 105

Ellis, D.G., 8, 123
Elon, A., 80
Emerson, R., 58
Epstein, L., 231
Erickson, 17
Error sensitivity
    in authoritarian dyad, 40
    in demagogic dyad, 66–67
    in undercommitted dyad, 94
Esterson, 24
Etzioni, A., 79

Falret, J., 11
Family, 47
Family of origin
    of masochistic agent, 47–48
    of masochistic insufficient,
        76–78
    of masochistic patient, 24–25
    of sadistic agent, 32
    of sadistic insufficient, 85–86
    of sadistic patient, 59
Fernando, T.J., 11
Ferreira, A.J., 36
Festinger, L., 40, 144
Fish, R., 94
Folie à deux, 11–12
Fox, W.S., 60, 89
Frank, S., 252
Freudenserger, H.J., 264
Freud, S., 3, 13n, 23, 35, 64, 85,
        88, 105, 108, 113, 141,
        202, 204, 217–219,
        246–247, 305
    "A Case of Obsessional
        Neurosis," 286–288, see
        also Rat Man
    Dora, case of, see Dora
    "From the History of an
        Infantile Neurosis,"
        295–296, 301, see also
        Wolf Man

    on neurosis and psychosis, 15
    on perversions, 197–198
    repetition compulsion of, 14n
    on transference, 195
    typology in cases of, 274–304

Gallanter, E., 147
Gamson, W.A., 58, 76
Gardiner, M., 295, 304
Garfield, C., 21
Gibb, C.A., 26
Gill, M., 216, 257
Giovacchini, P.L., 55
Gitelson, M., 208
Glauser, D., 145
Glover, E., 215
Gralnick, A., 11, 114
Gratification, 39
Green, K.J., 14, 66, 102
Greenson, R., 258
Greimas, A.J., 143
Grinberg, L., 20, 196, 216
Grinder, 61
Grinker, R.R., 63, 67, 125
Guilt, 105
Gunderson, J.G., 67

Haas, E.G., 89
Haley, J., 251
Hauser, R.M., 34
Heimann, P., 204, 258
Henderson, S., 85, 115
High performers, 20–21
Hill, M.A., 31, 59, 89, 111, 141,
        199
Holder, A., 206
Honesty (so-called), 84
Husband, "caretaker," 26

Inheler, B., 94
Insufficients, 8–9, 102

masochistic, *see* masochistic
   insufficients
neuroticizing, 17–18
sadistic, *see* sadistic
   insufficients
Interpersonal authority, 6–7
Interpersonal defenses
   of masochistic agent, 54
   of masochistic insufficient, 81
   of masochistic patient, 29–30
   of sadistic agents, 36–37
   of sadistic insufficients, 89–90
   of sadistic patients, 61–62
Interpersonal reality testing
   (IPRT), 150–151
Interpersonal submissiveness,
   246–249
Interventions, 242–244
Intrapsychic defenses
   of masochistic agents, 54
   of masochistic insufficients,
   81
   of masochistic patients, 30
   of sadistic agents, 37
   of sadistic insufficients, 90
   of sadistic patients, 62
Introjective identification, 13n,
   145
Inversion, 13

Jackson, D.D., 11, 47, 50, 107,
   253, 262
Jacobson, E., 55, 62, 91
Johnson, W.T., 78

Kadushin, C., 53
Kallman, F.J., 29
Kant, O., 22
Kanzer, M., 262
Katz, E., 127
Keohane, 88

Kernberg, O., 17, 55, 57, 58, 63,
   107, 219, 251
Kessler, R.C., 4
Kiraly, S.J., 35
Klauber, J., 262
Klein, M., 7n, 13n, 108, 147,
   199, 214, 218, 241, 266,
   306, 308
Kohut, H., 13, 31, 108, 113, 242
Komarita, S.S., 85
Kuhn, T., 4n

Lacan, J., 4n, 108, 147, 243, 306,
   308, 311
Laing, R.D., 24
Laird, P.N., 94
Lane, R.E., 6, 116
Langs, R., 76, 210–211, 242–245,
   265, 267
Larson, E., 21
Laruelle, F., 243
Lasch, C., 12, 87, 108
   The Culture of Narcissism, 74
Laseque, C., 11
Layman, W.A., 11
Lazarsfeld, P.F., 127
Lefcourt, H.M., 124
Leslie, G.R., 32
Lévi-Strauss, C., 14n, 141
Little, M., 212
Loberg, T., 57
Loewenstein, R., 243
Loss-gain strategy
   in authoritarian dyad, 40
   in demagogic dyad, 66
   in undercommitted dyad, 94

Macalpine, I., 270
MADDS, *see* multiaxial
   diagnostic decisions
   sheet

Mahler, M., 19, 50
Manderscheid, R.W., 8, 122
Marlat, G.A., 57
Marlow, D., 66
Masochistic agent, 10, 46-57,
    212-217
  basic traits of, 46
  clinical interview with, 46-47
  compulsive depressive
      subtype, 121-123, 167
  compulsive hypomanic, 123,
      172, 177
  defenses of, 53-54
  family of origin of, 47-48
  misqualification and reality
      testing of, 54-57
  object relations of, 48-53
  as scapegoat, 60
  social and family roles of, 48
  socioeconomic monopoly by,
      215-217
  submission and sacrifice by,
      213-215, 257-258
  subtypes of, 121-123
  testing therapist, 212-213
  treatment of, 256-261
Masochistic insufficient, 10,
    75-84, 224-230
  avoidant depressive, 132-133,
      188
  avoidant hysteric, 133-134,
      182
  basic traits of, 75
  clinical interview with, 75-76
  defenses of, 80-81
  family of origin of, 76-78
  misqualification and reality
      testing of, 81-84
  object relations of, 78-80
  social and family roles of, 78
  socioeconomic restriction of,
      228-230

  submission and sacrifice by,
      226-228
  subtypes of, 132-134
  testing therapist, 224-225
  treatment of, 265-270
Masochistic patient, 10, 23-30,
    202-207
  anxious subtype of, 119-120,
      160
  basic traits of, 23
  clinical interview with, 23-24
  conversive subtype, 117-118
  defenses of, 29-30
  depressive, 116, 154
  dissociative, 118
  family of origin of, 24-25
  neurasthenic, 117
  object relations of, 26-29
  obsessive, 120-121
  phobic subtype, 120
  schizoid subtype, 118-119
  social and family roles of,
      25-26
  socioeconomic dependence
      of, 205-207, 249-250
  submission and sacrifice by,
      204-205
  subtypes of, 115-121
  testing therapist, 203-204
  treatment of, 245-251
Masochists, 7, 9, 102
Masterson, J., 55, 259
Mavericks, 111-112
McCarrick, A.K., 8, 122
McNeil, J.N., 8, 102
Meier, R.F., 78
Menaker, E., 253
Mensh, I.N., 23
Mental health, 20-21
Mental illness, 3
  shared, 12
Merloo, J.A., 24

Metalon, B., 94
Mickey, J.S., 29
Millar, F.E., 7, 9, 27, 103
Miller, G.A., 147
Mirrorism, 108–111
Mirsch, S.I., 52
Mischel, W., 148
Money-Kyrle, R., 222
Monotheme, 141–142
Multiaxial Diagnostic Decision
    Sheet (MADDS), 141,
    149–153, 275–276
  clinical application of,
    154–192
Muslin, H., 257
Myerson, P., 246

Narcissism, 13
  and mirrorism, 108–111
Narcissistic personality, 31
Narrowing, 145
Nathan, P.E., 57
Naturalization, 145
Neri, C., 19, 243, 259
Neuroticizing, 106
Neurosis, 15–19
Neurotics, 105
Newell, A., 147
Nye, J.S., 88

Objective reality, 3
  and social control, 5–6
Object relations
  of masochistic agent, 48–53
  of masochistic insufficient,
    78–80
  of masochistic patient, 26–29
  of sadistic agent, 33–36
  of sadistic insufficient, 86–89
  of sadistic patient, 60–61
Omnipotence
  loss of, 57

of sadistic agent, 36
Organizations, attitudes
    toward, 111–113

Paracountertransference, 199
Paranoid-schizoid position, 7n
Paratransference, 199
Parkinson, C.N., 79
Patients, 8, 102
  masochistic, see masochistic
    patient
  sadistic, see sadistic patient
Payne, D.E., 60, 89
Pearling, L.I., 26
Perez, J.F., 59
Perversion, 197–198
Phillber, W.W., 60, 89
Potter, S., 36
Power
  and information, 6
Pribam, K., 147
Priest, T.B., 60, 89
Prins, S.A., 27
Projective identification, 13n,
    145
Psychosis, 15–19, 308–310
Psychoticizing, 106
Pulver, S.E., 39

Qualification, diagnosis of,
    103–104

Racker, H., 196, 200, 202
Rae, D.S., 8, 122
Rangell, L., 239, 271
Rank, O., 306–313
Rappaport, A., 77
Rat Man, 286–294
  treatment plan for, 293–294
Reality, 3–7
Reality testing
  diagnosis of, 105–107

Reality testing (continued)
    interpersonal, 150–151
    of masochistic agent, 54–57
    of masochistic insufficient,
        81–84
    of masochistic patient, 30
    of sadistic agent, 37–38
    of sadistic insufficient, 90–92
    of sadistic patient, 62–64
    socioeconomic, 150–151
Reich, A., 203
Reid, W.M., 60
Repetition compulsion, 14n
Repression
    in acting off, 145
    through inversion, 13
Risk
    in authoritarian dyad, 40
    in demagogic dyad, 66
    in undercommitted dyad, 94
Robinson, R.V., 87
Rogers, L.E., 17, 19, 104
Rogers-Millar, L.E., 7, 9, 27, 103
Rokeach, M., 95
Roles
    of masochistic agent, 48
    of masochistic insufficient, 78
    of masochistic patient, 25–26
    of sadistic agent, 33
    of sadistic insufficient, 86
    of sadistic patient, 59–60
    of therapist, 19–20
Romanticism, 45
Rosecrance, R.N., 95
Rosenberg, M., 26
Rosenfeld, H., 267
Rossel, Y., 306
Rychoff, I.M., 52

Sadistic agent, 10, 31–38,
    207–211

basic traits of, 31
clinical interview with, 31–32
compulsive hypomanic, 114,
    154
compulsive paranoid, 115, 160
defenses of, 36–37
domination by, 208–210
family of origin, 32
misqualification and reality
    testing by, 37–38
object relations of, 33–36
omnipotence of, 36
socioeconomic monopoly by,
    210–211
subtypes of, 113–115
testing therapist, 207–208
therapist as, 245–246
treatment of, 251–256
Sadistic insufficient, 10, 84–92,
    230–237
basic traits of, 84
clinical interview with, 84–85
defenses of, 89–90
domination and abuse by,
    232–235
family of origin of, 85–86
intrusive hypomanic, 130–131,
    188
intrusive paranoid, 131–132,
    182
misqualification and reality
    testing of, 90–92
object relations of, 86–89
social and family roles of, 86
socioeconomic restriction of,
    235–237
subtypes of, 130–132
testing therapist, 231–232
treatment of, 270–273
Sadistic patient, 10, 57–64,
    217–224

basic traits of, 57
clinical interview with, 58
defenses of, 61–62
dissociative explosive,
    128–129, 172
domination and abuse by,
    218–221
family of origin of, 59
histrionic subtype, 124–125,
    167
hypochondriac, 125–126
misqualification and reality
    testing of, 62–64
object relations of, 60–61
paranoid depressive, 127–128,
    177
paranoid schizophrenic,
    129–130
psychopathic, 126–127
social and family rules of,
    59–60
socioeconomic dependence
    of, 222–224
subtypes of, 124–130
testing therapist, 217–218
treatment of, 261–265
Sadists, 7, 9, 102
Sadomasochistic alternative, 7
Sand, G. (Amandine Aurore
    Lucie, *née* Dupin), 68–73
Sandler, J., 203, 206
Saroyan, A., 31
Savage, G., 38
Schachter, S., 49
Scripts, 14
Searles, H., 16, 25, 55, 75, 106,
    196, 205, 249, 265
Segal, H., 207, 247
Seligman, M.E.P., 105
Sewell, W.H., 34
Silbergeld, S., 8, 122

Simon, H.A., 147
Singer, P., 67
Slater, P.E., 59
Sluzki, C.E., 9, 103
Sobieszek, B., 9, 104
Social context, 4
Socioeconomic control, 5–6,
    254–256, 258–260
Socioeconomic reality testing
    (SERT) 150–151
Socioeconomic restriction,
    266–269, 272–273
Solomon, J.G., 11
Solomon, S.M., 11
Soni, S.D., 12
Speech, 310–313
Stein, A.A., 95
Stone, L., 268
Strachey, J., 252
Strategic goals, 238–240
Structural analysis, 142–143
Sturges, S.G., 33
Subjective reality, 3
    and interpersonal authority,
    6–7
Submissiveness, 246–249,
    265–266
Substitution, 145
Suicide, 58

Tarnopolsky, A., 9, 103
Tauber, E., 223
Taylor, M.G., 14, 66, 102
Theory, 19
Therapeutic reactions, 245
Therapeutic setting, 243–244
Therapist, 313–315
    as masochistic agent, 261–262
    as masochistic patient, 251
    role of, 19–20
    as sadistic agent, 245–246

Therapist (*continued*)
  sadistic agent's view of, 31
  as sadistic insufficient, 265
  as sadistic patient, 257
  and social context, 4–5
  testing of
    by masochistic agent,
      212–213
    by masochistic insufficient,
      224–225
    by masochistic patient,
      203–204
    by sadistic agent, 207–208
    by sadistic insufficient,
      231–232
    by sadistic patient, 217–218
Ticho, G., 258
Todorov, T., 143
Toffler, A., 23, 47, 78, 241
Transference
  and acting off, 200–201
  of authority and control, 199
  and countertransference,
    195–196
  of the neurosis, 196–197
  as reality twice removed,
    197–199
Transference-
    countertransference,
    201–202
Transference neurosis, 196–197
Treatment, 238–273
  of masochistic agent, 256–261
  of masochistic insufficient,
    265–270
  of masochistic patient,
    245–251
  of sadistic agent, 251–256
  of sadistic insufficient,
    270–273
  of sadistic patient, 261–265
  strategy of, 315–316

tactical stages of, 240–241
technical procedures of,
    241–244
Treatment plan, 277
  for Dora, 284–285
  for Rat Man, 293–294
  for Wolf Man, 302–304
Trivers, R.L., 21, 121
Tucker, L.S., 24
Turilazzi Manfredi, S., 19, 200,
    241

Undercommitted dyad, 12,
    74–100, 103
  analysis and diagnosis of,
    182–192
  breaking of, 95
  cognitive structure in, 93–94
  complementarity in, 93–95
  in consultation, 95–100
  diagnosis of, 98–100
  subtypes of, 135

Vernon, 9, 103

Wallsten, T.S., 77
Wason, O.C., 94
Watts, A.W., 7
Watzlawick, P., 11, 47, 53, 94,
    240, 269
Weakland, J., 94
Webster, M.J., 9, 104
Werble, B., 67, 125
Winnicott, D.W., 235, 265
Wolf Man, 295–304
  treatment plan for, 302–304
The Wolf Man by the Wolf Man
    (Wolf Man), 295, 303,
    304
Wynne, L.C., 52

Young, O.R., 94